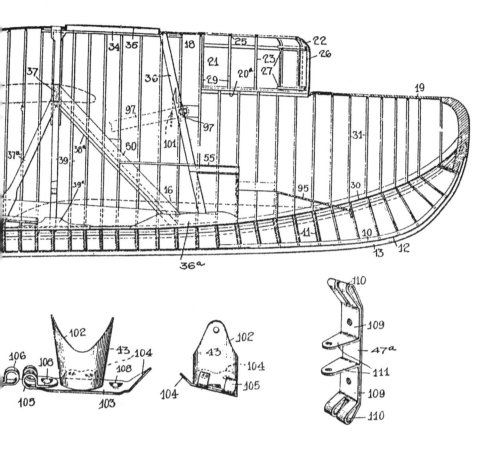

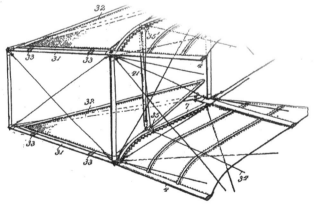

Hell-Rider
to King of the Air

Glenn Curtiss's Life of Innovation

Other SAE books of interest:

Edsel: The Story of Henry Ford's Forgotten Son
By Henry Dominguez
Order Number R-329

Hot Rod Pioneers
The Creators of the Fastest Sport on Wheels
By Ed Almquist
Order Number R-228

Advanced Engine Development at Pratt & Whitney
The Inside Story of Eight Special Projects, 1946–1971
By Dick Mulready
Order Number R-252

The World's Most Significant and Magnificent Aircraft
By David B. Thurston
Order Number R-285

For more information or to order this book, contact SAE at 400 Commonwealth Drive,
Warrendale, PA 15096-0001; (724) 776-4970; fax (724) 776-0790;
e-mail: CustomerService@sae.org; website: www.sae.org.

Hell-Rider
to King of the Air

Glenn Curtiss's Life of Innovation

Kirk W. House

Warrendale, Pa.

For permission and licensing requests, contact:

SAE Permissions
400 Commonwealth Drive
Warrendale, PA 15096-0001 USA
E-mail: permissions@sae.org
Tel: 724-772-4028
Fax: 724-772-4891

Library of Congress Cataloging-in-Publication Data

House, Kirk W.
    Hell-rider to king of the air : Glenn Curtiss's life of innovation / Kirk W. House.
       p. cm.
    Includes bibliographical references and index.
    ISBN 0-7680-0802-6
    1. Curtiss, Glenn Hammond, 1878–1930. 2. Aeronautics—United States—Biography. 3. Aeronautical engineers—United States—Biography. I. Title.

TL540.C9H68 2003
629.13'0092—dc21
[B]   2003045607

SAE
400 Commonwealth Drive
Warrendale, PA 15096-0001 USA
E-mail: CustomerService@sae.org
Tel: 877-606-7323 (inside USA and Canada)
Tel: 724-776-4970 (outside USA)
Fax: 724-776-1615

ISBN 0-7680-0802-6

SAE Order No. R-314

Printed in the United States of America.

To My Father

Harold B. House,

A Fine Mechanical Engineer in His Own Right

Contents

✶ ✶ ✶

Foreword

⋆ ⋆ ⋆

Glenn Curtiss was one of the most significant figures of pioneering aviation and engine development. He was also one of the most controversial—and one of the most complex—figures of his time. Although he was a quiet man, he showed a flair for racing that earned him the nickname "Hell-Rider." He was a man whose face inevitably froze into a stern expression whenever a camera turned his way, yet he was remembered decades after his death for his kindness. A formally uneducated man, he took the lead in multiple fields of engineering and entrepreneurship. Widely renowned as a man of character, he went to his grave accused of fiduciary irresponsibility and patent theft.

The historiography of Curtiss is almost impossible to separate from his mythology, both positive and negative aspects. Long and bitter patent actions brought against him by the Wright brothers have only provided tinder for this blaze of confusion. History reads better if it has heroes and villains, and a beginning, a middle, and an end. Either Curtiss is the villain and the Wrights are heroes, or the other way around.

Life is rarely so simple.

Curtiss was a pioneer in several fields: airplanes (in general); seaplanes (in particular); internal combustion engines; motorcycles; dirigibles; community development; and trailers (by way of his fascination for articulated, independently suspended road vehicles). In some cases, he was the original innovator in his field. In others, he seized existing innovations, developed them further, and made them practical and salable. Curtiss loved experimenting, but he never lost sight of sales.

Curtiss's work was always intensely personal. Therefore, to understand his work, we need to follow the thread of his life along with a deeper scrutiny of his technological efforts. As a young man, Curtiss worked for the Eastman Company and briefly supported himself as a photographer. We'll borrow from his art in organizing the chapters of this book, using "Panoramas" to cover his life story and setting and "Close-Ups" to examine his work in several fields.

As a very young man, Curtiss gained fame as an inventor and racer, perhaps the last in a line of know-how, can-do Yankee tinkerers who parleyed their limited educations into fortune and fame by creating or elaborating new technologies. Curtiss was 32 years old when a boys' adventure novel called *Tom Swift and His Motor Cycle* was published. The character of Tom was a young inventor and racing daredevil who had a plant in Shopton, a small town on the shores of fictional Lake Carlopa in upstate New York. Author "Victor Appleton" used many men as models in his 1910 creation of Tom Swift, but it's clear that a generous portion of the original mix consisted of Glenn Curtiss. [1, 2]

Tom and Glenn both remain forever young. Glenn Curtiss accomplished all that he achieved in only 52 years.

Back in those exciting turn-of-the-century days, especially in aviation, the focus was on who was first for one accomplishment or another. Historians studying the period frequently find this to be nearly impossible to sort out, especially given early aviation's second nature as a branch of show business. All we can say for this book is that assertions of firsts are good-faith efforts, and we're always ready to cheerfully correct our understandings in the face of better evidence. We also need to remember that *independent development* is not infrequent in times such as these.

It's also the case, however, that often more important than questions of *primacy* are questions of *influence.* Glenn Curtiss was one of the most influential men in the development of the motorcycle with its industy, the airplane with its industry, and the travel trailer with its industry—not to mention the development of southeastern Florida. A good portion of our transit through the sky and along the roads rests on work done by Glenn Curtiss. If his contributions are often neglected nowadays, that would probably be all right with him. Glenn was a quiet guy. He always hated a fuss.

REFERENCES

1. Dizer, John T., *Tom Swift and Company,* McFarland & Company, Jefferson, NC, 1981.

2. Swift, Earl, "The Perfect Inventor," *American Heritage of Invention and Technology,* vol. 6, no. 2, Fall 1990, pp. 24–31.

Acknowledgments

✷ ✷ ✷

Just as Curtiss couldn't have done his work in a vacuum, neither could this book have come to be without the work of many individuals. Although I am the only person responsible for what was written on these pages, the number of pages would have been far fewer without many others to whom I turned for elucidation and help.

Anyone toiling in the Curtiss vineyards owes a tremendous debt to three men who helped to create and sustain the Glenn Curtiss Museum, while also gathering archives and artifacts and exploring the life and work of the man. Otto Kohl, who founded the museum in 1961, had worked as a mechanic in Curtiss's Hammondsport plant. Merrill Stickler, a museum curator, was the great-nephew of Damon Merrill, one of Curtiss's key mechanics. Tony Doherty, museum director, was the son of Gink Doherty, one of Curtiss's star pilots. Lindsley Dunn and Samantha Worden also contributed to the gathering and interpretation of material about Curtiss.

In my time at the museum, I had the privilege of working with Jim White and Chris Geiselmann, both tireless researchers who could also tell when it was time to take a break and come back to earth for a while. Photographs and other illustrations appear courtesy of the archives in the Minor Swarthout Library at Curtiss Museum (abbreviated GHCM in references). Thanks go to Chuck Mitchell of the Photographic Center in Penn Yan, New York, for all he did in preparing photo images. Chuck and I collaborated on an earlier photo-biography, *Glenn H. Curtiss: Aviation Pioneer.*

Norm Brush, Art Wilder, and Jack Farmer are only three members of the large volunteer team that restores, conserves, reproduces, and, on a few exciting occasions, even flies Curtiss aircraft for the museum. Their work and research have been strong contributions not only to this book but also to our understanding of Curtiss aircraft as a whole. It is interesting that in their work they have several times found themselves bewildered as to why the Curtiss hands had constructed a certain feature in ways that seemingly could have been done much more simply. Inevitably, the original reasoning became clear several steps down the line. These men and women in the shop have also become expert at extracting construction data from photographs of wrecks, because the manner in which things come apart often reveals a great deal about how they were constructed.

Besides being ever ready to discuss technological details with me (always to my enlightenment), Jack and Norm read through and commented on the original manuscript of this work, as did Chris Geiselmann. Norm and I spent many enjoyable hours carefully examining the 1937 Curtiss Aerocar from stem to stern. Leo Opdycke (publisher of the invaluable *World War I Aero*) and Lou Casey (formerly of the National Air and Space Museum) paid the supreme compliment of reading and critiquing the manuscript before publication. Not all the differences raised have been resolved, but the work is certainly stronger for their insight.

Geoff Stein at the New York State Museum has done an expert job in pulling together the history of the Curtiss motorcycle business, while Larry Rinek's studies of Curtiss engines are first-rate. Glenn Bator at Otis Chandler Vintage Museum and independent restorers such as Wes Allen and Charlie Darling have learned a great deal about what those early machines were like.

No one researching Curtiss aircraft can get along without the works of Lou Casey and Peter Bowers, while Tom Crouch and Fred Howard are equally invaluable on the Wright brothers. For corporate history, I treasured chances to speak with Lou Eltscher. Morgan Wesson is always happy to be helpful when it comes to Alexander Graham Bell, while Don Dean Eklund's doctoral dissertation on Thomas Scott Baldwin is a necessity for people studying those pioneer days, especially in Lighter-Than-Air (LTA). Roger White's article on Glenn Curtiss's "land yachts" is an excellent summary of that period and its technology.

The field owes a special note of thanks to the late Bill Webster and his family. When Glenn Curtiss died, his widow gave her husband's three-volume hand-bound set of the *Bulletin of the Aerial Experiment Association* to their business associate C. W. Webster. The Websters preserved this treasure in pristine condition and donated it to the Curtiss Museum in 2001. Harold Morehouse and Marvel Dyer likewise donated their multi-volume typescript biographies of aviation pioneers, many of whom they knew; although far from perfect, this is a remarkable resource that may never be matched.

I owe a great debt to the visitors of the Curtiss Museum, and especially to the three thousand or more school students who come through the doors in class trips each year. It was my privilege for more than six and a half years to work closely with adult and student visitors. Their interest, enthusiasm, and curiosity certainly helped to stoke the fires of my own work. Every kid who came through our In-Flight programs, our Document-Based Questioning classes, our Curtiss birthday parties, our memorial services, and ribbon-cuttings has a share in this book.

The gang at the Bath Area Writers' Group was a source of constant encouragement and stimulus, and I thank them for that, besides thanking them for sharing their own work—not to mention their cookies. I've been blessed with a family who cares what I'm doing from coast to coast, from my sister Deborah and her colleagues at Mystic Seaport to our cousin on the West Coast, writer Heather King. My parents, Harold and Carolyn House, have always been cheerleaders. My mother died near the completion of the manuscript, an event that halted the progress of the manuscript for eight weeks; I'm sorry I couldn't have told her that it was finished. Of course, to be perfectly honest, she would have been enthusiastic because of the author, not the content, but that's OK with me.

My wife, Joyce, and our two college-student sons, Erik and Joshua, actually lived with me while all this was coming together, on top of full-time work and other projects. When they asked, "What are you working on?" and I replied, "The book," they were generally kind enough to ask, "Which one?" That's the kind of thing a writer likes to hear, and they're the kind of family a writer likes to have.

Chapter 1

Panorama:
Young Man in a Hurry

✷ ✷ ✷

Auspicious beginnings can sometimes turn sour; but sometimes, great achievements can grow from sour turns.

The Methodist Episcopal parsonage in Hammondsport, New York, held two happy couples on May 21, 1878. Reverend Claudius Curtiss and his wife, Ruth, had a new grandson, Glenn Hammond Curtiss. The boy's father, Frank, ran a harness business in the Finger Lakes village. The new mother, Lua Andrews Curtiss, played the organ, sang in the choir, and painted. The boy was healthy; the weekly *Hammondsport Herald* reported, "Harness is cheaper, and Curtiss is happy." [4, 6]

Methodist ministers were moved every year or two in those days, and 23-year-old Frank had followed his parents from manse to manse. But with a young wife and a new son, he was ready to settle in one place. His parents helped him to buy a house and vineyard on a knoll overlooking town, hard by the glen for which the baby had been named. Claudius was nearing the end of his ministry. The big old house on Castle Hill would serve as a retirement home when the family reunited after one or two more pastorates.

Glenn's younger sister, Rutha, was born in the new house, a few steps from the parsonage. Eventually, the elder Curtisses joined their offspring, no doubt looking forward to spending their final days among old parishioners and young children. But the end came far too quickly. Claudius was stricken while taking a steamboat excursion on Keuka Lake and died shortly after being rushed home. Five months later, Frank Curtiss followed him to the grave, struck down by "an inflammation of the stomach." All at once, the cozy family group was reduced to an old woman, her daughter-in-law, a four-year-old boy, a girl two weeks short of her second birthday, and a harness business that was beyond their means to run. [5, 6]

The women were very different. Ruth, with a lifetime behind her as a minister's wife, was hard working, practical, well known, well thought of, and skilled at working with people. She put the property's vineyard to work, despite her late husband's position as a temperance lecturer; the 1890 census listed her as a businessperson. Lua was artistic. She enjoyed painting as well as singing and playing the organ. She was athletic, an ice skater, and a skilled driver of horses. Attractive, vibrant, and intelligent, the young widow frequently attracted gentleman friends. But she was flighty. She couldn't manage money. She interfered in her children's lives. The people of Hammondsport gossiped that she was the second-worst housekeeper in town, much as they had gossiped that her late husband had had a drinking problem. [2, 3, 5, 6]

As if the family's stresses were not already overwhelming, at age six Rutha suffered a severe attack of meningitis. She recovered, but she had to learn to walk all over again. Her hearing also rapidly deteriorated, leaving the little girl deaf.

How two such different women, unrelated by blood, managed a home and a family together, in the face of all these strains, we can only guess. In later years, Glenn left his mother as soon as possible, making his home with his beloved grandmother. In letters to his mother, he would sign, "Sincerely yours, G.H. Curtiss." [6]

As a young boy, Glenn once pestered his grandmother to let him have some old clocks. When she finally relented, he disassembled them, cleaned them, figured out how they worked, and put them together again—and they ran. For one of his dismantling projects, he placed each part in a separate drawer in the kitchen, so that he could keep track of their proper order. At an early age, he showed signs of mechanical genius, while his grandmother showed signs of monumental forbearance.

It was indeed his grandmother who seems to have brought up the children. Rutha's notes on their childhood, written decades later for her nephew Glenn Junior and for history club members at Hammondsport High School, repeatedly describe their grandmother as instructing and guiding the children, while making decisions and arrangements about their upbringing and about the household.

Once, Lua and the children went to Pleasant Valley Cemetery to lay flowers on their father's grave. As Glenn was getting down from the wagon, the horse lurched forward, throwing Glenn to the ground and running a wheel over his head. The caretaker's family rigged up a poultice and Lua hurried the children home, where their grandmother redressed the wound and took charge of the situation.

Or so she thought. Ed Garton, the hired hand, had promised to take Glenn ice-skating, and the boy would brook no contradictions. He went skating with Ed, poultice and all, and came home none the worse for wear.

There were men around to take an interest in the fatherless boy, and Glenn learned to fish, swim, skate, and handle boats. He gained a reputation for being able to fix nearly anything, and mechanical operations fascinated him. He once pieced a quilt for his bed, sitting on his mother's lap as she worked the treadle sewing machine, and that is perhaps the only warm anecdote ever recorded about the two of them. He was clearly a determined child and, even at an early age, a meticulous planner. People said that he would think for half an hour before doing fifteen minutes of work. [2, 3]

Glenn played tag and war games with other boys in town, [1] went to school, and apparently did well enough without being outstanding. No doubt he checked the time by the clock in the Presbyterian steeple, the same way Hammondsporters do today. He played tricks on his little sister, but he learned the manual (hand-sign) alphabet with her, looked after her, and cradled her head in his lap when she fell asleep in church. He pumped the Presbyterian organ for ten cents a session but went to Sunday school at the Methodist Church. [2, 3] He enjoyed the outdoors. He enjoyed listening to the stories and poems his grandmother read to him. One of their favorites, written by an old friend of his grandmother's, was "Darius Green and His Flying Machine." They both considered it hilarious. [6]

Life in Rochester was vastly different from life in Hammondsport. The village by Keuka Lake had about a thousand people, much as it does now. Even then, the city on Lake Ontario was the third largest city in the nation's most populous state. Among its many amenities was a school for the deaf, which led Lua and Rutha to settle there, later sending for Glenn to come and join them.

Lua probably relished life in Rochester, where the city directory listed her as an artist. She took the trolley to Geneseo for teaching courses at the Normal School, and she ran a storefront school of her own in the slums, teaching music and, for the girls, sewing. Once, Glenn and Rutha gave up their own Christmas festivities, so that they could provide a Christmas tree, with small presents, for the children in the school.

Much as he missed his grandmother, Glenn seems to have thrived in the big city. He worked in a grocery store while finishing school through the eighth grade, where he excelled in math and did adequately in spelling. A growth spurt brought him to an impressive height, which he toned and toughened by joining the YMCA swim club. Glenn and his friend Ward Fisher got up before dawn to swim the aqueduct. Deciding that it was unnecessary to wake the family, Glenn rigged up a silent alarm clock that tugged a string tied to his big toe. [2, 3]

The Eastman Company was already booming because of its innovation of popular photography. Young Curtiss got a job stenciling film cases but found the work too slow and too dull. So he assembled a device to speed up the process, smuggled it into the plant, and suggested to the bosses that they put everyone on piece rate. When they agreed to try it, Glenn increased his output tenfold. Management quickly ferreted out his handiwork, duplicated it, and adopted it as the company's own. [6]

Curtiss also learned photography at Eastman and even built his own camera. However, he missed the outdoors. He saved his money, bought a bicycle, and went to work for Western Union. He had earlier bought a broken-down high-wheeler, refurbished it, and ridden it around town. The bike he used at Western Union, however, would have been a safety bicycle, that remarkable new technology that made drastic changes in the U.S. lifestyle, only to be overshadowed by the oncoming internal combustion technology. Glenn and Ward Fisher both got bicycles. They raced together and often took long trips, enjoying the freedom, friendship, and physical achievements. [2, 3]

When Rutha was old enough to board at her school, Lua married an old beau, J. Charles Adams, who owned a vineyard and orchard at Rock Stream on Seneca Lake. Glenn moved with her. He worked in the vineyard, helped his stepfather to build a couple of houses, and frequently cycled twenty miles to see his grandmother, who lived one lake to the west. But vineyard work was too hard for him, according to Rutha (the only thing anyone ever described as being "too hard" for Glenn—it may have simply taken more patience than he possessed). When their half-brother, Carl, was born, Glenn, in Rutha's words, "went home to Grandma for good." [2, 3, 6]

Despite occasional trips and summer visits, Glenn had been away from Hammondsport for most of his teen years. He would have to start village life all over again, and the tall young fellow making a home at his grandmother's must have seemed like a stranger to his old friends. On top of that, he didn't seem to do much! He was bright and mechanical, but neither his Eastman stenciling skills nor his Western Union delivery skills seemed to have much application in Hammondsport. He did a little racing, and he worked for a local photographer at the Saylor Studio, specializing in out-of-town jobs to which he would travel by bike. He didn't seem to want to work at anything agricultural. It wouldn't be surprising if village gossip dredged up memories of his flighty, artistic mother and his over-indulging father. Glenn had a lot of promise, but it didn't look as though he was going to amount to much.

The young men of town felt differently. C. Leonard "Tank" Waters, who had moved to Hammondsport while Glenn was away, stood by the drugstore one day and eyed the "new" boy suspiciously. Tank was Hammondsport's number one "wheelman," and the tall fellow cycling through the park looked like a dangerous threat to Tank's popularity.

Running up to Glenn, Tank asked where the fellow had gotten his "fancy, racy bike," asked if he could try it out, and offered a ride on his own machine in exchange.

"How that boy could ride," Tank remembered halfway through the following century. "After that . . . he was always first while I was second." The two formed a deep friendship that endured until they were parted by death. Tank was even more impressed on learning that Glenn had rejuvenated his "snappy racer" from a dilapidated used machine that he had saved money to buy. "Right here is where his mechanical ability showed up for . . . you could not tell it from a new one."

Tank testified that between his cycling skills and his personality, Glenn attracted a gang of boys who looked up to him as their leader. The forbidding face Glenn presented for cameras makes descriptions of an attractive personality sound odd. But if he smiled only rarely before the lens, he seems to have done it quite frequently when safe from photographers. He may have been quiet, but he had close friends, and former students, workers, and neighbors spoke of him enthusiastically decades later.

One cycling feat in particular set the stage for later triumphs on motorcycles and in early airplanes. Vintner Harry Champlin let the boys race their bikes at the trotting horse track on the grounds of his Pleasant Valley Wine Company. One way into the track was over a five-foot plank, twelve inches in width, which was laid across a muddy ditch three feet deep. Any weight bowed the plank down, tipping bike and rider into the mud. No one else in town ever made it across the plank. Glenn Curtiss never missed. Tank attributed this success to Glenn's speed in taking the plank. While this no doubt contributed to his success, Glenn seems to have had an almost preternatural sense of balance. This control and awareness of himself in space, combined with a sharp eye, would contribute to his later success with shooting, driving, or riding at speed, and in controlling primitive aircraft.

Glenn also revealed at this time a deep competitive streak. His first prize competition was a bicycle race at Bath Fair, the Steuben County fair that traces its roots back to 1796, soon after the first white settlement. Tank and Glenn decided that their only real competition would be a "rich boy" who owned a Columbia with a spring fork that meant for easier riding on ruts but cut down the speed (because some energy otherwise expended on forward motion went into spring action). Glenn and Tank took a hoe to the fairgrounds early on the morning of the race and cut ruts along the fence in the backstretch, after which they sailed past the rich boy in the race.

If Glenn's mechanical flair and leadership skills re-emerged later in life, so did his tendency toward sharp practice. And so too did his dry New England-style wit and his penchant for practical jokes, all the more effective because people didn't expect them from him. He raised rabbits for a while, and there was a stir of interest in a strain of red rabbits that was predicted to revolutionize the meat market. Glenn announced that he had one of these in his hutch, enlisting Tank's help to dye the creature. When other breeders begged to buy a pair, the boys washed the dye out and sadly reported that the lagomorph had died. Tank recalled that unlike most practical jokers, Glenn enjoyed a joke even if someone played it on him. [7, 8]

Jokester Glenn doubtless enjoyed the scheme of druggist and bicycle agent Jim Smellie, who smuggled into town an advanced Stearns racing bike, on which Glenn appeared at the starting line of a free-for-all race sponsored by one of Smellie's competitors. When the disgusted competitor canceled the race, Smellie immediately took it over, making good on the prizes, and cheerfully watching Glenn sail to easy victory. Smellie urged Stearns to take Glenn on as a professional racer, describing him as "a zany fellow" (Fig. 1.1). [6]

His sense of humor, inventiveness, and sharp eye for dollars combined during one grape-picking season, when Glenn asked the boss if he could get half again as much piece rate by doubling his output. When the boss agreed, Glenn rigged up a cutter blade to fit over his thumb. He filled twice his rate of trays, got his raise, and made more cutters for his friends. None of the other workers used them long, though, finding them very tough on the thumbs.

Fig. 1.1 Notice the toe clips and dropped handle bars—not to mention the determined face. Even at an early age, Curtiss allied first-rate equipment with first-rate skills to make a name for himself.

Glenn must have made an odd figure around the village, quiet but with an unpredictable streak, soft-spoken but athletic, magnetic within a certain crowd, at once generous and quick to spot a buck, mechanical and incisive but living with his grandma while working odd jobs. Always active, always thinking, always working at mechanical items to improve them, and reportedly able to fix anything, he was, Tank Waters wrote, "never idle a moment, and nights when other boys would be calling on their girls Glenn would be home in bed reading one of the two foreign and one American bicycle periodicals." [7, 8]

Glenn apparently preferred a rifle approach to a shotgun approach. Once, when he was visiting his grandmother while still living in Rochester, he had gone cycling one afternoon, noticed an attractive young girl picking grapes, and asked her for a glass of water. Sixteen-year-old Lena Pearl Neff, according to Glenn's sister, "had large brown eyes, brown hair with a glint of gold, was very pretty, very quiet and ladylike. She was fond of music and sang in the M.E. [Methodist Episcopal] choir. . . . He escorted her to Sunday evening service, choir practice, went on long hikes with another couple, took steamboat rides on the lake—and went on Sunday School picnics—Glenn easily became her favorite beau." [2, 3]

Lena was, by all reports, Glenn's only girl—except for proposing to one of the Arland girls when she was three and he four. Quiet and ladylike Lena certainly was, but she would also ride bicycles and motorcycles, purchase and drive autos at a time when many Americans had never seen one, work in the office of the motorcycle factory, and travel the world with her husband, supporting and encouraging him through financial reversals, technological roadblocks, and legal travails. She was 17, and he was only ten weeks short of 20, when they were married in the parsonage of the Presbyterian Church in Hammondsport (Fig. 1.2). They didn't announce their marriage beforehand, and Glenn falsely reported his age as 21 on the paperwork. Curtiss's biographer C. R. Roseberry has suggested that he did this to evade seeking permission, which would not have been forthcoming, from his mother. Lua Curtiss invested a good deal of energy over the years into breaking up the marriages of both Glenn and Rutha—unsuccessfully, in Glenn's case.

Glenn and Lena moved in with Grandma. Lena's mother worried over Glenn's lack of obvious prospects or even having a current income worthy of note. Mr. Neff assured her that the boy had a great future and would one day do well, but her concern was certainly justified. Apart from part-time photography, odd jobs, and the occasional bicycle race, Glenn wasn't earning much money.

However, Glenn had always fixed the other fellows' bicycles, and bikes were becoming more and more common. Slowly the repair work became steady, and Glenn had a business. Malinda Bennitt, a local businessperson and cofounder of the weekly *Hammondsport Herald*, had always kept a close eye on local young people, encouraging them whenever she could in practical ways. She had watched Glenn grow up, and she now let him use a vacant store she owned on Pulteney Square, directly across from the bandstand in the

Fig. 1.2 Betrothal portrait, with Lena in her wedding dress. We know that Curtiss took self-portraits, and this appears to be one; the position of his hands suggests a concealed bulb.

park. Glenn opened a bike shop, selling a sideline in his father's former field of harnesses from a barn in back. Bennitt had unwittingly become the godmother for a giant industry.

Besides his own work, Curtiss helped out on the side in the bicycle agency of druggist Jim Smellie. Through 1900 and 1901, Smellie divested himself of the bike business, transferring parts, sales, and service lines to Curtiss and taking out display advertisements urging his customers to patronize the new business on the other side of the square (Fig. 1.3). As a young man, Curtiss might have struggled not only with the fact of his own youth but also with villagers' memories of his parents' behavior. Perhaps this encouraged him to add maturity to his appearance by growing a new mustache.

Curtiss set up seasonal branch stores nearby in Bath and Corning. He contracted a machine shop in Addison, New York, to make bicycles from his designs, using the brand name "Hercules." Besides the bike and harness businesses, he sold sewing machines. He ran an apple press. The vineyard at his grandmother's house remained in operation. Curtiss set up an acetylene lamp system in own shop—electricity in Hammondsport, a brand-new proposition, reached only a few buildings and was available only part-time. Other businesses, including the post office, contracted with Curtiss for acetylene lights. [6]

Curtiss, at last, was amounting to something, flourishing under the best influences a small town can offer. Life was so busy by 1900 that he may not have noticed news of a new product coming out of Buffalo, the Thomas Auto-Bi, the United States' first production

Fig. 1.3 Curtiss (far left with military-style cap) and what he later called his "industrial incubator." He ran the harness business out of the barn in the rear.

motorcycle. In 1901, Lena gave birth to Carlton Curtiss, but their joy was alloyed by the baby's heart and respiratory problems. Even so, in the week of June 23, Curtiss combined business with pleasure, joining several friends to follow the track already trod by numerous Hammondsporters, making his way to the Pan-American Exposition in Buffalo. [4]

REFERENCES

1. Curtiss, Glenn H. (and Augustus Post), *The Curtiss Aviation Book,* Frederick Stokes Company, New York, 1912.

2. Curtiss, Rutha, to "Dear Friend" (probably Nina Arland), undated manuscript, GHCM Yorkers Collection.

3. ———, "Little Known Facts About Little Known People—As Observed and Told to Me—R. C. Written for Glenn H. Curtiss Jr. by His Aunt Rutha 1952," manuscript in GHCM Curtiss Family File.

4.   The *Hammondsport Herald,* published weekly throughout Curtiss's lifetime, includes multitudinous references to Curtiss, his works, and his times. (Curtiss Museum holds a microfilmed set.)

5.   Mitchell, Charles R., and Kirk W. House, *Glenn H. Curtiss, Aviation Pioneer,* Arcadia Publishing, Charleston, SC, 2001.

6.   Roseberry, C. R., *Glenn Curtiss: Pioneer of Flight,* Doubleday, Garden City, NY, 1972.

7.   Waters, C. Leonard, to Nancy Hutches, undated typescript, GHCM Yorkers Collection.

8.   ———, to Nancy Hutches, undated typescript, GHCM Yorkers Collection.

Chapter 2

Close-Up:
Hammondsport on the Brink

What technology did young Mr. Curtiss find available as the twentieth century dawned in 1901, and what attitudes toward technology and innovation had helped to form his growing mind?

Hammondsport and the Finger Lakes lie in the heart of the so-called Burnt-Over District of western New York. Now regarded as a bastion of rock-ribbed conservative Republicans, the region has indeed been Republican since the party was born. But at that time, it was a party of daring innovations, and western New Yorkers were among the most radical people in the nation.

In the town of Seneca Falls, which was two lakes to the east, a meeting in 1848 had counterpointed Europe's year of revolution with a Declaration of Sentiments that began, "We hold these truths to be self-evident, that all men and women are created equal." Frederick Douglass, who had left his home in Rochester to attend the conference on women's rights, enthusiastically signed the declaration. An escaped slave, Douglass was a newspaper publisher, writer, speaker, and tireless warrior for abolition. Douglass orchestrated Underground Railroad routes throughout the lakes and into Canada. Although he had long been at rest in Rochester's Mount Hope Cemetery by 1901, his old comrade in arms, Susan B. Anthony, kept her house on nearby Madison Street, ceaselessly battling for women's suffrage.

Settled largely by New Englanders pushing west with the frontier, the region bore in its villages, architecture, society, and intellectual interests the marks of that region. It was a place of intellectual and social ferment as early as the Second Great Awakening, a series of evangelical Christian revivals that bred passions for abolition, women's rights, education, and temperance. The ferment of the Awakening also set the stage for newer religious ideas—Mormonism, Spiritualism, Seventh-Day Adventism, and the Jehovah's Witness movement all sprung from the soil of western New York. Shakers founded two settlements in the area. Perfectionists announced "Bible Communism," Complex Marriage, and an elegant new design of flatware at Oneida. Even before the Second Awakening, Jemima Wilkinson, the Public Universal Friend, had ruled her own religious community near the north end of Keuka Lake, not far from the spot where skeptic campaigner Robert Ingersoll would later be born.

A century of ideological turmoil had exhausted residents of the region. As the new century dawned, the old issues of temperance, education, and women's rights remained important. New issues had a hard time engaging the passions of the past, although a Hammondsport clothier advertised in 1901 that he never sold sweatshop products, and a high school senior in nearby Bath delivered a commencement address denouncing trusts. [4]

Although social and political innovation were growing less important to Hammondsporters and their neighbors, technological innovation now stirred their blood vigorously. George Eastman in Rochester was making a fortune and building an empire. "You take the pictures and we do the rest!" he cried, prying photography away from the realm of alchemy by placing its joys in the hands of ordinary people. Elmira businessman Mathias Arnot was backing the work of Augustus Herring on hang gliders, as he puzzled over ways to make men fly. Corning Glass Works, in the same county as Hammondsport, was slowly making progress in creating a type of glass that would hold colors truly and consistently, while withstanding almost instantaneous extremes of temperature and humidity. In addition to finally standardizing railroad signals and lanterns, Corning's work would enter American kitchens as Pyrex glassware.

Hammondsport valued learning. Its academy (a public school) maintained a twelve-year program, a postgraduate teacher-training course, and a 600-volume high-school library. The public library held more than 2,000 volumes. (Its first acquisition in 1875, *The Scarlet Letter,* is still in the collection.) The *Herald* reported scientific news regularly in 1901, informing readers that doctors had concluded that yellow fever was spread by mosquitoes and plague by rats. Readers also learned news from scientific publications suggesting that currents, rather than lunar gravitation, caused tides and that there were proposals for contacting the planet Mars.

News from Cornell University and Geneseo Normal School helped to fill the columns of the newspaper, along with news of Keuka College, located near Penn Yan on the northern end of the lake. Keuka was struggling to raise $25,000 to qualify for a $50,000 challenge grant from the Ball brothers, canning-jar magnates of Muncie, Indiana. They eventually succeeded; a hundred years later, Ball Hall remains the central feature of Keuka's campus. [4]

If the small town of Hammondsport was soon to become a very unusual town, in 1901 it was typical—a small village with indifferent road connections, teetering on the brink between the nineteenth century, with a way of life a thousand years old, and the twentieth century, with ways of life beyond human experience and, almost, beyond imagining.

HAMMOND'S PORT

When Judge Lazarus Hammond bought the land and incipient village in 1807, he probably did not recognize its full potential. However, when the Erie Canal was completed in 1825, it sparked an economic boom in the state of New York. Hammondsport was on the fringe of this excitement until 1830, when the 6-mile Crooked Lake Canal along Keuka Outlet linked Penn Yan (on Keuka Lake) to Dresden (on Seneca).

By itself, the new waterway might not have been especially significant. When the Erie Canal sparked a canal craze across the Northeast, many poorly managed (or poorly sited) ditches soon went broke. However, another canal, leaving Seneca Lake at Geneva, joined the main Erie route. Hammondsport suddenly was the final port—or, more to the point, the first port—in a water-shipping route that could circle the globe.

Westward traffic on the Erie Canal reached Buffalo, Cleveland, Chicago, and Duluth; or, turning downstream from Buffalo, it found its way to Quebec and Montreal. Heading eastward from Geneva, Hammondsport cargo reached Albany and New York, which was rapidly becoming the busiest port and biggest city in the booming new nation. Past New York, the seas of the world were open.

The 30-ton schooner *Sally* had plied Crooked Lake (as Keuka was then called) as early as 1803, but the canal connection gave rise to the center-wheel steamer *Keuka* in 1835. From a five-county area of New York and Pennsylvania, goods were hauled by team to Hammondsport, then set on steamboats for shipping to Penn Yan and transfer to barges.

King Steam ruled the nineteenth century, and approximately 30 steamboats (some of them small launches) cruised "Crooked Lake" in the next 90 years. The 80-foot *Keuka* had twin hulls, producing a shallow draft that allowed her to run up onto landings cleared along the shore. However, landings soon became more sophisticated and had permanent docks. *Keuka*'s successors usually had walking-beam engines. By 1892, the *Mary Bell* was built as a 150-ft steel-hulled, twin-screw vessel, capable of traveling at 20 mph and carrying more than 400 passengers. In the 1890s, three shipping companies competed on Keuka Lake. Passage between Penn Yan and Hammondsport—a distance of 22 miles—cost a dime. [4]

The low price reflected competition and economy of scale, rather than lack of demand. The northern and southern ends of the lake would never have direct, or even worthwhile, rail connections until after the death of Curtiss. Dirt roads joining them were poor. Mail went by steamer, with land carriage authorized for only those months when ice closed navigation. [4]

While Penn Yan and Hammondsport never had a rail link, Penn Yan had the advantage of a New York Central route, as well as a Northern Central route. Hammondsport had to rely on a short-line, the 10-mile Bath & Hammondsport (B&H). Opened as a narrow gauge in 1875, it was rebuilt with standard gauge in 1888. B&H joined the Erie in Bath, which was also served by the Delaware, Lackawanna, & Western (DL&W).

This access to the Southern Tier rail lines, combined with excellent steamer connections along the lake, was good for shipping in Hammondsport, especially for the wine and grape business, which had inspired the short-line in the first place. It also stimulated excursion and vacation traffic. The Erie Railroad aggressively marketed trips from Rochester, Elmira, and Binghamton, which included winery tours and a cruise on the lake. In 1901 (Figs. 2.1 and 2.2), organized groups were able to book cruises from Hammondsport as

Fig. 2.1 Hammondsport around 1901. At far right is the waterfront with its steam-boat wharves. In the foreground is Kingsley Flats, which would later become the Hammondsport flying field. Beyond the flats, the B&H Railroad tracks slide toward the waterfront. As was typical in those days, most land throughout the Northeast was cleared for pasture or tillage—in Hammondsport, vineyards were (and remain) prominent features of the landscape. The wooded cleft behind the village is the Hammondsport Glen, for which Curtiss was named. His middle name, of course, came from the village itself.

part of their rail package to or from the Pan-American Exposition in Buffalo. Resorts along the shore catered to visitors from New York City and other big cities. Clusters of summer cottages were built, including Corning Landing, a settlement favored by people from the nearby glass-making center.

A voyage from Hammondsport to Penn Yan by steamer (five trips daily in 1901) took about three hours. To Bath by rail (six trips a day) was about thirty minutes, although both trips could be delayed by flag and whistle-stops. If you were in a hurry to get from Bath to Buffalo, the DL&W express could do the job in slightly more than two hours. A 7:47 P.M. Erie train got Hammondsporters to New York City eleven hours and ten minutes later. Morning papers from New York arrived in Hammondsport in the early afternoon.

Fig. 2.2 The large white house on the knoll in the right foreground is the Curtiss homestead, later the site of both the motorcycle factory and the aircraft factory. This photograph reverses the view of Fig. 2.1. The Curtiss home sat near the glen.

If you had business or pleasure in Pulteney, 10 miles up in the hills to the northwest, you could take the stage, which arrived from Pulteney at 11:00 A.M. and started its return trip at half-past noon. Another option was to ride the steamer for an hour to Pulteney Landing, then find your way 1.5 miles up a steep slope. [4]

No one in Hammondsport owned an automobile in 1901. As far as we know, no auto had ever passed through town.

POWER AND LIGHT

The rapid spread of electric power was a hallmark of late-nineteenth-century America. It didn't reach Hammondsport until 1898, when P. G. Zimmer installed a 3-kW DC generator to light the waterfront B&H machine shop, where he was superintendent. However, this miracle was too great to waste on machinery. The B&H directed Zimmer to deliver power to its office and docks. Other lakeside businesses quickly signed on, and Zimmer faced an immediate demand to extend his lines uphill for shops and residences. The process would have gone more smoothly if Zimmer been more knowledgeable about electricity.

Before Zimmer set up his electrical generator, and even as his web of wires was extending into the village, young Glenn Curtiss generated acetylene for his own shop, the post office, and several other stores, giving them a light more brilliant than that from oil or kerosene. (Candles and kerosene were still standard features of homes and businesses, even where electricity was already in use.)

From his reading, Curtiss understood that acetylene gas could be developed from carbide, but he had no information on creating an apparatus. Making his own without a pattern or guidance, he created equipment that had a reputation for being economical on carbide. Curtiss used a heavy cast-iron lid to cover the tank and serve as a safety valve; too much gas would lift the lid and escape. One night, the water valve was not turned off tightly, and acetylene continued to generate. The lid, unfortunately, stuck tight. In the early morning hours, the tank exploded, waking the neighbors and blasting the cast-iron lid through the roof of Curtiss's shop. Because no flames were nearby, no fire resulted. [8]

As William Manchester has observed with respect to the Middle Ages, the world of 1901 in a small town such as Hammondsport was still a world lit mainly by fire. Streetlights burned kerosene, and the village appropriated a dollar a year to buy matches for "the old lamplighter."

Electricity was used primarily for lighting in 1901. The village had requested lighting for the bandstand almost as soon as it became available but required that Zimmer run his line up the Glen Creek rather than befoul the streets. The town's fastidiousness did not last for long; by 1901, Zimmer's lines and poles were lining Lake Street. When the Wheeler barn was moved in May from Vine Street through Lake to Main, workers had to remove the wires first. [4]

As the web extended, residences hooked onto it at $1.50 per light. The Presbyterian Church on Pulteney Square and the Methodist Episcopal Church on Lake Street both signed up, observing that the new system would make summer services much cooler. The Methodists paid for their installation by voluntary subscription.

Zimmer bought at least three major pieces of equipment in 1901, including a Westinghouse dynamo and a Corliss gasoline engine (perhaps the first internal combustion device in town). However, high demand, low capital, and limited understanding always seemed to conspire in frustrating both Zimmer and his customers. Even after World War I, electricity in Hammondsport was not constant. It came on at sunset and shut down at eleven, with additional hours Wednesday mornings for using washing machines and vacuum cleaners. [4]

Power for purposes other than lighting continued to rely mostly on steam. Public water came to Hammondsport in 1895, and engineers located the reservoir high enough in the hills for its head to throw a stream of water above the steeple on the Presbyterian Church. Later, a new source was established with a coal-fired steam pump.

Zimmer's hectic work wrought one change in 1901 that, while trivial in and of itself, no doubt provoked an unsettling sense of change for Hammondsport children and parents. Beginning in May, nightly curfew was sounded not by the town hall bell but by the whistle at the electric light plant. [4]

LIFE AT HOME

No radio, no television, no telephone, no modern conveniences to break down, no automobiles allowing people to scurry around frantically—life must have been simpler and richer in those days.

Maybe.

If a person wanted to wash clothes back then, he or she might have used a Centennial Star washing machine, patented in Hammondsport in 1876. In the early days, the machine was filled by hauling buckets of water from a hand pump. By 1901, a hose from the public water system was used. After adding soap and dirty clothes, a person would agitate the washing machine by working an upright handle back and forth, while pushing a horizontal handle in and out. It clearly took some muscle to work water, soap, and clothes between two huge paddles, but at least the person wasn't tied to the clock of an automatic timer; he or she could stop laboring whenever the clothes seemed clean enough. Then, the plug was pulled to drain the well. The clothes needed to be rinsed thoroughly (more pumping, more carrying, more agitating, more draining), wrung, dried, pressed, folded, and put away, after which it was no doubt time for lunch or supper, or maybe even bed. Or maybe a second load of wash.

National prosperity and Yankee ingenuity were combining to make Hammondsport homes very different places from those of a half-century earlier. Coal heating had become commonplace. It is not clear how cooking was performed, but it may still have depended largely on wood-fired ranges because there were no gasworks, and electricity was available for only a few hours each day. There was another option, however. Kerosene stoves were heavily advertised in the *Herald,* and all that expenditure presumably meant that people were buying them. Kerosene stoves, of course, would be vastly more convenient and compact than woodstoves, in addition to being much cooler during operation. Moreover, they would eliminate the need for cutting, storing, and hauling wood. It is not clear where villagers bought their kerosene, but presumably it was available from the merchants who sold the stoves.

In no place was change more evident than in the bathroom, which was developing into a separate place for washing and elimination. Public water, of course, made this logical— bringing pipes and drains to a single location was more efficient—but a truly reliable siphon toilet did not appear until 1895. It is impossible to know the elimination procedures of Hammondsport in 1901, but photographs from the period show that nearly every tiny yard has a little house behind the residence. If these are indeed outhouses (which seems likely), we can only hope that villagers were all hooked into the new water system, rather than depending on wells in those same crowded yards.

The recognition of mosquitoes as vectors for yellow fever closely followed a development that probably was first thought of as a matter of comfort. Mass-produced window screens had become available in the previous twenty years, and screen doors in the previous five. Recognizing that there was no air conditioning, it becomes easy, if a little frightening, to imagine sleeping (or trying to sleep) through sweltering heat with all windows tightly closed, or with all windows open, admitting mosquitoes and flies with any welcome stray breeze.

Consider also the kitchen, when nothing could be cooked without a wood fire, either closed up tight against the insects or opened wide and offering them a feast. Combine this dilemma with the inability to chill more than small quantities of food, and that not very reliably, not to mention the frequent lack of running water, which was often of questionable quality.

It has been suggested that screens were the first step in the increasing isolation of U.S. families, tempting them to stay sealed in their homes rather than sitting on their porches or strolling through their neighborhoods in the evening. (It was cooler outside, and the insects were no worse outdoors than indoors.) The suggestion is probably correct. However, screens were also, for many, the first step in increasing the life span of U.S. families. Combined with the contemporary discoveries of Pasteur and of Semmelweiss, public water, siphon toilets, and even the humble window screen meant an excellent chance to live past childhood and live to what previous generations would have considered a prodigious age.

With a huge lake nearby, Hammondsport had easy access to ice. Iceboxes, however, were usually small contraptions and were not reliable for keeping food safe in any but small quantities and for short periods.

Innovations such as the hand-cranked "record player," which employed wax cylinders, were also creeping into U.S. households. However, in most homes, the most complex piece of machinery was probably still the treadle sewing machine. Indeed, although these innovations were available and even becoming commonplace, huge numbers of U.S. homes continued to lack basic features such as electric light, running water, and indoor plumbing until midway through the twentieth century. [3, 5, 6]

GETTING AROUND ON YOUR OWN

No matter how up-to-date your home is or how well it shields you from the elements, most people want to get out of it sooner or later. As we have seen, Hammondsporters in 1901 had the train and the steamboat available, not to mention small sailing, rowing, and canoeing craft on Keuka Lake. Apart from walking, most individual travel relied on horses. (There probably was not much riding going on, and little use, in this region, of oxen or mules.)

A decade earlier, an explosion had burst on the U.S. scene. Its effects had reached Hammondsport five years later, and those effects were still swelling.

The explosion was preceded by two short-lived boomlets. The first, around the time of the Civil War, was the velocipede or "boneshaker," an early two-wheeler with pedals directly driving the front axle. With metal or wooden wheels and a seat covering that often was limited to a single layer of carpet, these uncomfortable contraptions certainly earned their nickname. Moreover, because a single revolution of the pedals produced a single revolution of the front drive wheel, speed could be increased only by pedaling faster. Riders quickly reached their upper limits.

Increasing the circumference of the wheel, however, gave greater road distance for each revolution. This insight led to the high-wheeler "ordinary" or "penny-farthing" bicycle, some of which offered such optional equipment as spoon brakes. Spills, which were common, generally pitched the rider head first from a perch five or six feet above the road. This led to moving the high drive wheel to the rear. Spills continued to be common, but the rider was more likely to slip back, instead of forward, giving him a fighting chance of landing on his feet.

Both velocipedes and high-wheelers enjoyed crazes, but both crazes sputtered out when their shortcomings overwhelmed their novelty. Variations such as three-wheelers failed to catch on. [1]

Around 1890, however, the aptly named safety bicycle arrived from England. Wheel sizes were closely, and often exactly, matched. Moreover, these bicycles were about the size of modern bicycles, which means that the rider was set low on the frame—low enough for his or her toes to touch the ground. The frame had its still-familiar diamond pattern. The drive pedals transmitted power to the rear wheel by means of a chain and sprockets. Coaster brakes and pneumatic tires completed the picture. The modern bike had come to the land of the free.

Americans embraced the new immigrant enthusiastically, instantly grasping that it would make them even more free. Earlier versions, such as the high-wheeler that Glenn Curtiss had repaired and ridden as a boy in Rochester, became quaint curios of a benighted past. Curtiss bought a safety bike to get his Western Union job, rode one to earn the loyalty of Hammondsport boys, and fixed safety bikes to make a living. Other emerging entrepreneurs such as Henry Ford and the Wright brothers were following similar paths.

Observers have often commented on the independence that automobiles offered Americans, and particularly young Americans, who could suddenly get out of town unchaperoned. The rapid adoption of automobiles after 1903 has overshadowed the fact that the process began a decade earlier. Young women took to bikes as enthusiastically as their beaux and brothers did. Bloomers, (relatively) short skirts, and split skirts became more popular and more acceptable. Women could ride the roads on their own, in groups, in couples, or even in the company of men.

By 1899, the United States had nearly 10 million cyclists. A single Chicago store at that time sold 1,000 bikes a day. The horse population dropped by 7 million in three years (a trend abetted by the spread of electric streetcar lines). Three hundred manufacturers took in a total of $60,000,000 a year. [2] On the square in Hammondsport at the beginning of 1901, there were three dealers—George Lyon, the jeweler; Jim Smellie, the pharmacist; and Glenn Curtiss, the harnessmaker. Curtiss spent far less on advertising than did either of his competitors. [4]

What was Curtiss's bicycle like? He manufactured at least a few batches before becoming caught up with motorcycles, but no record or description survives. When he raced, he used a startlingly modern machine. There were no gears to shift—these would not arrive for another year or two—but photographs show that he had toe clips and dropped handlebars. This may have been a Stearns machine. Jim Smellie was a Stearns dealer, and in correspondence with the Syracuse firm, Smellie urged them to somehow accommodate the "poor zany" boy who couldn't afford the $70 top-of-the-line racer, but whose patronage and endorsement would provoke a host of sales among the local fellows, not only in Hammondsport but throughout the region.

The market imploded, of course, when automobiles became available in large numbers. Bikes, for several generations, were what you rode until you got your license. However, it was pointed out that "Several bicycle innovations, such as the chain drive, differential gears, and shock absorbers, were crucial to the development of the auto. The bike boom years stimulated the production of better steels, rubber compounds, ball bearings, and tubings; they accelerated improvements in tools, machinery, engineering, assembly lines, and distribution." [2]

The popularity of bicycles also stimulated attention to streets and roads. The town of Urbana, which includes the village of Hammondsport, had 71 highway supervisors in 1901, each responsible for a stretch of road, probably near his home. However, the roads were all earth, and the village relied on a horsed-drawn sprinkler, repeatedly making its rounds, to keep the streets in condition and hold down the dust. Penn Yan, in contrast, operated a steamroller on its streets. [4]

Mud, dust, urine, and horse manure were all hazards of negotiating the streets, as were the washouts, ruts, and potholes that are common to dirt or gravel roads. When cyclists crowded their way onto wooden sidewalks with pedestrians, the results were extremely annoying to all concerned.

Streets were upgraded, and a new class of public official came into being—the county sidepath commissioner. Cinder sidepaths were established along country roads throughout Steuben County. Paid for by mandatory annual bicycle tags, the sidepaths separated bicycles from automobile traffic. Ironically, sidepaths probably gave cyclists a surface far superior to that of the roads they paralleled. [4, 7, 8]

There are two striking facts about the 1890s safety bicycle. First, the basic machine remains almost unchanged more that 100 years later. Second, the safety bike is in some ways a retro production, leaping back almost half a century to the general configuration of the early boneshaker. If the dead-end high-wheeler phase is ignored, it seems that the bicycle sprang into existence almost complete, became mature with the adoption of a rear-wheel chain drive, and has since been fine-tuned, most notably by the addition of differential gearing and caliper brakes.

One very simple innovation, however, still eluded manufacturers of 1901. The kickstand was only a dream.

If a person were more traditional, not up to the physical demands of cycling, or had a load to carry, a horse was the logical choice. Buggies and wagons were commonplace, and Curtiss's mother was known as an expert driver. While sleighs would have been a necessity in certain circumstances, they seem to have been regarded more as pleasure vehicles than as working vehicles. Sleighing in 1901 began in the third week of January but later that year resumed by the beginning of December. [4]

Not everyone had a vehicle, and not everyone had a horse. If a young man wanted to take his lady friend to see the bright lights of Bath, he could rent a horse and buggy. The livery at the Steuben House hotel offered "buss" service throughout the village, in addition to renting and stabling.

Even if a person had a horse, it was not necessarily available all the time. A horse that had worked all day in the vineyard, or in front of a dray, needed to be cared for and rested when the day was over. If someone wanted to hitch up the horse for courting or traveling, he either gave it a day off beforehand or hitched up a second animal. Trucks and automobiles, when they arrived, were delightfully versatile and theoretically available at a moment's notice, for any purpose, 24 hours a day.

Deliveries, of course, were handled by horse-drawn conveyances, including, in 1901, A. D. B. Grimley's new ice wagon. That summer was the hottest on record, and the *Herald* reported an intriguing innovation that was appearing on the East Coast—a horse hat to keep off the sun. Within a month, the newspaper reported that D. H. Talmadge had tried out the idea, apparently with satisfactory results, on his blind dray horse. [4]

The fire companies depended on muscle power in 1901, and the Curtiss Museum collection includes several pieces of apparatus from the period. The hose truck of the Citizens Hose Company was hand-drawn by four firefighters. The ladder truck of the Hammondsport Hook and Ladder, drawn by a pair of matched grays, was a gorgeously decorated showpiece and obviously a source of community pride, but it also was used in action. (There is fire damage along one side.) A one-horse pumper also was in use, not to mention a high-wheeled tank apparatus that would have been hurried to the scene by two firefighters on foot.

Human nature never changes, and having horses in the mix only added another set of complications. Horse-drawn accidents outnumbered automobile accidents in news reports as late as 1918. [4]

Vineyard horses worked on the hillsides. Small, intelligent, and marvelously patient, these animals were trained to instantly come to a stop in case of a snag, lest they tear up any of the precious vines. Winemaking was a field of innovation as well as tradition. Lena Neff Curtiss's Uncle Frank had invented a wire hood to use in place of wax on champagne bottles, and manufactured these in shops by the lake. *Harpers Weekly* had earlier profiled Hammondsport winemaking. No one seems to have taken up the suggestion the *American Wine Press* made during 1901 that cannon fire could break up approaching thunderstorms. [4]

Although telephones were used in the village and in many surrounding communities, Hammondsport residents depended on the telegraph to keep in touch with the outside world *without* traveling. A new world was on the verge of being born.

On what brink did Hammondsport tremble in 1901? In the village, elderly people, such as Malinda Bennitt, had known veterans of the American Revolution. Elsewhere in New York, veterans from the War of 1812 still clung to life. The town supported an active Grand Army of the Republic post for Union Civil War veterans, the youngest of whom were now in their early fifties. Some of these men no doubt cradled newborn grandchildren on their knees in 1901. In 1908, they might have taken those grandchildren to see the first airplane flights in Hammondsport. Those same grandchildren would surely remember that day when they sat before their color television sets, newly retired with Social Security, to watch Neil Armstrong take one small step on the Moon.

REFERENCES

1. Berkebile, Don, "Bicycles," in Andrea DiNito [mng. ed.], *The Encyclopedia of Collectibles: Beads to Boxes,* Time-Life Books, Alexandria, VA, 1978.

2. Crown, Judith, and Glenn Coleman, *No Hands: The Rise and Fall of the Schwinn Company, an American Institution,* Henry Holt and Company, New York, 1996.

3. Curtiss, Rutha, undated manuscript describing Curtiss home in Hammondsport, GHCM Yorkers Collection.

4. The *Hammondsport Herald,* published weekly throughout Curtiss's lifetime, includes multitudinous references to Curtiss, his works, and his times. (Curtiss Museum holds a microfilmed set.)

5. Ierley, Merritt, *The Comforts of Home: The American House and the Evolution of Modern Convenience,* Clarkson Potter, New York, 1999.

6. ———, *Open House: A Guided Tour of the American Home, 1637–Present,* Henry Holt and Company, New York, 1999.

7. Mitchell, Charles R., and Kirk W. House, *Glenn H. Curtiss, Aviation Pioneer,* Arcadia Publishing, Charleston, SC, 2001.

8. Waters, C. Leonard, to Nancy Hutches, undated typescript, GHCM Yorkers Collection.

Chapter 3

Panorama:
Two-Wheeled Terror

★ ★ ★

Curtiss left no record of his trip to the Buffalo Pan-Am (a World's Fair) in the week of June 23. He accompanied Frank Smith and Arthur Stanton, presumably taking advantage of excursion rates on either the Erie or the DL&W. They probably stopped over at least one night, perhaps staying at a boardinghouse or hotel, or taking a room in one of the many private homes that were cashing in on the spectacular attraction. Perhaps they stayed with Tank Waters, who was practicing nursing in Buffalo, or with some other friend or relative. The *Herald* sardonically reported that many Buffalo residents were receiving the attentions of acquaintances from whom they had not heard in years. [6]

It is not known whether the three friends crossed paths with Geronimo, who visited in the same week, or what they might have thought of the Scottish Games. We can only wonder whether they took in one of the many concerts during Saengerfest Days, or whom they might have known among the 250,000 visitors jamming the fair each week. If they were Oddfellows (Glenn wasn't), they might have joined lodge brothers for special activities on June 26. We can be certain that Glenn Curtiss visited the Machinery and Transportation Building. His own mechanical inclinations would have driven him there, but it was also the showcase for the latest innovations in his various businesses.

William Ayers and Son of Philadelphia presented horse blankets, as did L. C. Chase and Company of Boston. William Hengerer and G. N. Pierce, both of Buffalo, each showed off their latest bicycles, as did National Cycle of Bay City, Michigan—one of Curtiss's suppliers. Buffalo Metal Goods offered bicycle fittings. Emery Tire, Pennsylvania Rubber, Revere Rubber, Fisk Rubber, and Goodyear offered tires, while the brashly named Twentieth-Century Company provided vehicle lamps.

This showcase of products probably made part of the visit a business trip, but the restless Curtiss surely looked over the seven makers of horse-drawn vehicles, the four boat builders, and the fifteen companies selling automobiles. If he had visited number 69 on an alphabetical list of 78 exhibitors, at location A-21, next to the Pierce bicycles, he would have found "Thomas Motor Company, Buffalo, N.Y. Motor cycles, etc."

The Motor cycle was a Thomas Auto-Bi. Thomas had a 175-lb model with a 1.5-hp engine retailing for $200, and a 110-lb 2.25-hp racer for $250. In both models, the single-cylinder engine lay high in the frame along the front diagonal tube, above and parallel to that tube, with the cylinder head squeezed into the junction of the horizontal tube, front diagonal, and front down tube. Because the racing engine weighed 50 lb and even the road engine weighed 20 lb, there must have been balance drawbacks with the design. Likewise, the long belt that ran between the rider's legs to a large drive pulley mounted on the rear wheel must have been a nuisance. However, Edwin R. Thomas's brainchild, backed by strong capital that allowed for swift manufacturing and delivery, was running away with the business it had essentially originated. [13]

Although it is not known for certain whether Curtiss met his future in the Machinery and Transportation Building, several things support this notion. First, Curtiss later reported that the Thomas Auto-Bi was the only motorcycle he had ever seen before starting his own work in the field. Second, he went into that work almost immediately after returning from the Pan-Am. Third, for his powerplant, he selected a mail-order engine from Thomas.

What Curtiss got for his money disgusted him. The engine was rough-cast, needing milling to finish it. There was no carburetor. There were no instructions. Curtiss grimly set about making things good. Lena's uncle, Frank Neff, ran a wire hood factory at the waterfront, and Curtiss delivered the single-cylinder motor to him for finish milling. He created a carburetor from a tomato can, and as for instructions, wasn't he the boy who dismantled and reassembled clocks, the youngster who rebuilt dilapidated bikes into snappy new racers, and the man who could fix nearly anything? [12]

There are no secrets in a town as small as Hammondsport, and Curtiss's efforts were viewed with cynicism, amusement, wonder, or eagerness, depending on the individual dispositions of his friends and neighbors. When he finished hooking up the engine to a bicycle frame, he had an audience. Even if people did not gather to see Curtiss's project, a crowd would have been magnetized by the shocking, unprecedented racket of the tiny engine. According to persistent local tradition, Curtiss ran his first motorcycle down the street and into the lake, having forgotten to install brakes.

Alternate accounts claim that Curtiss ran into a tree instead of the lake, or had to pedal back from outside of town, having forgotten about fuel consumption. These might be separate incidents, although all seem to be out of character for Curtiss, who even as a boy was famed for meticulous planning. Augustus Post, Curtiss's first (although not always reliable) biographer, specifically denied these tall tales. [10]

At any rate, Curtiss clearly considered his first motorcycle to be a simple experiment, to see whether he could actually do it. Now ready to get serious, he wrote again to Thomas, ordering the biggest engine they had.

Curtiss was now 23 years old. He had a 20-year-old wife, a sickly son, and an ailing grandmother who was losing her eyesight. He carried on his bicycle business, including the two branch stores, and even launched into manufacturing. He also kept up the harness business, which was getting the lion's share of his advertising money in the *Herald.* He collected 60-cent fees for bicycle sidepath tags. He sold sewing machines, ran an apple press, and presumably continued, or at least rented, Grandma Curtiss's 7-acre vineyard operation. Because Zimmer's power lines were spreading rapidly through town, it is likely that the demand for acetylene was dwindling rapidly.

However, none of these activities tore him away from his new experiments. Curtiss was clearly possessed by the new internal combustion gasoline engine and by the speed possibilities that the motorcycle offered.

Speed had long been a passion with Curtiss, and it would remain so for the rest of his life. Rutha said that he had developed this urge while cycling over the hills and valleys between his newly remarried mother's home in Rock Stream and his old haven with Grandma in Hammondsport. It is also possible that this was an obsession, a form of so-called dry alcoholism. Alcoholism ran in his mother's side of the family. Although she is not reported to have suffered directly, problem drinking would manifest in her two husbands, her daughter, her son-in-law, and others. It is also possible that Curtiss's speed passion reflected some form of Learning Disability—his mind might have worked in such a way that it was only when things were racing that they seemed "normal." For whatever reason, speed was an important goal for Curtiss, and motorcycles offered it to him.

After proving to himself that he could actually make a working motorcycle, Curtiss ordered the biggest engine castings Thomas had (56-lb, 3-hp, designed for trikes and quads) and created a more practical machine. Again, the engine needed to go through the process of milling at the wire hood factory, but soon Curtiss had a powerful, if still rather crude, vehicle, capable of handling the hills around Keuka Lake. By this time, he had decided that he could do better than the Thomas company when it came to powerplants. He sketched out what he wanted and took the designs to the Kirkham foundry in Taggerts, which was halfway between Hammondsport and Bath. In Kirkham's little operation, some time late in 1901, the first Curtiss engine (soon trademarked "Hercules") appeared. [12]

The engine was installed in its frame not as a jury-rigged experiment but almost as a prototype. By January 22, 1902, the *Herald* reported, "He has the principle down fine and can now manufacture, should he care to, with no fear of failure." [6] Curtiss cared to and apparently had no fear. In March, the *Herald* reported that Curtiss had sold this first "production" machine to a Pennsylvania man, would soon be working on a tandem, and even planned to specialize in motorcycles. [6]

Although the sales, technical successes, and recognition from his community were exciting and gratifying, there was a pall over them. Between the two newspaper notices, Glenn and Lena buried their son, one month short of his first birthday. [12]

Curtiss was not inclined to air his feelings in public, but his son's death—even if presaged by Carlton's ill health—could not have been anything but devastating (Fig. 3.1). It extended a pounding pattern of loss in the young man's life. He was only 23 years old, but he had already been through his grandfather's death, his father's death, his sister's deafness, his removals to Rochester, to Rock Steam, and back to Hammondsport, and his mother's odd mixture of distance and vibrancy. Now he laid his baby boy to rest alongside

Fig. 3.1 Carlton Curtiss with his mother.

two men he could at best only scarcely remember, but whose absence must have loomed large in his life. He had an uncle, his father's brother, but Adelbert lived at a distance and involved himself little with the Hammondsport clan, even when his father and brother died suddenly. The men of his mother's family likewise lived at some distance. Curtiss must have felt very lonely as he stood in Pleasant Valley Cemetery, the only survivor by the graves of three generations of Curtiss males. To make matters worse, his grandmother and Lena's father were both declining rapidly.

There may have been another dimension of loss at this time. Curtiss biographer C. R. Roseberry states that Lena was determined not to have another child, fearing to face another loss. (While not citing his source for this information, Roseberry interviewed old family friends and Glenn Curtiss, Jr., in the course of his research.) Birth-control information, while available, was illegal in New York, as in most states, at the time. Margaret Sanger, who grew up in nearby Corning, was 19 in 1902, and her birth-control crusade still lay years in the future. May there have been sexual withdrawal (perhaps promoting drive in other fields) at least for a time, within the young couple? If so, it does not seem to have affected their other relations. Observers frequently commented on the closeness of the couple. Glenn and Lena were both quiet, preferring to keep to a small circle of intimate friends.

It is difficult not to see the impact of Carlton's death in Curtiss's career over the ten years that would intervene before the birth of Glenn Junior. While continuing most of his other businesses, Curtiss threw himself into engines and motorcycles. Building a tandem, he rode with Art Stanton 30 miles to reopen his seasonal store in Corning, where he immediately sold the new machine. He made a 200-mile circuit of the Finger Lakes, swinging out west to Geneseo and as far north as Rochester before wending south through Palmyra and Canandaigua to home—an impossible trip even five years earlier. He put a telephone in his store and another in his home. He received the first special-delivery letter ever seen in Hammondsport. [26]

Curtiss' trade name was Hercules, which may have been borrowed from the brief period of bicycle manufacturing. Classical mythology was part of the cultural literacy of that time, and the name Hercules gave a reassuring sense of endurance and strength. The motorcycle business was only two years old, and Curtiss was manufacturing in a wide-open field (Fig. 3.2). By Labor Day of 1902—6 months after his first sale, 7 months after Carlton's death, and 14 months after his trip to the Pan-Am—he was at Ocean Parkway in Brooklyn, finishing second in a time race and third in a 10-mile distance race sponsored by the New York Motorcycle Club. "He gave them a race for their lives," the *Herald* noted. Boosterism aside, the newspaper was probably correct. With a stack of new Hercules orders in hand, Curtiss added more help, set up the G.H. Curtiss Manufacturing Company, recruited investment from vintners and other leading businesspeople of the village, and jettisoned the harness business, converting the barn into a small manufacturing shop. [6, 7, 13]

In December, the company brought out its first catalog, while Curtiss swapped a Hercules for a steamer, one of the first automobiles in Hammondsport. In January 1903, he made his first trip to what would become the site of an annual pilgrimage—the New York Auto Show. [12]

Despite spending his teen years in Rochester, Curtiss was still very much a country mouse at this point, as Tank Waters recalled with amusement half a century later. In all the excitement of getting his motorcycle ready for shipping and exhibiting, Curtiss was at the DL&W depot in Bath before he realized that he had left home without any cash. Two men, including the station agent, dug into their own pockets to get him on his way, after which the Pratt Bank wired funds to New York. Curtiss and Waters, who had come along to help set up the exhibit, visited a cafeteria in the big city. Not realizing they were supposed to carry their trays and load up at the counter, the two men sat down at a table and waited. "After sitting quite a while we started to walk out and as we reached the door a man said to us '[D]id you forget to pay the cashier[?]' 'For what[?]' Glenn said. I will bet that man thought, here is a couple of rustics just out of the big woods." [15]

Fig. 3.2 The early motorcycle shop was not a large operation.

In future years, the auto show became an annual outing for Glenn and Lena, besides being a good stimulus for sales. The motorcycle business seemed so promising that Curtiss decided against reopening the Corning bike shop. Instead, he dedicated the end of 1902 and the beginning of 1903 to a new inspiration—the two-cylinder motorcycle (Fig. 3.3). All U.S. motorcycles, if not all motorcycles worldwide, had been singles until this point. Curtiss, determined to get more speed by increasing power while keeping down weight, decided that a V-twin could do the job. Using the same cylinders as the ones on his existing single, he doubled output to 5 hp. The 60-lb twin used roller bearings, and these were quickly added to the single (which had depended on ball bearings until this point). Each model used flat belts to a large drive pulley attached to the rear wheel. The engines were installed at the lowest point of the diamond frame, upright, and on the centerline. The twin required a slightly larger frame and longer wheelbase. [7, 12, 13]

Fig. 3.3 The Hell-Rider, with the world's first V-twin motorcycle. Notice the flat belt.

Curtiss apparently envisioned this new motorcycle as a racer but quickly realized it could be marketed as a superior road machine. Thus, he had a lot of potential business at stake, in addition to his personal racing pride, when he returned to New York on Decoration Day and took his place in line at N.Y.M.C.'s Riverdale hill climb. Horses, steamers, and electrics (not to mention cyclists) all faded on hills, so the new gasoline technology offered great opportunities in the field, and hill climbs were an important form of "comparison shopping."

The grade on this particular hill ran from 5 to 14%, and no one was surprised when Charles Gustafsen and Oscar Hedstrom, professional riders on chain-driven Indians, finished first and second, respectively. Then Curtiss took off, lying flat across the frame in his accustomed style, and took the slope in 51 seconds, tearing 4-2/5 seconds off Gustafsen's time. After collecting his gold medal, Curtiss roared uptown to Yonkers, where he jumped into the National Cycle Association's big race. Leaving his eight competitors in the dust, Curtiss won the 10-mile race, became the first American Amateur Champion, and set his first world speed record—1 mile in 56-2/5 seconds. [4, 12, 13]

Prestigious victories in hill climbing and in flat racing, under two different auspices, in two separate locations, on the same bike by the same rider, on the same day, with an industry-leading engine innovation, did no harm whatever to the Curtiss business. Respected in the infant industry beforehand, he now established himself in a lightning stroke as a major force.

By the first half of 1904, Curtiss was experiencing strong lobbying efforts to bring his operation to Owego, New York. Electing to stay in Hammondsport, he erected a two-story, 20′ × 60′ manufacturing shop next to the home he and Rutha had jointly inherited after their grandmother's death, resulting from a fall, the previous year. Work up to this point had apparently gone on either in outbuildings or in the harness barn near the square. Although the new building was noted for having plenty of light (a common feature in succeeding Curtiss plants, to judge from photographs), it was the beginning of a ten-year haphazard process of conglomerating structures that would overwhelm the house, which itself eventually was turned into offices. [12]

Curtiss clearly loved racing. It complemented his athleticism, his craving for speed, his fiercely competitive nature, and his passion for mechanics and gadgetry. Moreover, it was advertising. Do well in a race, and the newspapers would blazon forth your achievement—at their own expense! Curtiss, indeed, was his own best publicity, offhandedly creating highly effective celebrity marketing.

In January 1904, Curtiss made his debut in the town and state with which his name would later become inseparably linked—Ormond Beach, Florida. On the flat sands there, he set a 10-mile world speed record at 8 minutes 54-2/5 seconds, a rate that would not be broken for seven years. [9, 11]

In Waltham, Massachusetts, still using the only twin in the race, Curtiss roared home to victory on the fifth lap of a tricky 5-mile course before any of the competition had finished a fourth lap. At the 1905 New York State Fair in Syracuse, he set three world records on one day. Newspapers called him "that amazing Mr. Curtiss." Some, aghast at his close corners, frightening speeds, and shocking maneuvers, called him "the Hell-Rider."

Curtiss took chances, and he took spills. But his frightening maneuvers masked the fact that he was committed to safety. He would not race, and he would not let his riders race, if he did not like the look of the track. In fact, Curtiss studied each course carefully, enlisting it as an ally rather than fighting it as an obstacle. Every one of his heart-stopping stunts in the course of a race was planned and calculated. Although he often pushed the envelope, he never made a move he did not believe he could do safely. This preliminary study and careful calculation, aimed at squeezing every advantage from rider, track, engine, and frame, put Curtiss repeatedly in the winner's circle.

"At Providence," wrote Tank Waters, "he leaned his mc [motorcycle] at so great an angle that he actually rode the curbing on a street corner and won the race because all others slowed down greatly on the turn. At Waltham, Mass. he earlier in the day placed some boards over a small ditch and rode a steep bank on a turn while all others stayed in the dirt road and this let Glenn win the race. Glenn was the best judge of distance I ever knew." (Was the placing of boards over a ditch cheating? If so, it seems odd that Waters would crow about it to school students, even fifty years later. He seems to be describing a long-distance endurance run in 1907, which may have given riders some latitude as to the details of their route. At any rate, his point seems to be that Curtiss preferred to take advantage of the risky steep bank, rather than relying on the safer road route.) [15]

In addition to eschewing races he considered unsafe, Curtiss also declined to start in races where he did not think he had a strong chance of victory, arguing that there was no point in the effort if you already knew you could not win. Despite his impressive string of victories and records, he also lost from time to time, and once in Chicago was disqualified from an apparent victory on the grounds that his machine was overweight. Although there is no record of Curtiss being a sore loser, he freely admitted, "I didn't like to lose." [12]

After the Owego overtures, Elmira and Rochester both weighed in with unsuccessful bids to relocate the Curtiss operation. By 1905, he was reluctantly using his own name on the product, having discovered that the trade name Hercules was already registered to another company. C. C. Jenkins, village barber and part-time artist who worked in the Curtiss plant off and on, designed the familiar script emblem that carried over into the airplane days; contrary to legend, it was not based on Curtiss's autograph. Curtiss victories on Curtiss motorcycles could, of course, only stimulate sales further.

The G. H. Curtiss Company, capitalized at $40,000, was incorporated in October, quickly increasing its workforce from 20 to 40—significant figures in a village of 1,100 residents. Although Curtiss held the majority of the stock, 14 other local men were also shareholders. A new 20 × 50 ft building was built, a sidecar attachment was offered, and the price of the twin machine was actually reduced by $25. Curtiss set up his own foundry, dropping the subcontract under which the Kirkhams manufactured his engines. A sales agency was opened in England. By 1907, two more large buildings had been added to the property, and the plant was running 24 hours a day. Curtiss engines and motorcycles were shipped worldwide in boxcar loads, with even cash orders sometimes laid off because of backlogs. After a year of incorporation, the company paid a dividend on preferred stock. Wages had totaled more than $11,000. This rose to $38,000 in 1908, with profits for the year of $120,000. By 1909, Curtiss was employing 100 men—nearly 10% of the population of the village. Many family men had to give up their Curtiss jobs, unable to find housing. [12, 13]

By 1909, a new dimension had been added to the Curtiss business. Aviation had entered the picture in the flurry of orders following the 1902 Labor Day race in New York, when a Hercules engine was delivered to "a New York aeronaut." In 1903, Curtiss and Charles Kirkham rode their motorcycles to Frankford, near Utica, New York, delivering an engine they had made for "Mr. Benbow," who was hoping to fly a dirigible at the Louisiana Centennial Exposition in St. Louis. This was surely Thomas C. Benbow, who made an unsuccessful attempt at the World's Fair in 1904. Presumably, he was in Frankford at the Balloon Farm, where Carl and Carlotta Myers pursued their own lighter-than-air work. [6]

The only successful aeronaut at the fair was Captain Thomas Scott Baldwin, whose *California Arrow* had first flown at Oakland in July, making a circular flight (even before the Wright brothers) a few days later. Most accounts consider these to be the first successful dirigible flights in the Western Hemisphere (Fig. 3.4). At the fair in October, Baldwin—nearly 50 years old and already a prominent citizen (he was overweight, in other words)—recruited wiry young Roy Knabenshue, a balloonist, and took him into the business on the spot. Knabenshue, a fast learner, made 23 ascents, including 9 round trips. A month later, Baldwin descended from the B&H at Hammondsport, announcing to the startled citizens that he, the famed aviator of whom they had heard so much in the past few weeks, had powered his creation with a Curtiss motorcycle engine.

It must have been similar to the Music Man coming to town, but Baldwin, flamboyant as he might have been, was genuine. A former circus acrobat who had added balloons and parachutes to his act, he had toured before the crowned heads of Europe (acting on advice from Buffalo Bill). If his airship did not measure up to those of Count von Zeppelin or Santos-Dumont, it was certainly the best the United States had to offer.

When villagers steered Baldwin to the Curtiss shop, the quiet Hammondsporter was probably taken aback by the extroverted, spectacular midwesterner. Baldwin, on the other hand, had not expected to find an obviously very young fellow in coveralls on the shop floor, needing to wipe off the grease before he dared to shake hands.

The captain explained expansively how he had had nothing but frustration with his experiments, because he could not find a single engine with a power-to-weight ratio high enough

Fig. 3.4 Captain Tom (on sawhorse) in St. Louis, with his California Arrow *powered by a Curtiss V-twin motorcycle engine.*

to lift balloon and pilot, until he heard a cowboy purring along with a strong, steady motorcycle. Accosting the rider, he found that the engine came from the G. H. Curtiss Manufacturing Company, immediately placed an order, and at last found success. (At least, that is how he usually told the story. With a lifetime of show business behind him, Baldwin cheerfully tailored his tales to his audience.)

Curtiss was no doubt pleased but also considerably confused. Apparently, he remembered the order only vaguely and had no idea that the airship at the World's Fair, faithfully reported in the *Hammondsport Herald,* had used one of his engines.

Baldwin saw a great future in airships (at least for exhibition purposes) and wanted more engines. Curtiss, who rather disdainfully considered aeronautics a sort of crackpot diversion, still appreciated the business and was happy to oblige. However, something deeper began to develop that day in November.

On the surface, it is hard to imagine an odder couple than Captain Baldwin and Glenn Curtiss. A quarter century separated their ages. One was gregarious, the other withdrawn; one flamboyant, the other understated. One gave florid interviews on any topic at the drop of a reporter's hat, while the other would learn to evade demands for banquet speeches with a single memorized sentence. However, they were both competitors. They were both entranced by gadgets. They were both future-oriented. Curtiss took Baldwin home and put him up for the duration of his visit. The two men forged a close bond that would endure until the older man's death in 1923. [5, 12, 14]

Using motorcycle engines for aeronautics was a good starting point, but Curtiss, no doubt with input from Baldwin, began to press ahead in two directions. The first, although effective and obvious, was also limited. Curtiss lightened the engine largely by perforating internal components such as the valve stems. This must have played hob with engine life, but dirigible operators were mostly flying short hops before paying crowds. Presumably they were willing to make more frequent engine purchases if what they got for their money had a low enough specific weight to keep them flying.

The second—more promising—approach was elaboration of the original engine. There was a brief flirtation with the V-4 configuration. (This was in doubt for some time; we're all indebted to Wes Allen and Geoff Stein for turning up documentary evidence that it actually existed.) The innovation that finally took hold, however, was a four-cylinder inline engine (Fig. 3.5). Both engines used the original motorcycle cylinders, and all engines

Fig. 3.5 Curtiss's staff at work while Captain Baldwin (rear) admires the new I-4. The singles, doubles, and fours all employed the same cylinders.

continued to be air-cooled. Although air-cooling tended to limit endurance, Baldwin and others were mostly in show business, flying short hops and circles for the crowds at fairs. Water-cooling would have added weight to aircraft that were still barely getting off the ground.

With Baldwin's success, other aeronautic dreamers clamored for Curtiss engines. Although he liked Baldwin, who had a record of proven accomplishment, Curtiss continued to sniff at most of the starry-eyed visionaries who beat a path to his door or his mailbox. However, he found that aviators would pay higher prices for the same engines than motorcyclists would. While no doubt confirming his assumptions about their fuzzy-headedness, at least it was good for business, although aeronautic work was definitely only a sideline.

When Baldwin lost his shop and most of his stock during the San Francisco earthquake, he decided that he had no reason to rebuild on the West Coast. In Hammondsport, he had his engine source and a very good friend. The Curtisses enthusiastically welcomed Baldwin into their home, where he became part of the family. (They referred to him, even in the third person, as Captain—"Captain says" or "Captain will be home next week"—as though that were his given name. He signed his post cards to Lena as "Captain.") Near the Curtiss plant, in the mouth of the glen, Baldwin set up his own shop for balloons and dirigibles. Native son Curtiss had indirectly brought a new business to his village.
[5, 12, 14]

Baldwin's exhibitions were also staged out of Hammondsport, and Curtiss began traveling with him as a ground engineer to ensure that the powerplants performed properly. Back home, Curtiss developed a three-wheeled wind wagon to test propellers (Fig. 3.6). This outlandish road warrior terrified all the horses in the neighborhood, and Curtiss, always willing to turn a few extra bucks, sold a handful of them as novelty vehicles. [6, 7, 12, 14]

Motorcycles remained the main business, and Curtiss was able to do another favor for Hammondsport on the heels of Captain Baldwin's relocation. His old cycling friend Tank Waters, practicing in Buffalo as a nurse and muscle therapist, had started a sideline of motorcycle conversion kits for bicycles. By 1905–1906, he was ready to manufacture complete units under the Erie name, and Curtiss successfully lobbied him to return home and set up shop in Hammondsport. The little village was now roaring into the twentieth century with two motorcycle factories and an airship shop. [13]

In 1905 and 1906, Curtiss continued his seemingly haphazard additions, building at least two more shop buildings on his property, including one to house offices and the enameling department. He installed a new gas engine, probably to generate electricity—the plant

Fig. 3.6 When an elderly couple's buggy horse was spooked by the wind wagon one day, Curtiss jumped out to grab the bridle and bring the animal under control. "Don't worry about him, son, take care of the old lady," the husband said. "She's more scared than the horse is." Notice that Glenn has nothing to shield him from the drive belt and wheel at his back.

produced its own, rather than relying on Zimmer's part-time village system. In January 1906, the plant worked 13 to 15 hours a day, but everything closed down on the Fourth of July (this apparently was unusual) so that workers could travel to Rochester and watch Curtiss race—a first for most of them. (He won a 5-mile race and a 1-mile race.) Also that year, worker David Brandow narrowly escaped death when a brazier head exploded. The fire was contained but scorched the grapevines immediately outside. [6]

Curtiss set up a suggestion system with incentives for implemented ideas (unfortunately, none were recorded for posterity) and hired his first office manager, old friend Harry Genung. Encountering the housing shortage, Genung told Curtiss he was going to have to give up the job and find work in his fiancée's hometown of Elmira. Loath to lose either his friend or his friend's services, Curtiss moved the young couple into his own house. Besides the two Curtisses and the two Genungs, the household also included Captain Baldwin, Lena's widowed mother, and any relative or business associate who happened to be passing through town. Curtiss's sister was there from time to time. Frequent visitors were his mother and his half-brother Carl. Lua's second husband was succumbing to alcoholism, and the marriage broke up in 1907, when Lua moved in with a sister in Buffalo.

Lena continued to work in the office while her mother acted as housekeeper. Both women must have sometimes felt as if they were running a boardinghouse. At least it was a big place, with seven bedrooms and a sleeping porch after Glenn modernized it, although it is not known exactly when that occurred. A maid was hired eventually (taking up one of those bedrooms), and we can only hope for the sake of Lena and her mother that the maid was already on the job at this time. They only had one bathroom, though. [1, 2, 3]

In 1906, Curtiss and Baldwin had traveled together to the automobile show in New York, where the fledgling Aero Club was staging a joint exhibition. Baldwin showed off his latest dirigible, and Curtiss emphasized aero engines in his own display. Here he was honored to meet Alexander Graham Bell, who was experimenting with kites and speedboats at his summer home on Cape Breton Island. Bell studied the Curtiss engines and ordered a two-cylinder unit soon after leaving the show. They met again at the next year's show, when Bell ordered a four-cylinder engine. Upon learning that Curtiss was heading south in a few weeks, Bell invited the engine man to stay overnight at his home in Washington, D.C.

Curtiss made his visit in January 1907, on his way to what would turn out to be his final trip to the races in Ormond Beach. Here, while sitting on his motorcycle with Tank Waters awaiting their next race, he witnessed the spectacular crash of a Stanley steam racer. Decades of arguments about details of the crash could have been settled by recourse to a meticulous letter from Curtiss published in *Scientific American* on February 7. [11]

Because Curtiss was sensitive about his lack of education, he was always working on his writing skills. He published several articles during the airplane days, and there has always been a question whether they were his own work or that of a publicist. They all bear the stamp of this letter, being direct, lucid, and vigorous. Because the letter could scarcely have come from another hand, it tends to validate the later works published under Curtiss's name. It seems that he did not need to be so sensitive about his writing skills after all.

That week Curtiss set a new world record mile at 46-2/5 seconds, again using one of his V-twins. However, the immortal highlight of the day was the performance of his newest creation: the world's first V-8 motorcycle.

Captain Baldwin appears to have been satisfied with his straight fours, but other aviation visionaries such as Captain Jones and Captain Mattery were clamoring for more. Arranging two of his inline fours in a "V" formation gave Curtiss one of the first eight-cylinder engines in the world, and he had at least three assembled in his shop as starters.

Neither Captain Jones nor Captain Mattery would chalk up much aviation success, but their demands proved vital for an industry in its infancy. Motorcycle engines had powered airships, and now Curtiss dreamed of reversing the process. Why shouldn't the new 40-hp aero engine power a motorcycle? The men in Curtiss's shop tried to dissuade him, but he fabricated an 8-ft custom frame, installed one of the airship engines, and shipped the monster to Ormond Beach.

Officials at the Carnival of Speed barred the vehicle from any races but offered an official time test. On January 24, the racing man mounted the saddle, supported on one side by his old biking and motorcycling friend, Tank Waters, and on the other by his new aeronautical friend, Tom Baldwin. (The crossover of technologies, and the support by representatives of each field, blended together by Curtiss and his vehicle, would be considered too contrived even for fiction).

Curtiss cracked that Baldwin had not worked so hard in years. Baldwin puffed and Waters trotted until Curtiss left them in a spray of sand, tearing down the beach for his 2-mile run to the starting point. He passed this point at speeds no one on earth had ever seen. Only 26-2/5 seconds later, he was over the finish line, one mile away. A mile after that, he finally coasted to a stop (Fig. 3.7). The record was unofficial, as Curtiss freely acknowledged, but the speed was in excess of 136 mph. No auto, no motorcycle, nor even

Fig. 3.7 A man and his monster. Charles Oliver Jones, Socialist lecturer, artist, and aviation visionary, created the background and retouched the photograph. Jones died when his airship caught fire in 1908. Despite the retouching, the bevel-geared direct drive is clearly visible.

a locomotive had ever approached that speed. Glenn Curtiss was the fastest man on earth. [5, 11, 12, 13, 14]

With business booming following the auto show, the aero show, and the Ormond–Daytona races, Curtiss uprooted some of the vineyard to build another machine shop. He had been one of the first manufacturers in the new field of motorcycling. His products were distributed across the globe, bringing him at least moderate wealth and a position of respect in his hometown, not to mention the approbation of eminent men such as Alexander Graham Bell. He had developed the first V-twin machine and the first V-8. He had turned his motorcycle engines into successful aero engines. He had won race after race and set record after record, often on the same day. He had made that explosive run at Ormond Beach, causing the Chicago *Daily News* to crow, "Bullets are the only rivals of Glenn H. Curtiss of Hammondsport." Moreover, his Ormond Beach record, however unofficial, was enduring. It would not be beaten (by an automobile) until 1911 and would stand as a motorcycle record as long as Curtiss lived.

What was there left to do in the motorcycle business?

The restless Curtiss seemed to be asking himself the same question. On June 28, as Baldwin was trying out his new dirigible in Hammondsport, Curtiss quietly suggested that if he took it up, he could get a better feel for the performance of the engine. The effusive aeronaut agreed. After two years of traveling with Baldwin and servicing his aircraft from the ground, Curtiss took to the skies. Going up solo for his first trip into the air, Curtiss surprised no one by revving the airship up to 20 mph. "It is delightful," he told his neighbors after landing. Nothing ever changed Curtiss's opinion that the aviation field was crowded with cranks, but never again would he see flying itself as a crackpot venture. Exactly six years after his trip to the Pan-Am in Buffalo, Curtiss had again found his future. [5, 13]

Curtiss said that the Ormond Beach run had satisfied his speed craving, but that was true only in relative terms. It would be eminently satisfying from a literary perspective to close his motorcycle career at that point, but in fact he had at least one more meet in him. At the end of July, he traveled to Providence for the F.A.M. (Federation of American Motorcyclists) races. Albert Cook, one of the prime racers in the Curtiss stable (a new mid-range model would later bear his name) won the diamond medal in the curtain raiser—a New York to Providence endurance run.

Curtiss and Cook finished first and second, respectively, in a single-cylinder race, with Curtiss setting his last world land speed record (1 mile in 52-2/5 seconds). Curtiss also entered the hill climb—it might have been the race in which Waters described him as taking the turn on the curve of the sidewalk. There was indeed a bad turn immediately before the finish line. Curtiss crossed the line under control, winning the race, but crashed seconds later. From his hospital bed, with serious injuries to his hand and knee, he ordered Cook off the course, declaring it too dangerous. [12, 13, 16]

Curtiss came home with a cane, and his wife sat him down for a serious conference, forcefully suggesting that at age 29, he end his motorcycle-racing career. Still limping, Curtiss agreed. Anything from this point would probably be anticlimactic. The Curtiss brand would endure until 1912, and he would stay in the business possibly until 1914. But Curtiss had been on the road a lot that summer. He made three or four trips assisting Captain Baldwin (but not flying) at airship demonstrations. He also had gone to Providence from Cape Breton Island, where something new was seizing his attention.

REFERENCES

1.   Curtiss, Rutha, to "Dear Friend" (probably Nina Arland), undated manuscript, GHCM Yorkers Collection.

2.   ———, undated manuscript describing Curtiss home in Hammondsport, GHCM Yorkers Collection.

3.   ———, "Little Known Facts About Little Known People—As Observed and Told to Me—R. C. Written for Glenn H. Curtiss Jr. by His Aunt Rutha 1952," manuscript in GHCM Curtiss Family File.

4.   "Curtiss Was the Star," attributed to *Motor Age*, circa 1903, typed transcription in GHCM Motorcycle Files.

5.   Eklund, Don, "Captain Thomas S. Baldwin: Pioneer American Aeronaut," Ph.D. dissertation, University of Colorado, 1970.

6.   The *Hammondsport Herald*, published weekly throughout Curtiss's lifetime, includes multitudinous references to Curtiss, his works, and his times. (Curtiss Museum holds a microfilmed set.)

7.   "Hercules Motor Cycles," G. H. Curtiss Manufacturing Company, Hammondsport, circa 1903, GHCM Motorcycle Files.

8.   "Here's the Wind Wagon," unattributed, typed transcription in GHCM Motorcycle Files.

9.   "New World's Record," transcribed from *Museum of Speed Newsletter,* Winter 1958–1959, original publication unknown, typed transcription in GHCM Motorcycle Files.

10. Post, Augustus, "The Evolution of a Flying Man: Incidents in the Experience of Glenn H. Curtiss with Motors and Aeroplanes," *The Century Illustrated Monthly Magazine,* vol. 81, no. 1, November 1910.

11. Punnett, Dick, *Racing on the Rim: A History of the Annual Automobile Racing Tournaments Held on the Sands of the Ormond-Daytona Beach, Florida, 1903–1910,* Tomoka Press, Ormond Beach, FL, 1997.

12. Roseberry, C. R., *Glenn Curtiss: Pioneer of Flight,* Doubleday, Garden City, NY, 1972.

13. Stein, Geoffrey N., *The Motorcycle Industry in New York State: A Concise Encyclopedia of Inventors, Builders, and Manufacturers,* The University of the State of New York, Albany, NY, 2001.

14. Studer, Clara, *Sky Storming Yankee: The Life of Glenn Curtiss,* Stackpole Sons, New York, 1937.

15. Waters, C. Leonard, to Nancy Hutches, undated typescript, GHCM Yorkers Collection.

16. ———, to Nancy Hutches, undated typescript, GHCM Yorkers Collection.

Chapter 4

Close-Up:
The Curtiss Motorcycle

✯ ✯ ✯

The most desirable feature in a motorcycle is plenty of power; another a good strong frame and forks; and when the long wheel base and large tires, which are most essential for easy riding, are used, the weight of the machine is found to be considerably over 100 pounds. However, the riding qualities of the heavier built machine compare with the 75 pounders as the riding of a Pullman to that of a street car. . . . [W]hat the rider wants most is a good, safe, reliable machine, on which he can ride with comfort to his destination.

—Glenn H. Curtiss, "The Problems of Motorcycling,"
written to the editor of *Motor Age* around 1904 [8]

FRAMES, STYLES, AND ACCESSORIES

Curtiss's first production motorcycle in 1902 was, similar to all others of the time, a single-cylinder. Little would be known about it today without a surviving catalog and a photograph or two. Three standard dry cells and a coil, all in a square case behind the seat, provided spark. A torpedo-like fuel tank was located between the horizontal tubes. "While we believe that the motorcycle belongs more to the bicycle family than to the automobile," the 1904 catalog averred, "we have found it wise to depart somewhat from the style of construction of the present day cycle," by adding a second horizontal member at the top. Likewise, of course, Curtiss used heavier gauge tubes and fittings. [23, 27]

Sometimes two tanks were mounted, presumably for long-distance work. The V-twin, introduced in 1903, had two tanks, at least in some versions; it also used three horizontal tubes. A surviving photograph (see Fig. 3.3) shows Curtiss on a two-tank two-cylinder number, wearing a leather suit, still possessed of nearly all his hair, and with a bit of curl at each end of his mustache. In this photograph, he also shows us his habitual and successful racing position, bent forward from the hips, laying his upper body prone along the horizontal member, and craning his neck enough to set his face forward.

One unit of the next version survives, in the collection at the Glenn Curtiss Museum. This unit, the only extant Hercules known, is probably of the last type marketed with the Hercules name. The torpedo tanks have now been replaced by a large boxy tank supported between the horizontals, secured by metal straps and clamps. Grooves along the centerline provide upper and lower seating. The tank presents a high narrow cross section, and the front is slightly chamfered or tapered—perhaps in a crude attempt to provide some streamlining. Surviving photographs, and the 1903 catalog illustration, suggest that this style was introduced for the tandem, but quickly replaced the cylindrical tank on the single-seaters (Fig. 4.1). The oil reservoir was set to the rear of the gas tank,

Fig. 4.1 The Waters (left) and Curtiss (right) couples on an outing. Curtiss's V-twin machine shows the large boxy tank that succeeded the torpedo tanks. Notice the throttle lever on the right side of his tank (twist controls are in the future), and the bulb horns on the handlebars. The women are wearing split skirts. Bicycles provided an impetus for more practical women's clothing, and, naturally, those styles transferred directly into motorcycling.

extending the profile. This arrangement also must have served with the earlier torpedo-tank models. The rider regulated oil feed through a sight valve. [23]

Pedals provided assistance on hills and for cycling when gas ran out or equipment broke down. Backpedaling engaged a bicycle-style coaster brake in the rear wheel; there was no front brake. Because this brake seems unlikely to quickly slow a motorcycle running at speed, the rider must have throttled back at the same time.

A flat lever on the left, about midway along the frame, engaged a tension roller clutch to tighten the flat drive belt, thus delivering power to the 20-in. wheel mounted on the rear hub attached to the 22-in. road wheel.

A second lever on the left operated a hit-or-miss spark advance and retard. It seems likely that this mechanism also included a cutoff switch that connected for ignition and disconnected when the motorcycle was idle, so as not to drain the four dry cells in a square case behind the seat. A coil (on the rear diagonal member) was located midway between the batteries and the engine; a hot wire ran from the coil to the spark plug. The rider throttled with a third lever, on the right side of the tank.

More familiar are the three later versions, one of which was the first to bear the Curtiss name and logo. Once multiple versions became available, this type was designated the Standard-frame (sometimes called O-frame or Regular-frame) model (Fig. 4.2). The gas tank–oil tank combination now presented a more or less square cross section. The single-cylinder Standard, "complete with grip control and full road equipment," retailed for $200 in the 1905 catalog, the first year in which this tank style appeared. [2, 13]

The twin-cylinder cost $300. A stripped-down V-twin was marketed as "the 110," taking its name from its weight, which was the maximum allowed for the light motorcycle class in competition. The 110 had a shorter wheelbase, making it "unsatisfactory for road riding." This racer sported drop handlebars and a special set of batteries in a tube along the back of the seat post. Getting down to 110 lb meant sacrificing exhaust pipes, idler, "unnecessary fittings," and mudguards. It also took the smallest tires in the Curtiss stable, at 1-3/4 in. [2]

The two road models resemble each other strongly, and they superficially would appear to differ only in the engines. Both use the same handlebars and the same 22-in. frames (58-in. wheelbase, 1-1/4 in. tubing, 3/4-in. forks and stays). They use the same gas and oil tanks. This makes sense, because Curtiss was always enthusiastic for standardization and interchangeability: "**All parts are built to guage** [sic—a frequent misspelling in Curtiss catalogs] **and are interchangeable**," the catalog had emphasized as far back as 1903.

Fig. 4.2 This Standard-frame single (circa 1904) houses three dry cells in the triangular case beneath the seat; the coil is just forward, beneath the lower horizontal. Curtiss engines were always mounted low and upright. The engine is an F-head type, and the flat belt has given way to a segmented V-belt. The Hercules name is gone, and the Curtiss logo is now in use. This image clearly shows the frame's heritage as a reinforced bicycle frame.

Even the 110 racer uses as many standard parts as possible and closely maintains the standard profile. [2, 23]

All 1905 models use Curtiss's twist-grip controls. All were normally enameled in black (including rims, guards, tanks, and grips) with nickeled bright work, including the cylinder and head. The aluminum crankcase was "nicely scraped and polished," and customers could order any other color they wanted for enameling—for an added charge, of course.

There are subtle differences between the standard single-cylinder and double-cylinder machines. The double uses a 2-in. belt, while the single's belt is 1-1/2 in. The double carries four batteries in its case, with two coils mounted under the horizontal member. The single houses three batteries and one coil in the same square case behind the seat. The pedal of the V-twin machine has 45 gears; the single-cylinder has 46. The twin normally used a 5-in. engine pulley, making a 4:1 ratio with the wheel pulley. However, the twin also had optional engine pulleys at 4 in., 5-3/4 in., or 7 in. The single-cylinder motorcycle typically operated at 6:1, with 4:1 for racing. The V-twin machines used 2-1/4 or 2-1/2 in. tires; the tires of the single were 2 in. [2]

By 1907, the price of the two-cylinder motorcycle had dropped (those were hard-money days) to $275. Changes after 1905 were few. There were now three dry cells, and the case was located beneath the rear stays, while the coil had been improved. The belt was now a patented segmented 28° V-belt, a style already popular abroad. The single, still retailing at $200, likewise betrayed few changes apart from battery and coil changes corresponding to those on the double.

A combination luggage carrier and stand was now available for $4. The stand, which could be used without disturbing the carrier, used a thumbscrew to lock it up or let it down. It had four legs, pivoted in pairs to either end of the rear axle. The four feet anchored a flat framework, all of which raised the rear wheel a couple of inches. This seems a little awkward to manage, but it certainly appears to be stable and was a worthwhile feature at a time when most cycles had no stand of any sort. [12]

In 1908 (early 1909 catalog), stands were standard on all models. This simplified version employed a frame formed roughly in a squared-off "U." The frame ends pivoted freely on the axle ends, and a clip on the fender secured it when not in use. The driver simply kicked the stand off the clip after dismounting, lowered it, and rocked the bike backward to lock the stand into place, again raising the rear wheel while leaving the front on the ground. Rocking forward and kicking the stand freed the lock. Although not as stable as the optional model of the previous year, it was much easier to use. [13]

A new frame model appeared for the first time since 1904, designed by and named for Henry Wehman, a Curtiss racer and dealer. The Wehman tank, now cylindrical with parallel angled and wedged ends raking forward, was constructed integrally with the single horizontal member. It lay atop this member and was welded at its forward point to the front tube. It gave an appearance of streamlining, and the seat was set low, taking advantage of the angled rear of the tank to place the rider on the same level as the tank; all previous models had perched him above. Curtiss claimed that the 17-in. frame produced the lowest saddle position in the world. Customers could now order a machine finished in either black or gray, with each of the four enamel coats separately baked and hand-rubbed, following an anti-rust coating. The V-twin model had a magneto option for an extra $25—apparently, the first time magnetos were used in the Curtiss production. [10, 13]

The Standard-frame models were available in single-cylinder, V-twin, and fan three. This last model had a 60-in. wheelbase, as opposed to the typical 58 in. This number developed 10 hp (called the "most powerful cycle motor made") and weighed 175 lb. Powerful it may have been, but it ran rough, was heavy, raised the price to $350, and never appeared in another catalog. [13]

Only the Wehman frame appeared in the sole Herring-Curtiss catalog, which must have appeared late in 1909. The ignition system by now was down to two dry cells and a coil, although $25 would add the magneto option. Spring forks, previously an option and briefly dropped altogether (as unnecessary given the excellent ride of the machine), were now standard. This catalog was choked with superlatives: "the machine that has no equal"; "lowest saddle position in the world"; "best transmission in the world"; "simplest and best [lubrication] system ever incorporated in a motorcycle"; "more power and speed from this carburetor than any other in the world"; "most effective [muffler] in the world." And all of this was only the single-cylinder model. [10]

But what a single it was! In 1909, Curtiss motorcycles incorporated his new Model G engine. This engine was rated at 4-1/2 hp, whereas the 1907 twin-cylinder had developed only 5 hp. Yet, the new battery-ignition motorcycle retailed for only $200 and weighed a mere 125 lb. Again, the V-twin machine offered in 1907 had cost $275 and weighed 150 lb; on top of that, it came only in black. [13, 34]

For $275 in 1909, you could buy a 150-lb Wehman-style machine with an 8.5-hp V-twin version of the Model G. Engine and motorcycle were both outstanding performers, but marked the climax of Curtiss's motorcycle career. This was the last of the Curtiss motor-cycle engines, and it would still be used on the Marvel line three (perhaps even five) years later (Fig. 4.3). Curtiss's businesses were always very personal. After his Ormond Beach triumph, his Providence accident, and his *June Bug* airplane success (1908), the Hell-Rider was evolving into the King of the Air. From this point, the motorcycle business would start to languish. [13, 32, 34]

Albert C. Cook, fellow Hammondsporter and one of Curtiss's top racers, endowed the next model with his own name by 1911. In a Cook-frame motorcycle, the upper horizontal member angled below the horizontal about halfway back on the tanks, giving it an appear-ance, if not a reality, of more streamlining than a Standard-frame model. Oil and gas tanks gave the appearance of a single unit. The oil reservoir was now forward and the gas tank aft. Because both tanks were squeezed between the horizontals, the gas tank followed the upper tube, narrowing at a rearward angle from the top.

The Standard and Cook models, similar to the earlier Hercules, used grooves, straps, and clamps to fasten the tank, whereas the Wehman model made the tanks a more integral part of the construction of the motorcycle. Marvel, which was Curtiss's partnership effort with Tank Waters and his swan song in motorcycling, took yet a further step. The 5-in.-diameter fuel tank actually formed the horizontal member. The 4-in.-diameter oil tank formed most of the upright member supporting the seat. For more detail on the period, see Refs. 3, 7, 9, 14, 16, 19, 22, 24, 25, 35, and 40.

Curtiss and Waters had created the Marvel Motorcycle Company in 1909, possibly to help Curtiss hedge his bets against the looming Herring debacle (see Chapter 5). Waters

Fig. 4.3 The Marvel motorcycle employed the powerful Model G, the last of the Curtiss motorcycle engines.

had been manufacturing Erie motorcycles in facilities near the Curtiss plant, but he dropped the Erie line for the new Marvel. Marvels were powered by the single-cylinder Curtiss Model G throughout their existence. A fine machine with elegant lines, innovative construction, and a powerful Curtiss engine, the Marvel caused a stir when it first appeared late in 1909 or early in 1910. Changes in the Marvel over the next several years were mostly changes in details only; production might have run to a thousand units a year. I know of only two still in existence, both owned by collector Wes Allen.

The last motorcycle manufactured under the Curtiss name appeared in 1912. Marvel production probably also ceased the same year, although there is some evidence that it continued as late as 1914. (Business in replacement parts seems to have continued for a time, which might have been limited to stock on hand.) For all its innovative lines and features, the Marvel employed some outdated elements, such as the V-belt drive rather than a chain drive. Curtiss and Waters were obviously not sticks-in-the-mud, and they had solid reasons for preferring belts. However, throughout their careers, they had manufactured what were essentially light motorcycles. [34] The business as a whole was declining, and

Americans in overwhelming numbers were opting for heavy machines. Waters went back to his previous parts and supply business, while Curtiss turned completely to aircraft for World War I. I am not aware of any records that would place Curtiss on a motorcycle later than 1907 [33], although there are vague suggestions in 1908.

ENGINE DEVELOPMENT

The overall motorcycle package was very successful in the early days of the industry, but the key component was the engine. Because the gasoline engine was in its infancy in 1902, Curtiss quickly vaulted forward as a pioneer in this field as well.

Curtiss's first production engines were single-cylinder 3 × 3 in. four-stroke units, reportedly developing 2-1/2 hp (Fig. 4.4). Because most ratings were derived by formula rather than by test, all ratings (by Curtiss and by most other makers) are open to question. Each engine will be described with its contemporaneously designated horsepower, noting exceptions where known. [23]

Because of his racing perspective, Curtiss was already insisting on low weight. From the beginning, the crankcases were constructed of aluminum or aluminum alloy. Upper portions were cast iron. Cylinders were oriented vertically, and Curtiss placed the engine at the lowest point of the frame. Indeed, it actually formed the lower part of the frame, because the upright tube and front diagonal tube were fastened to it about midway on opposite sides of the curved perimeter of the crankcase. The 1904 catalog expressed the belief that Curtiss had originated use of this position—upright, low, and forward of the crank hanger. [27]

Not surprisingly, construction was rather simple and straightforward. The cylinder was built with an F-type head, employing suction intake and pushrod mechanical exhaust. As already noted, a sight-tube feed was used for lubrication. Curtiss used ball bearings in this initial effort. [23]

In the following year, Curtiss introduced roller main bearings on the crankshaft. He also introduced his V-twin, and the two innovations quickly catapulted him out of obscurity (Fig. 4.5). The V-twin, employing the same cylinders as the single, now developed 5 hp at 1800 rpm. [27]

The 1903 catalog stated, "Our new throttle control allows a much greater range of speed than when the engine is controlled entirely by advancing or retarding the spark," suggesting that this latter approach was used on the first production models. [23] By 1904, the spark advance, exhaust valve lifter, and switch were controlled by a single lever on the single-cylinder model. Twist-grip control was an option now. "[A] twist of the grip closes

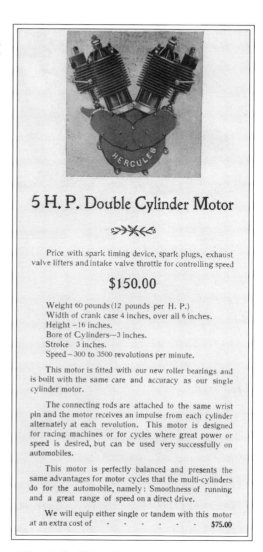

Fig. 4.4 Hercules single 2-1/2-hp engine (1903 catalog), $90.

Fig. 4.5 Hercules V-twin 5-hp engine (1903 catalog), $150.

the compression and makes the electrical connection in starting, and a further twist of the grip advances the spark for speed." [27]

Curtiss noted that this was done "by use of the famous Boden wire, which is used almost exclusively in England for controlling rim brakes and other features." The previous catalog had noted that the low upright engine arrangement was being adopted almost universally in England. It would seem that Curtiss was following his practice from bicycle days of keeping up closely with developments abroad. [27] By 1905, twist control was standard.

Right grip advanced the spark and closed the exhaust valve. Left grip worked a switch that could be thrown in or out at any time, regardless of the position of the commutator. [2]

The 1905 catalog relayed a fair amount of basic detail about the engine. The main shaft used roller bearings, whereas all other bearings were "best bronze." The gears were hardened steel, the valves and connecting rods drop forged. Pistons were fitted with four rings. Weight (60 lb), displacement (3 × 3 in.), and horsepower (5) were identical to those listed in the 1903 catalog. Dimensions had altered slightly in two years: height was now 14 in. as opposed to 16 in.; crankcase depth was 3.5 in. as opposed to 4 in.; overall depth was 7 in. as opposed to 6 in. In 1903, the price of the engine was $75. No separate price was listed in 1905, but the two-cylinder machine overall cost $100 more than the single-cylinder, suggesting that price was relatively steady.

The catalog reported that the company had conducted "continual experimenting with all systems of lubrication" before selecting the approach they found "by far the most satisfactory." Feed took place through a sight valve. Curtiss equipped the crankcase with a ball valve compression relief, designed to allow air to escape. Oil escape was prevented when the ball valve formed a suction seal on the upstroke of the piston. The catalog assured customers that excess oil (and *only* excess oil) would blow out, preventing fouling, while a positive feed was maintained throughout. "The rider has but to turn on the oil in starting and is sure of perfect lubrication of all parts of the motor with no danger of fouling the plugs." This must have been attractive advertising in a day when engines and vehicles were paradoxically simple in construction and tricky in operation. [4]

The Bicycling World reported in 1906 that Curtiss frames had been modified so that they could mount either the single engine or the twin. The publication also noted the segmented V-belt, describing it as "the first of the sort made in this country," whereas the "carburettor of Curtiss design" was startlingly light at 12 oz. *The Bicycling World* was especially impressed with the simplified exhaust valve operation, in which a single gear replaced a train of five. [36]

By 1907, roller bearings (previously used only for crankshafts) were being used throughout on the single. [10] A single gear and cam now lifted both exhaust valves on the twin, while the exhaust valve stem was made larger and fitted with a hardened screw cap. A new kick-lever worked the muffler cutout. Valves were now seated at 30° (rather than 45°), adding an additional 1/2 hp to each engine.

In 1908, glass oil sight gauges were added directly to the crankcase, while connecting rods on the twin model were being attached to the same pin. [4] "We are the pioneer manufacturers of two-cylinder cycle motors in America and are some years ahead of the others in experience," the catalog observed. [15] *The Bicycling World and Motorcycle Review* supported this view, saying that the two-cylinder motorcycle by 1907 had been so refined that "no considerable improvement has been found possible." The magazine in another 1907 issue reported several changes that, although minor, "prove . . . that where improvement was possible it has been made." [37, 38]

The 1909 advance sheet picked up this theme, listing the single as "the original roller bearing motor." This sheet noted features considered to have originated with the Curtiss company that were now being copied by other manufacturers: trussed frame and fork construction; upright engine in front of the crank hanger; roller bearings; V-belt transmission; and two-cylinder motorcycles. The sheet advised: "Experience is the best teacher. The CURTISS has been through the experimental stage. Avoid imitations." It is interesting to note that there is no claim to originality with the twist grip, which had often been attributed to Curtiss. [1] A contemporary writer stated that with the 1907 auto show, Curtiss and Merkel were making the entry of "two more well known machines into the leverless class." [36] However, twist-grip controls had been a Curtiss option as far back as 1904 and apparently had been standard equipment since 1905. [2]

The Curtiss carburetor was singled out for special catalog attention beginning in 1908, when it was described as having central draft and central "gasolene" supply, perfectly automatic with adjustable automatic air supply. "Much of the success of our engines is due to the efficiency of this carburetor," which weighed 15 oz and sold separately for $8. Float feed was adopted the following year.

By 1908, the V-twin had been upgraded to 6 hp at 1500 rpm, partly by increasing displacement to 3-1/4 × 3-1/4 in. Weight had dropped to 55 lb, height had climbed to 18 in., and crankcase depth had edged downward to 3-1/8 in. Retail price, on the other hand, was now $150. Intake and exhaust valves were "Both made with the new 30 degree seat, with which 200 revolutions per minute more can be obtained than with the old style valve seat." Cylinders, now cast from "special air-furnace iron," were ground after boring "to assure absolutely perfect bore." **An important feature**, which the catalog proclaimed in bold print, was operating both exhaust valves by a single gear and cam, which "decreases the number of moving parts and greatly simplifies the engine" (Fig. 4.6). [4]

Although the Model G engine made some significant departures from its predecessors, it clearly built on their successes. To achieve constant lubrication, Curtiss installed a metal float attached to a lever in the crankcase oil well. When moved to a given point by the rising float, the lever engaged a plunger in the supply pipe to cut off the flow. A strainer was also used. The oil levels were factory set "so that no further attention is necessary except to replenish the supply."

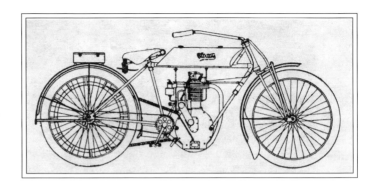

Fig. 4.6 Wehman-frame motorcycle with Model G engine, from the Herring-Curtiss catalog (but retaining the Curtiss logo on the product).

The new engine had a 3-1/4-in. bore with 3-5/8-in. stroke. It used 1-11/16-in. overhead valves in place of the old F-head construction. A single rocker arm, push rod, and cam served both valves. The catalog also claimed that this was the first motorcycle to use an offset cylinder (Fig. 4.7). A large (18-lb) flywheel promoted, it was claimed, "a smooth running, easy starting motor that is practically vibrationless." All these changes reduced friction, wear, and heat while increasing compression, making for a more efficient and powerful engine. [10]

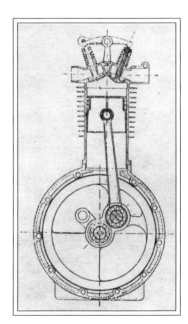

Fig. 4.7 The offset cylinder as diagrammed in the sole Herring-Curtiss catalog, published in 1909.

THE BRIDGE TO AERO ENGINES

In the 1904 catalog, Curtiss observed, "Although designed for the cycle, this motor is suitable for use on automobiles, airships and other purposes where a light powerful motor is required. It develops one horsepower to each twelve pounds of weight and will not overheat, having 150 square inches of radiating surface on each cylinder head." [27]

This catalog was probably issued in early 1904, which was late enough to tout Curtiss's official world record of 10 miles in 8 minutes 54.4 seconds at Ormond Beach on January 30, naturally using a two-cylinder. Thus, the airship suggestion predated Captain Baldwin's St. Louis success by several months, showing that Curtiss was at least aware of the prospect of aeronautic sales and had probably taken note of those few sales (to failed experimenters) that had already taken place. [28, 31, 33]

In 1998, Ed Marshall and volunteer Bill Blackwood of the National Air and Space Museum brought the NASM Curtiss V-twin engine, which was used on an airship, to the Curtiss Museum. Curtiss volunteers Norm Brush and Jack Farmer had already removed a V-twin from a Curtiss motorcycle on exhibit. Working together, Marshall, Brush, Farmer, and Blackwood dismantled, compared, and reassembled both engines. The NASM engine had already been noted as being lighter than the Curtiss Museum unit. This had been achieved by perforating pistons, connecting rods, and flywheel. Clearly, this would lighten the engine, but it also seriously threatened structural integrity and durability. Because most contemporary dirigibles were being used for short exhibition flights, this factor presumably was not a serious concern.

Larry Rinek (engineer and senior consultant with SRI International) has summarized Curtiss's technical success with engines as owing to "minimal weight consistent with acceptable reliability, advanced (but not too far out) mechanical features, careful machining, lots of expensive materials of construction, and high efficiency of operation." [29, 30]

These features—valuable as they were in the motorcycling world—were meat and drink in the aeronautic world. Light reliable engines with low specific weights were vital in those early days of aviation.

A catalog issued in late 1907 or early 1908 lists nine "High Powered and Light Weight Motors for Airships and Other Purposes." However, this listing is only a small box on page 11 of the catalog, and aero engines were clearly a sideline to the motorcycle business. Engines ranged from a single-cylinder 2-hp air-cooled model weighing 20 lb to a V-8 100-hp water-cooled engine at 350 lb. No prices were listed, and interested parties were invited to request a detailed motor catalog. [4]

This is presumably the catalog issued in May 1908, after the *Red Wing* (Chapter 5) flights but before the *White Wing*. The company was suddenly described as making "Aerial and Cycle Motors" (note the order). Thirteen models were described as being "regularly built." [15]

Simply put, this seems unlikely. It would be astounding to find that there was a regular demand for these engines, especially those at the high end in cost, weight, and power. It seems more plausible that these engines were made on order. However, the aggressive interchangeability probably meant that they could be produced quickly. Which models were available to motorcyclists, aviators, and other dreamers in the early months of 1908? Thanks to this catalog, we have detailed descriptions, including illustrations, costs, and even model designations—something that had been rather haphazard, and at any rate unnecessary, before this point. The following descriptions are drawn from Ref. 15; see also Refs. 5, 6, 11, 17, 18, 21, 29–31, 33, and 39.

| Model A1 | 20 lb | 2 hp | $50 | Single | Air-Cooled |

An unusual offering of a two-cycle engine "specially adapted for use in working models of flying machines, converting bicycles into motorcycles, etc." Uses 2-3/4-in. cylinders with 2-3/4 in. stroke, unique among the Curtiss offerings.

| Model B1 | 38 lb | 3 hp | $80–$100 | Single | Air-Cooled |

The basic motorcycle engine.

| Model B2 | 50 lb | 6 hp | $150 | V-twin | Air-Cooled |

The basic two-cylinder motorcycle engine (Fig. 4.8).

| Model C1 | 40 lb | 3 hp | $150 | Single | Air-Cooled |

"Airship Motor . . . built on the same lines as the cycle motor." The aero version of the B1.

| Model A2 | 50 lb | 7 hp | $260 | V-twin | Air-Cooled |

"Airship Motor . . . standard for exhibition dirigible balloons." The aero version of the B2.

| Model A4 | 90 lb | 15 hp | $500 | I-4 | Air-Cooled |

"Light Weight Aeronautical Engine." This engine and all above, with the exception of the A1, have 3-1/4 × 3-1/4 in. cylinders.

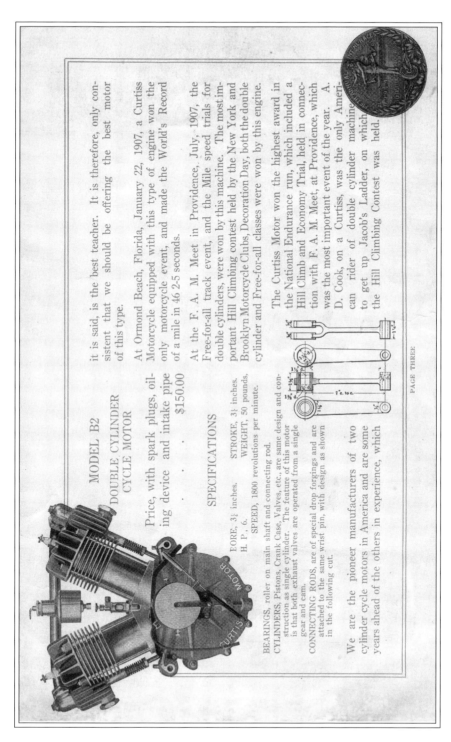

Fig. 4.8 As the aero era began, this model and the corresponding single were Curtiss's primary products. Each had a corresponding lighter-weight model for aero applications.

| Model B4 | 100 lb | 20 hp | $650 | I-4 | Air-Cooled |

"Light Weight Aeronautical Engine." Almost identical with the A4, except that cylinder bore is now 3-5/8 in.

| Model C4 | 110 lb | 25 hp | $750 | I-4 | Air-Cooled |

"Light Aeronautical Engine . . . designed especially for the government war balloon, and is of a somewhat different construction than our other engines" (Fig. 4.9). The cylinders are 3-5/8 × 4 in. The "government war balloon" seems to refer to one of the abortive Signal Corps bids of early 1908, which had been voided, leading to the August creation of *SC-1* (Chapter 5) with its innovative engine. It is also possible that this engine was originally designed, and found wanting, for *SC-1*.

| Model D4 | 110 lb | 25 hp | $900 | I-4 | Water-Cooled |

"[I]dentical with Model C4 excepting that it is water cooled. It is recommended for marine work or where the added weight of the water-cooling system is not objectionable." These last two engines presumably formed the basis for creating the *SC-1* engine.

| Model A8 | 140 lb | 30 hp | $1,000 | V-8 | Air-Cooled |

"Light Weight Aeronautical Engine. . . . The cylinders of this engine are the same as the other Type A engines [3-1/4 × 3-1/4 in.]. . . . [T]he general construction is similar to the four-cylinder model, except that the number of cylinders are double and placed in the form [of] a V on a single case. This V type of engine gives us the greatest power per pound weight obtainable, and is now being used most successfully for racing cars and aeronautical purposes abroad."

| Model B8 | 150 lb | 40 hp | $1,200 | V-8 | Air-Cooled |

"Light Weight Aeronautical Engine." This model matched the A8, except that the cylinders were 3-5/8 × 3-1/4 in. This type had been used for the V-8 motorcycle (with two carburetors) and for *Red Wing* (with eight). It would shortly be used in *White Wing*. The type garnered great admiration in the 1907 auto show following the Ormond Beach record, but Curtiss had no takers at this price.

| Model E4 | 250 lb | 50 hp | $2,000 | I-4 | Water-Cooled |

"[D]esigned for large dirigible balloons, racing motor boats, or any purpose where a reliable and durable light engine, which will stand up under constant usage and heavy load, is required." The cylinders were 5 × 5 in.

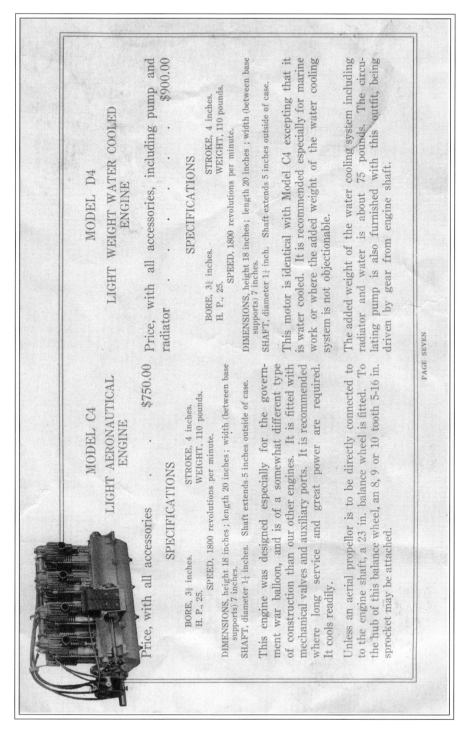

MODEL C4
LIGHT AERONAUTICAL ENGINE

Price, with all accessories . . . $750.00

SPECIFICATIONS

BORE, 3⅛ inches.   STROKE, 4 inches.
H. P., 25.   WEIGHT, 110 pounds.
     SPEED, 1800 revolutions per minute.

DIMENSIONS, height 18 inches ; length 20 inches ; width (between base supports) 7 inches.
SHAFT, diameter 1¼ inches.   Shaft extends 5 inches outside of case.

This engine was designed especially for the government war balloon, and is of a somewhat different type of construction than our other engines. It is fitted with mechanical valves and auxiliary ports. It is recommended where long service and great power are required. It cools readily.

Unless an aerial propellor is to be directly connected to the engine shaft, a 23 in. balance wheel is fitted. To the hub of this balance wheel, an 8, 9 or 10 tooth 5-16 in. sprocket may be attached.

MODEL D4
LIGHT WEIGHT WATER COOLED ENGINE

Price, with all accessories, including pump and radiator $900.00

SPECIFICATIONS

BORE, 3⅛ inches.   STROKE, 4 inches.
H. P., 25.   WEIGHT, 110 pounds.
     SPEED, 1800 revolutions per minute.

DIMENSIONS, height 18 inches ; length 20 inches ; width (between base supports) 7 inches.
SHAFT, diameter 1¼ inch.   Shaft extends 5 inches outside of case.

This motor is identical with Model C4 excepting that it is water cooled. It is recommended especially for marine work or where the added weight of the water cooling system is not objectionable.

The added weight of the water cooling system including radiator and water is about 75 pounds. The circulating pump is also furnished with this outfit, being driven by gear from engine shaft.

PAGE SEVEN

Fig. 4.9 The C-4 led directly to water-cooled airship engines.

Model E8	350 lb	100 hp	$3,000	V-8	Water-Cooled

"Large valves, liberal bearings and strong construction make these engines adaptable to marine work and hydroplanes [boats, not aircraft] or any service requiring great power and absolute reliability. The cylinders were 5 × 5 in.

These models mark a dramatic (and abrupt) departure for the Curtiss company. Only a short time earlier, the company had been making those two motorcycle engines and their corresponding aero versions, which were presumably introduced in 1905 or later. (It is not clear, at least to me, how long the two-cycle was in production.) At some point after that time, the I-4s were introduced, with the first V-8 coming out at the end of 1906. Motor-cycle engines were clearly the heart of the business, with aero engines as an elaborated sideline.

It is interesting to observe that Curtiss doubled up the cylinders from his early engine to form a V-twin. The next logical step would seem to be to link two V-twins and form a V-4. This type of engine was created, but it soon vanished in favor of the I-4. These straight banks of four would be linked to form the V-8 models. Curtiss progressed not by linking his twins but by lining up his singles.

The I-4 models seem to have been crafted specifically for aero work, although Bell's interest in marine versions probably helped to hasten progress. A marvelous photograph, apparently taken at Bell's estate, shows Curtiss cradling a straight four in his arms—an eloquent demonstration of his prowess as a skilled maker of lightweight engines.

The original V-8 was created for airships and later imported into airplanes, although it received most of its fame in the monster motorcycle. Of the twelve engines (excluding the two-cycle) offered in this catalog, half of them use the 3-1/4 × 3-1/4 in. cylinder of the B-1 basic motorcycle single. A straight four in the Curtiss Museum collection, lacking any original marking but almost certainly a Curtiss engine, shows that these cylinders are iden-tical to those on the two-wheelers. However, the introduction of water-cooling (perhaps still in prototype), the proliferation of four-cylinders and eight-cylinders, and the emphasis on aero applications (seven engines of thirteen are designated for aero in their titles) were pushing the original motorcycle engines into obscurity. Only two engines are designated for motorcycle applications, and they were the only two suited for it. Glenn Curtiss was obviously lifting his eyes to the sky (Fig. 4.10).

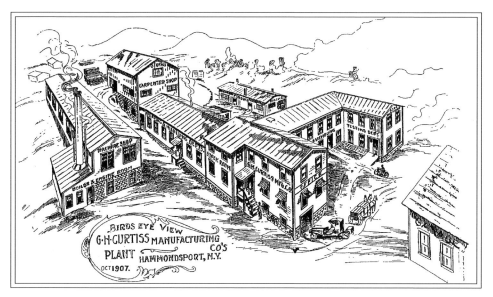

Fig. 4.10 A somewhat sanitized view of the Curtiss shops and outbuildings that sprawled around—and finally swallowed—his house on the hill. The Aero Department (at the time the Aerial Experiment Association [AEA] was formed) is the second floor of the wing to the far right. Notice that a bike, an auto, a motorcycle, and a dray are all in use.

REFERENCES

1. "Advance Sheet: Curtiss Motorcycles for 1909," G. H. Curtiss Manufacturing Company, Hammondsport, circa 1909, GHCM Motorcycle Catalogs File.

2. "Annual Catalogue 1905: The Curtiss Motorcycles and Motors," G. H. Curtiss Manufacturing Company, Hammondsport, circa 1906, GHCM Motorcycle Catalogs File.

3. "Broke the World's Record," unattributed, probably from the *Hammondsport Herald,* typed transcription in GHCM Motorcycle Files.

4. "The Curtiss," catalog circa 1907–1908, GHCM Motorcycle Catalogs File.

5. "The Curtiss Double-Cylinder Motor" (advertisement), *The Bicycling World,* undated but after February 21, 1905, p. 138, photocopy in GHCM Motorcycle Catalogs File.

6. "Curtiss Engines," unpublished two-page typescript, GHCM, Kleckler Collection.

7. "Curtiss Gets into Armory Show," unattributed, possibly *Hammondsport Herald.* typed transcription in GHCM Motorcycle Catalogs File.

8. Curtiss, Glenn H., "The Problems of Motorcycling," attributed to *Motor Age* circa 1904, typed transcription in GHCM Motorcycle Catalogs File.

9. "A Curtiss Motorcycle as a Record Breaker," attributed to *R.F.D. News,* typed transcription in GHCM Motorcycle Catalogs File.

10. "Curtiss Motorcycles," The Herring-Curtiss Company, Hammondsport, circa 1909, GHCM Motorcycle Catalogs File.

11. "Curtiss Motorcycles 1906," G. H. Curtiss Manufacturing Company, Hammondsport, circa 1906, GHCM Motorcycle Catalogs File.

12. "Curtiss Motorcycles 1907," G. H. Curtiss Manufacturing Company, Hammondsport, circa 1907, GHCM Motorcycle Catalogs File.

13. "Curtiss Motorcycles for 1909," G. H. Curtiss Manufacturing Company, Hammondsport, circa 1909, GHCM Motorcycle Catalogs File.

14. "Curtiss Motorcycles. Curtiss Mfg. Co., Hammondsport, N.Y.," *The Bicycling World and Motorcycle Review,* undated, p. 228, photocopy in GHCM Motorcycle Catalogs File.

15. "Curtiss Motors," G. H. Curtiss Manufacturing Company, Hammondsport, circa 1907, GHCM Motorcycle Catalogs File.

16. "Curtiss Was the Star," attributed to *Motor Age,* circa 1903, typed transcription in GHCM Motorcycle Files.

17. "Curtiss's Powerful Machines," *The Bicycling World,* April 26, 1905, p. 123, photocopy in GHCM Motorcycle Files.

18. "Curtiss's Worst Case: 'Experts,' Irate Purchaser and Lawsuit Involved—What Caused it All," unattributed, typed transcription in GHCM Motorcycle Files.

19. "Dinner to Curtiss with Curtiss Absent," attributed to *The Bicycling World and Motorcycle Review,* November 7, 1908, typed transcription in GHCM Motorcycle Files.

20. Eklund, Don Dean, "Captain Thomas S. Baldwin: Pioneer American Aeronaut," Ph.D. dissertation, University of Colorado, 1970.

21. "For Starting Without a Stand: Wehman Evolves a Free Engine Arrangement to Effect the Result," unattributed, typed transcription in GHCM Motorcycle Files.

22. *The Hammondsport Herald,* published weekly throughout Curtiss's lifetime, includes multitudinous references to Curtiss, his works, and his times. (Curtiss Museum holds a microfilmed set.)

23. "Hercules Motor Cycles," G. H. Curtiss Manufacturing Company, Hammondsport, circa 1903, GHCM Motorcycle Catalogs File.

24. "Hot Going," unattributed, 1907, typed transcription in GHCM Motorcycle Files.

25. Mitchell, Charles R., and Kirk W. House, *Glenn H. Curtiss, Aviation Pioneer,* Arcadia Publishing, Charleston, SC, 2001.

26. Molson, K. M., "Early Curtiss Aircraft Engines," *A.A.H.S. Journal,* Summer 1966, pp. 133–137.

27. "1904 Motorcycles and Motors," G. H. Curtiss Manufacturing Company, Hammondsport, circa 1906, GHCM Motorcycle Catalogs File.

28. Punnett, Dick, *Racing on the Rim: A History of the Annual Automobile Racing Tournaments Held on the Sands of the Ormond–Daytona Beach, Florida, 1903–1910,* Tomoka Press, Ormond Beach, FL, 1997.

29. Rinek, Larry M., "Curtiss Aviation Engines: An American Success Story." Photocopy.

30. ———, "Glenn H. Curtiss: An Early American Innovator in Aviation and Motorcycle Engines," SAE Paper No. 940571, Society of Automotive Engineers, Warrendale, PA, 1994.

31. Roseberry, C. R., *Glenn Curtiss: Pioneer of Flight,* Doubleday & Company, Garden City, NY, 1972.

32. Rudd, Clarence P., to Rosa Lee Nudd, October 3, 1959, manuscript, GHCM Yorkers Collection.

33. Stein, Geoffrey N., *The Motorcycle Industry in New York State: A Concise Encyclopedia of Inventors, Builders, and Manufacturers,* The University of the State of New York, Albany, NY, 2001.

34. Studer, Clara, *Sky Storming Yankee: The Life of Glenn Curtiss,* Stackpole Sons, New York, 1937.

35. Untitled description of Curtiss Motorcycles at New York Auto Show, *The Bicycling World,* January 26, 1906, pp. 362, 363, photocopy in GHCM Motorcycle Files.

36. Untitled notice and illustration on new Curtiss line, *The Bicycling World,* Spring issue, April 27, 1907, photocopy in GHCM Motorcycle Files.

37. Untitled notice on upcoming Curtiss exhibit, *The Bicycling World and Motorcycle Review,* November 2, 1907, p. 179, photocopy GHCM Motorcycle Files.

38. Untitled report on 1907 New York Auto Show, *The Bicycling World and Motor Review* (page and date illegible), photocopy in GHCM Motorcycle Files.

39. Untitled typescript table (one page) describing Curtiss aero engines from 1906 to 1911, GHCM Curtiss Engine Files.

40. "Wehman Enters the Motorcycle Trade," attributed to *The Bicycling World and Motorcycle Review,* December 5, 1908, typed transcription in GHCM Motorcycle Files.

Chapter 5

Panorama: "Prove to the World That We Can Fly"

★ ★ ★

Even as a boy, Alexander Graham Bell had been fascinated by flight, experimenting with kites and whirligigs. As a revered elder statesman of science and technology, he continued his interest. As a wealthy man, between his earnings on the telephone and his wife's fortune, he had the luxury and resources to indulge his interest. Unfortunately, he was investing heavily in a dead-end approach.

Bell, a regent of the Smithsonian Institution, had been a close friend of Samuel Pierpont Langley, the secretary (actually the director) of the institution. Although their doctorates were honorary, both men had parleyed their not-entirely-formal educations into outstanding accomplishments in several fields and prominence in learned circles. Both men would come a cropper on aeronautics, and Langley's reputation would never recover.

Bell joined Langley aboard a houseboat on the Potomac River in 1896, eagerly photographing the flight of an unmanned, steam-powered aircraft with a 14-ft wingspan. The catapult launching was successful, and results were exciting. The aircraft flew perhaps a mile, repeatedly describing circles, before going down into the water. Of course, it had not been under control. Regardless, it was finally a form of powered heavier-than-air flight, however impractical it remained. [18]

As the Spanish-American War erupted, the U.S. Army poured $50,000 into Langley's experiments, hoping that he could quickly produce a machine with military potential. On the lighter-than-air side, the army turned to Ivy Baldwin, erstwhile partner of Captain Tom and Tom's brother Sam. (Ivy had assumed the Baldwin moniker as a stage name in order to pass as a third brother.) Neither Ivy Baldwin's work nor Langley's work produced anything worthwhile. At any rate, the war had ended so quickly and so decisively that there was neither time nor need to develop air power. [15, 31]

Langley continued his work, and in 1903, well aware of the Wright brothers' activities at Kitty Hawk, he attempted two launches with a scaled-up version of his 1896 aircraft. The 1903 *Buzzard* had a five-cylinder radial engine and a pilot, Langley's assistant Charles Manly. Neither attempt showed the slightest success or encouragement. On both occasions, the catapulted aircraft dropped immediately into the river. Manly was recovered safely on both occasions, although he was quite cold after his December dunking. [2, 28]

Nine days later, the Wright brothers finally ascended into the air. This event was disappointing for Langley, but the mere fact of not being first was probably not the reason he gave up his experiments. Both attempts had been colossal, well-photographed failures. Press and public attacked him for wasting government money, although he had put in $25,000 of his own when the army's $50,000 ran out. The dismantled *Buzzard* was stored at the Smithsonian, and Langley died in 1906, devastated by public contempt.

Bell was thrilled by the Wrights' success, but he also felt that Langley had not been that far off the mark. After all, Bell had watched those 1896 trials and resented the excoriation his old friend had endured. However, he stretched his mind a bit. The Wright Flyer reportedly had two stacked wing planes. The *Buzzard* had two wing planes in tandem. Was there another approach, Bell wondered? Were wings even needed at all?

Working with kites, Bell discovered that lift could be generated using tetrahedral cells. Stacking many cells, he reasoned, would develop greater lift; by 1905, he found, enough to lift a person. If enough lift were generated to carry aloft not only a person but a powerful, lightweight engine, an aircraft of tetrahedral cells might offer a stable flying machine, while avoiding any patent problems with respect to the Wright brothers. With these thoughts in mind, Bell studied the new Curtiss engines at the 1906 Auto and Aero Show. [22, 31]

Despite the Langley fiascoes, the U.S. Army had not abandoned the prospect of aviation. Lieutenant Thomas E. Selfridge conferred with Bell on the topic during 1907, inspiring the older man to write his friend, President Theodore Roosevelt. The president quickly sent orders instructing Selfridge to work closely with Bell. Bell maintained his own laboratory and staff at his Cape Breton estate—indeed, he lived almost as a Scots laird, with entire families in his employ through multiple generations. In 1907, J. A. D. McCurdy, son of Bell's secretary, joined the team. Recently graduated from the University of Toronto, McCurdy recruited his classmate F. W. "Casey" Baldwin (no relation to Captain Tom). With these two young men plus the energetic, inspiring Selfridge, Bell felt ready for a serious assault on the problem of flight. However, he also wanted the man he called "the greatest motor expert in the country"—Glenn Curtiss. [3, 18, 19, 31]

The Curtiss engines had proven themselves on the ground and in the air. Bell had introduced them to the surface of the water, using catamarans to test their endurance and air propeller configurations. Curtiss himself had recently completed that spectacular 26-second mile race at Ormond Beach. Moreover, he must have been a pleasant guest during his visit to the Bell home in January. Bell's wife was deaf, and Curtiss's skills from life with Rutha seem to have facilitated their communication. (Both Rutha Curtiss and Mabel Bell used speech reading for receptive communication and vocal speech for expressive communication, rather than signing.) Bell, who was secure in his position and generous in spirit, was quick to identify and encourage young men of promise. Curtiss not only was congenial but also an expert engine manufacturer with great personal daring and highly honed physical skills. Although his experience with aeronautics was somewhat limited, not many men in the history of the race had had much more by 1907. Curtiss was just the man Bell wanted to complete his team.

On the other hand, Curtiss's accomplishments militated against any such goal on Bell's part. The energetic younger man was already a success, even a famous man. He was not about to become a retainer in the Bell household. Besides, he had a family and a good-sized business to run. The president of the G. H. Curtiss Manufacturing Company was unlikely to drop everything, run off to Nova Scotia, and work on flying machines.

Bell visited Hammondsport and convinced Curtiss to come for a short visit at $25 a day plus expenses, for the purpose of overseeing the engine being used in the tetrahedral kite experiments. Curtiss agreed, sandwiching his visits between the Providence meet, stints in Hammondsport, his first airship flight at Kingsley Flats, exhibitions with Baldwin, and an unsuccessful attempt to erect and fly his own dirigible in St. Louis. (This flop was Curtiss's only attempt at building an airship on his own.) [5, 15, 18, 19, 31]

Curtiss obviously was looking for new goals in life, and Bell capitalized on that fact. He described Curtiss during this period as "a well-known expert in the construction of light gasolene motors . . . his knowledge and experience with such motors will be invaluable— and indeed necessary to the successful conclusion of these experiments."

However, these experiments were limited to the tetrahedral kite, in which Curtiss had no confidence. He and the three younger men seemed to share the same opinion of the kite—although it might fly, it would never be practical. "We come together," dictated Bell in his notes one evening, "not to develop a flying-machine (which is probably their point of view), but to complete a flying-machine which has already been developed, without their aid." [22, 31] Bell had their point of view exactly.

When Bell aired a formal proposal for the Aerial Experiment Association (AEA), it met a hearty response. The group would be a five-man partnership among Bell, Curtiss,

Selfridge, McCurdy, and Casey Baldwin. Mabel Bell would finance operations in exchange for a share in any future profits, and Selfridge defined the goal: "to get into the air." [18]

Even Curtiss agreed. Henry Kleckler, his right-hand man in Hammondsport, would keep the plant going, and the AEA would pay Curtiss $5,000 a year to be the director of experiments (with half-pay whenever he was not actively on the job, a clause added at Curtiss's insistence). Roosevelt arranged new orders for Selfridge, who would be the secretary of the association. Bell would be the chairman, McCurdy the treasurer, and Baldwin the chief engineer. McCurdy and Baldwin would get $1,000 apiece; Selfridge remained on army pay.

Almost immediately, Bell was confronted with a polite mutiny. A bit exasperated but as generous as always, he graciously agreed to the scheme of his young colleagues. They would undertake not one flying machine but five. Each member would take a turn as lead designer, with the others assisting. Each successive machine would build on the experiences of its predecessors. The first aircraft would be Bell's kite. The next four would be aerodromes, or airplanes—which not one of them had ever seen. [4, 19]

The kite worked, more or less. Constructed of more than 3,000 cells—and "big as a house" in Bell's own words—it became airborne carrying a man. The *Cygnet* must have been an impressive sight as it rose from Bras d'Or, the ocean arm overlooked by Bell's estate (Fig. 5.1). Selfridge had the honor of piloting the unpowered flight, in tow from a steamboat. However, poor communications and bad visibility brought *Cygnet*

Fig. 5.1 A pilot (probably Selfridge) tries out the "cockpit" of Bell's kite. Bell standing (just visible) at far right.

unexpectedly back to the water after seven minutes, smashing the aircraft. Selfridge had to be pulled from the wreck, much as Manly had been four years earlier. Again, the young men asserted themselves. The Curtiss engine, and the new propeller, would have to wait. Kite experiments could be resumed when summer returned. Until then, the association should move to Hammondsport, take advantage of Curtiss's motorcycle plant, and get to work on Aerodrome #1.

Word was sent to the absent Curtiss to start working on building a glider—an assignment, he later confessed, about which he had not the slightest idea how to begin. Probably acting on long-distance guidance from Selfridge or Bell, he created a hang glider with Chanute-type biplane wings. Photographs show that these gliders underwent several variations, so the "experimental" part of the AEA name was taken seriously. Apart from Bell's kites and Baldwin's dirigibles, this glider work formed the group's initiation into aviation. Curtiss augmented their base of knowledge by tearing up and down the frozen lake on a sled powered by one of his engines with an aviation propeller.

Bell, who had endured years of lawsuits concerning telephone patents, demanded careful photo-documentation of all his work. Curtiss, who was once a professional photographer, saw the point. He contacted Henry M. Benner, whose studio (now a tavern) continues to stand near the village square. Benner became the semi-official photographer for Curtiss and the AEA. He did well financially for years, selling aeronautical postcards, portfolios, and similar products, and his work forms an unparalleled resource on early aviation. As a minor point, the photographs reveal that the glider work was conducted on slopes across from the current Curtiss Museum (Fig. 5.2). [1, 6, 18, 31]

*Fig. 5.2   Fun in the snow with their new hang glider, watched
by at least two photographers.*

Curtiss led the Bells, Selfridge, McCurdy, and Baldwin to his village, put them up in his home, and provided motorcycles for the younger men. These well-educated and unattached young men caused quite a stir in the social circles of the village, where dances and dinners were quickly planned but with no lasting business resulting. They obviously had a good time, however, and probably even enjoyed plowing through the snow at the end of their short rides in the hang gliders. [19, 31]

The wine aristocracy, already proud of Curtiss and awed by the eminence of Alexander Graham Bell, greeted "Bell's Boys" with open arms and popping corks. McCurdy and Baldwin, riding double on a Curtiss motorcycle, pulled up beside the porch of vintner Harry Champlin one day to chat and then roared off. Several hours later, Champlin was startled by a telephone call from his favorite hotel in Buffalo, which was 150 miles away. Two young men, both covered with mud and one wearing carpet slippers, had turned up without cash and asked for a room, assuring the clerk that Champlin would vouch for their solvency, their credit, and their good name.

Curtiss had made Hammondsport a vastly different place in the six years since the sale of his first motorcycle. Augustus Post—writer, balloonist, and opera singer—arrived in town, sent by the Aero Club to file full reports on the proceedings. The AEA brought with it William F. Bedwin, superintendent of Bell's shop in Nova Scotia. At the Curtiss plant, the association found several savvy men, notably Henry Kleckler, who had taken a lead in developing the original V-8 in addition to running the factory in Curtiss's absence. With increasing frequency, Kleckler was bringing into reality engine ideas sketched by Glenn Curtiss. Apparently working with Kleckler was A. L. Pfitzner, a former Austro-Hungarian military officer who had come to Curtiss by way of an engineering job with Buick. Pfitzner had his own aviation ideas.

So did J. N. Williams. Born before the Mexican War, Williams had made a fortune on a fanning mill. He later made a second fortune refining the new typewriter, which until that point had kept the paper concealed from the operator, leading to considerable frustration when keys jammed—as they often did—because the jam was not discovered until the page was removed. Williams created the first typewriter that exposed the page as the operator worked. He was now in Hammondsport, using Curtiss engines to power a helicopter (Fig. 5.3).

Charles Oliver Jones, whose order had inspired the V-8 project in the first place, had temporarily given up on LTA (Lighter-Than-Air) and was now in town, working on a monstrous ornithopter (wing-flapping) contraption but without any success. H. C. Gammeter, visiting for the same purpose but with a more refined design, was not doing much better (Fig. 5.4). Of course, Captain Baldwin, the most experienced airship operator in the United States, was also on hand. Hammondsport was a zesty place for aviation experimenters as winter melted into spring in 1908. [19, 24, 31]

Fig. 5.3 Williams (right) and a helicopter with a Curtiss V-8. The photographer was Glenn Curtiss.

Fig. 5.4 Gammeter's ornithopter, with a Curtiss V-twin.

Selfridge's swim in the Bras d'Or earned him first honors as lead designer, which was for the best because he had been ruminating about airplanes longer than the other three men. His work was the subject of earnest discussion at the shop and in the Curtiss home, and advice was welcomed from anyone with pretensions to useful knowledge. The aircraft that took shape on Kingsley Flats (near Baldwin's dirigible shed, because the motorcycle plant was overcrowded at the time) was a biplane with stacked wings having opposing dihedrals. The powerplant was one of the powerful Curtiss V-8 air-cooled engines, similar to the one used a year earlier in the motorcycle but now fitted with eight carburetors instead of two (Fig. 5.5). There was a single pusher propeller, a stern rudder, and a canard elevator mounted on bamboo outriggers in the bow. Absolutely no provision was made for lateral control, although the opposing dihedrals produced a good amount of inherent stability. The craft had two skids because there were plans to operate from the ice of Keuka Lake. The fabric was red silk left over from the kite project; Bell selected the vivid color because it would show up well in photographs. Selfridge named the aircraft *Red Wing*.

Fig. 5.5 *The engine of* Red Wing *was a Curtiss V-8 that had been used in the Ormond Beach motorcycle, with eight carburetors instead of two. Notice the large battery of dry cells and the tiny fuel tank.*

Similar to Curtiss, Selfridge had other commitments and obligations; therefore, *Red Wing* was finished while he was away on army business. It was understood that the lead designer on each machine would also be the first pilot, but Curtiss, with his local knowledge, interjected a sobering truth: It was already March, and the ice was not going to last. They finally made the obvious, if awkward, decision. They were going to fly *Red Wing* without Selfridge.

They invented the aircraft carrier before they flew an airplane. Because open water was already at the head of the lake (the Finger Lakes run north, so Hammondsport, on the southern end of Keuka, is at the head), *Red Wing* was trundled aboard the steam barge *Springstead* for a short journey to solid ice. Tank Waters fell in as they were unloading, but he was fished out safely. Because Mabel Bell had become sick, she and her husband had left for their home in Washington, D.C. The three remaining members drew straws, and Casey Baldwin took his place in the pilot's seat after Curtiss and Kleckler checked everything.

A crowd had gathered for the occasion. Not only had two dozen men, including photographer Benner, tagged along for the ride on *Springstead,* but the entire town watched from a distance. The beefy Kleckler cranked the prop, the men holding down the wings let go, and Casey skidded along the ice. Before anyone expected it, he flew, finally settling back down, bending the aircraft a little, after 318 ft 11 in. of adequately controlled heavier-than-air flight (Fig. 5.6). Dr. William Christmas reportedly had made a short flight in an airplane

Fig. 5.6 Red Wing *with skids, opposing dihedrals for stability, and no provision for lateral control.*

of his own design four days earlier near Washington, D.C. Apart from that, Casey's flight was the first in the Western Hemisphere outside the Wright camp, and the longest first flight made (by man or aircraft) in the world until that point. Now the AEA members could claim that they had seen an airplane, as could hundreds of Curtiss's friends and neighbors.

After repairs, *Red Wing* was back on the ice for St. Patrick's Day. Despite his lucky green tie, Casey treated the audience this time to its first airplane crash. There was no properly controlled flight on this attempt, despite being 120 ft airborne. When Selfridge finally returned to the fold the next day, all he found salvageable from his brainchild was the tail section and the Curtiss engine. Neither Selfridge nor the Bells ever saw *Red Wing* in a finished condition, let alone seeing it in flight. However, the AEA had created and flown an airplane, from scratch, in eight weeks. [1, 5, 6, 18, 19, 22, 24, 31]

The team started at once on Aerodrome #2, which was later named *White Wing,* with Casey Baldwin as lead designer. They had learned to put the engine controls where the pilot could reach them (the controls in *Red Wing* had been under the seat). They had also learned that lateral controls were absolutely essential; Casey's success on the twelfth was partly due to dumb luck because uncooperative winds could not have been managed. Furthermore, they recognized that because they would not be flying from ice again, skids were unusable.

Having rejected from the start the assisted takeoff favored by the Wrights (who used a catapult and monorail), Bell's Boys created the tricycle-wheeled landing gear. Apparently borrowed from Curtiss's old Wind Wagon, the configuration remains standard today. The dirigible-type propeller used on *Red Wing* was replaced with a sturdier laminated-wood model.

For lateral control, they had at the earliest point in their deliberations rejected the Wright brothers' wing warping approach as not only patented but ineffective. There were several possible approaches to the problem, but they quickly built on a suggestion from Bell. Movable flaps at the tips of the wings would change the amount of lift at each extremity, forcing one tip up and the opposite tip down (Fig. 5.7). Apparently unknown to the group, such devices were already being used in Europe. This appears to have been an independent development, and the first use in the Western Hemisphere of the device that the AEA called "wingtips." The term "aileron" would be imported months later after a conversation with French pilot Henri Farman.

Credit at least for ailerons was later claimed by Augustus Herring, who had arrived in the wake of the *Red Wing* crash. Herring had worked with aviation pioneer Octave Chanute, and Bell considered him to be the first man to have flown, based on experiments in the

Fig. 5.7 White Wing *in flight, with tricycle landing gear and ailerons (triangular wingtip flaps).*

Indiana Dunes with a hang glider (having a compressed-air engine added) as far back as 1892. Although it is possible that Herring may have done some hopping, skipping, and jumping into the air with this device, it was not controlled, powered flight. Despite the promise of his early work, Herring had produced little besides promises in the previous decade. He had plenty of chutzpah, however, and had even offered to give the Wright brothers a two-thirds interest in the airplane after their success at Kitty Hawk. Apparently, the Wrights never replied to this egregious offer. Any comments Herring made presumably went into the AEA hopper with everyone else's, but there is no trail of anything useful and no record that he actually employed innovations, such as ailerons, that he claimed to have originated.

The new control system was elegant, even instinctive. The pilot turned the wheel in the desired direction to engage the rudder. Pushing forward on the wheel tilted the bow elevator to pitch the nose downward, while pulling back pitched the nose upward. Cords from a shoulder yoke engaged the ailerons, so that a pilot wanting to turn, for instance, to the left, steered left and leaned left simultaneously—the same movement he would make on a bicycle or motorcycle. The machine would then bank into the turn, in the same manner as a two-wheeler. Virtually all the early pilots had cycling experience, and the AEA controls produced the same effect in the same situation with the same movement. It also was self-correcting; if a wingtip rolled down, the pilot would lean in the opposite direction to keep himself upright, dragging the yoke with him, engaging the ailerons, and regaining equilibrium.

There was a definite drawback if a wing dipped too far—the pilot would not be able to haul himself up against gravity, although some later saved themselves in these circumstances by grabbing a strut and hauling up that way.

Aerodrome #2 (except for the salvaged tail from *Red Wing*) was covered with white lightweight muslin and quickly christened *White Wing*. Harry Champlin, at whose trotting horse track Curtiss and other village boys had raced bicycles, offered his track as the AEA flying field, going so far as to grade earth and remove trees where that seemed helpful. A huge tent was nailed to the wall of a barn next to the track on the Pleasant Valley Wine Company grounds, and *White Wing*, in pieces, was shipped on the B&H the mile or so from Kingsley Flats to Stony Brook Farm, as Champlin called the place.

The usual crowd, including the *Hammondsport Herald,* observed the work, and Bell was back in town. Bell proved himself quite useful one day when all hands were puzzling over the apparent lack of lift in ground tests. It took the association chairman to realize that the cloth was too porous. Doping, he opined, would solve the problem; and so it did, with the added weight apparently no impediment. On May 18, Casey Baldwin took the aircraft up 10 ft for a 279-ft flight, ending when the wing fouled the prop. However, it was a controlled landing, and Bell was ecstatic, which he made clear in an impromptu press conference (Fig. 5.8). Selfridge took his maiden flight (the first by a U.S. military man) the next day,

Fig. 5.8 The AEA members with White Wing. *From left: Casey Baldwin, Selfridge, Curtiss, Bell, McCurdy (recovering from a motorcycle accident). At far right is Augustus Post of the Aero Club, and at Selfridge's feet is his dog, Jack.*

stopping after 100 ft when a wire fouled the prop. Clearing up the problem, he flew 240 ft on his next attempt, bending the front wheel a bit on landing. Baldwin and Selfridge both handled *White Wing* until May 21, when Curtiss took the pilot's seat, after removing the cloth windscreen—he wanted to see everything ahead. It was his thirtieth birthday.

Even the "veteran" pilots, Selfridge and Casey Baldwin, were startled and impressed by Curtiss's handling of *White Wing*. "The machine was in perfect control at all times," Selfridge wired Bell. The balance and control that Curtiss had repeatedly demonstrated on two wheels were now becoming useful in the air.

Even a short distance such as 1,000 ft placed Curtiss in a fraternity embracing perhaps a dozen men worldwide. Despite his self-deprecating description, his flight was fraught with significance. Baldwin and Selfridge, the two experienced pilots, marveled at his control. Whatever made Curtiss successful on bicycles and motorcycles was carrying over to airplanes. For his entire life, Curtiss was acutely aware of his own position in space.

From his testimony, the flight wrought a notable change in Curtiss. He appears to have been strongest at experiential and kinesthetic learning. Even a single flight, as subsequent events would show, seemed to have given him a deep knowledge of the early airplane and its dynamics. Quite likely, he could not have articulated *how* he knew the airplane, but the fact remains that he *did* know it. He wrote after the flight:

> Although I have given the subject of aviation much thought, it wasn't until I flew *White Wing* today that my ideas of how to operate a heavier-than-air flying machine are really tangible enough to be of service to another. . . The art of flying, even such a short distance as a thousand feet, gives a person something to work from, and his ideas follow on a more practical course. [3]

On May 23, McCurdy finally had his chance. The Canadian was taking a good deal of ribbing from his friends for frequent motorcycle spills and had even been on crutches after an accident. After 549 ft, he wrecked *White Wing*, unable to manage her in a foul wind. McCurdy was unhurt, and *White Wing* could have been serviceable after two weeks of repairs. However, that fact, although gratifying, was held irrelevant. *White Wing,* now junked, had been a drastic advance on *Red Wing*. It was time for Aerodrome #3. [1, 5, 6, 18, 19, 22, 24, 31]

Glenn Curtiss was the lead designer, a task he likely could not have managed with notable success if he had not had that birthday experience with *White Wing*. The changes he directed on Aerodrome #3 seemed almost superficial, but they led to dramatic improvements in performance. Curtiss discarded the cloth windscreen altogether, insistent on seeing everything before him. The wheelbase and mainframe were lengthened, the pilot and engine shoved farther apart, and the bow elevator extended. Wing surface was reduced, which necessarily reduced lift but also reduced drag; Curtiss found the exchange well warranted. Aileron surface was increased, making the aircraft more responsive to roll control. To further enhance lateral control, Curtiss created a shoulder yoke with a neck strap, maximizing the pilot's movements as he engaged the ailerons. The result—at least theoretically—would be an extremely sensitive aircraft.

Remembering how Malinda Bennitt had lent him a storefront for his bicycle shop, Curtiss personally chauffeured her by auto to Stony Brook Farm one day, showed her his new creation, and asked her to do him the honor of naming it. It must have been something of a letdown when Bennitt, who as a child had known veterans of the Revolutionary War, claimed that her old head simply was not up to the task. Bell gallantly stepped in, christening Aerodrome #3 *June Bug.*

Recognizing the risk that each new operator brought to the equation, Bell's Boys ruled that no one but Curtiss would fly *June Bug* until they were satisfied that they had squeezed from the aircraft all the information it had to offer. On June 21, exactly one month after his sole *White Wing* venture, Curtiss rolled out *June Bug* and conducted three flawless flights, the longest at 1266 ft and 34.5 mph. The delighted Bells moved to Cape Breton Island, while *June Bug*'s fabric was varnished yellow for the convenience of photographers. On June 25, Curtiss made two flights, the longest at 3420 ft. "We have telegraphed [the] secretary [of the] Aero Club of America that we are now ready to try for the Scientific American Cup," Selfridge wired Bell. "Hurrah."

The news took the secretary of the Aero Club aback. Despite regular reports from Augustus Post, he had not been expecting this news and was not certain he welcomed it. *Scientific American* had offered the huge silver trophy (now in the Curtiss exhibit at the National Air and Space Museum) to stimulate U.S. aeronautics, and the Aero Club had agreed to supervise arrangements. The problem was that sponsors had hoped the award would smoke out the Wright brothers.

Since their first successful flight four and a half years earlier, Wilbur and Orville Wright had continued to work, mostly near their home in Dayton, Ohio. They had handily beaten one requirement for the 1908 trophy award, a 1-km (0.6 mi) straight flight. However, the Wrights' activities, while not exactly secret, had been shielded from scrutiny as much as possible. There had never been an official, impartial observation of their flights. No knowledgeable person doubted their accomplishments, but it certainly would be inappropriate to grant a major award based on the participants' own word. If that were the case, they might as well give the trophy to Curtiss, who had already beaten the required distance (with newspapers and rubberneckers on hand, but without official sanction) on June 25.

The Wrights saw no reason to expose their invention to public scrutiny and considered exhibitions to be unseemly. They felt no marketing pressure because they were confident that no one could match their achievements within five years—unless, of course, the person stole their ideas. Moreover, their aircraft became aloft after being shot down a monorail by a falling weight. The *Scientific American* requirements insisted on an unassisted takeoff.

The secretary of the Aero Club offered to stall the Bell group if the Wrights would make a trial for the trophy. However, Wilbur was in Europe, and Orville replied that he was too busy preparing for U.S. Army trials of a Wright airplane in the fall. Moreover, he added, they simply could not spare the time to convert one of their machines for a wheeled takeoff, although he pointed out that it would be possible to do so. The Wrights simply were not interested in the trophy. Therefore, the Aero Club glumly turned to Curtiss, asking him to make arrangements to come to New York City for the official trial.

The AEA again riled the genteel Aero Club by responding that no rule specified the location or gave sponsors any right to choose the location. The AEA members and their airplane were in Hammondsport, and that is where the trial would take place. After some gnashing of teeth (and presumably some checking of maps), the Aero Club agreed. Bell's Boys were clearly a threat to good order.

Curtiss also set the date as the Fourth of July. "Advertise it," he said. "Invite everybody interested in flight. Draw a crowd to Hammondsport and prove to the world that we can really fly." [31] Pleasant Valley was about to host America's first air show.

People began arriving that Saturday at sunrise, by automobile, buggy, foot, bike, motorcycle, and special B&H trains. Karl Dienstbach was there, representing the Imperial German government. The Aero Club was there. *Scientific American* was there. The *Hammondsport Herald* and other newspapers were there. Daisy Fairchild (daughter of the Bells) and her husband, David, were there. Augustus Herring and other aeronautic experimenters were there. People from the movies were there, eager to catch the first film of an American airplane. Curtiss's friends and neighbors were there, making up a crowd of a thousand people on the Pleasant Valley grounds. *June Bug* was there, ready to show them all what she could do.

The only one missing was Glenn Curtiss. Despite his daredevil reputation and his confident promotion of the day, he remained passionately committed to safety. He didn't like the wind or the thunderheads looming in the distance. Conditions were not good, he decided, and until they were, he refused to fly.

The situation became increasingly awkward as the crowd became restive, beginning to wonder if they had been gulled by tricksters with their plausible talk of an implausible flying machine. Pleasant Valley Wine Company saved the day by throwing open its doors to serve up an impromptu wine tasting. The crowd, now satisfied for the time being, decided it could wait a little longer.

It would wait as long as Curtiss did, and he had plenty of patience when he needed it. David Fairchild whiled away his time photographing the empty streets and the empty motorcycle plant. Some rain passed through, which could not have improved dispositions on the Pleasant Valley grounds. Curtiss studied the sky and got into his auto. He was ready.

Times were still being standardized, and eyewitness reports vary by two hours when detailing the moment Curtiss and his colleagues wheeled *June Bug* out to her scratch line. Officials were appointed, a direction determined, and a kilometer paced off. The rules called for a straightaway flight, but Curtiss requested and received permission to weave while avoiding bad ground because of obstacles such as vineyards and trees. But he was cautioned that he would be given credit only for distance to the 1-km marker, which meant his trip would actually be a little longer.

"Oh, why does he fly so high?" Lena Curtiss cried out as he took off. Amused males have exaggerated her cry to create a picture of Lena as a whimpering Victorian woman, dabbing her eyes as her husband set off on frightening, incomprehensible exploits. However, Queen Victoria was long since dead, and Lena, although quiet, had never been a shrinking violet; she did ride motorcycles, after all. In an age when scarcely any woman (or man) worldwide had even seen an airplane, she was familiar enough to know when and how they were going wrong. Curtiss was indeed flying much higher than he had intended. In fact, he was shoving down on the elevator control with all his weight, trying desperately to get back to earth with himself and his machine intact.

He finally managed it, far short of his goal. Inspection revealed that the tail had been fastened at the wrong angle. There was no shortage of eager volunteers to wheel *June Bug* back to the starting point. Adjustments were made, and Curtiss again straddled the pilot's bench, working the yoke around his shoulders and the strap across his neck. Peering down the course, he spotted a photographer setting up—slightly short of the 1-km mark.

At that point, something apparently snapped in the quiet Hammondsporter. Grimly he fired up the engine, rumbled forward, and was airborne. This time he flew straight, low, and level, kicking up an impressive cloud of dust. Cheers exploded, and one woman was so engrossed by the sight that she was struck by a slow-moving train, breaking a rib. All eyes were on Curtiss as he flew past the offensive photographer and triumphantly over the 1-km mark...

... and kept going. The weather, the delays, the impatient crowd, and the false start had been enough annoyance for one day. The doubting photographer had been the final straw. "Just on account of Mr. B—," he wrote Bell, "who was standing at the finish with a camera to photograph the machine in case I fell short on the distance, I flew the machine as far as the field would permit, regardless of fences, ditches, etc." (Fig. 5.9). He was nearly a mile down the road to Hammondsport when he finally made a perfect touchdown, his air-cooled engine overheating, and the limits of safe landing ground reached. He had traveled at 39 mph and used less than a quart of gasoline.

Back in Pleasant Valley, they threw open the cellars a second time. [1, 5, 6, 18, 19, 22, 24, 31]

On Sunday morning, assembled dignitaries took a cruise on the lake, to be met by the town band on their return, while Selfridge and Casey Baldwin "carried Mr. Curtiss from the steamer, much to the discomfort of the unassuming gentleman." The band took one of the special trains to Pleasant Valley, where it played for a crowd even larger than that of

Fig. 5.9 July 4, 1908: The flight of June Bug. *The barn at the left continues to stand on the grounds of the Pleasant Valley Wine Company.*

the preceding day—"the entire population of Hammondsport and surrounding country," according to the *Herald.* Curtiss flew again, attempting a circle but giving it up to avoid flying over a vineyard.

In 1976, Mercury Aircraft of Hammondsport built a reproduction of *June Bug*, flying it as far as 10 miles in Hammondsport, Oshkosh, and Dansville, New York. David B. Thurston (now head of Thurston Aeromarine Corporation) "was asked to participate as structural designer and did so using current Federal Aviation Administration (FAA) Part 23 design regulations." In his words,

> [A]t least some of the designers of 1908 were more aware of what they were doing than many believed. For example, when going over the wire braced wing bays, I chased the loads increasing toward the center of the airplane and decided that double diagonal rather than the replica's single diagonal brace wires were required between bays. We had been working with what little we could find in the way of drawings from the museum, personal files, and local attics. Among the material was a detail showing double diagonal wires designed into the original airplane at the inner bay. Someone back in 1908 was using wing design loads similar to those of the FAA in 1974.
>
> When it finally became necessary to locate the center of gravity position for flight, I was faced with determining what Curtiss intended the dual aft fixed horizontal surfaces to accomplish. Because the forward elevator was movable to provide trim in flight, I decided that the fixed surfaces must be there for increased stability in level flight. Thus, the center of gravity was located at 26% of wing chord, a safe position for most aircraft, and to my relief the replica was flown very successfully . . . although the aileron roll power was rather marginal. [32]

After six months of airplane work, the AEA had a smashing success on its hands. Moreover, the wide publicity of this first exhibition flight, and the movies shown nationwide, forced airplanes at last into the public consciousness. Bell was calling in his patent lawyers, and Wilbur Wright was writing Orville from Europe, recommending that he query Curtiss on whether the latter would like a license for exhibitions, but withholding any manufacturing rights. [34, 35] Both Wrights were convinced that it would not be possible to create an airplane without using their patented features. Focusing on 30-year-old Mr. Curtiss, rather than on the eminent Dr. Bell, was a sound tactical move. At any rate, it was clear by now that Curtiss and Selfridge were the main spark plugs in the Bell team. [1, 5–8, 18–20, 22, 24, 31]

Bell was reasserting his leadership now, albeit in a conservative direction. He set patent applications in motion. He firmly vetoed a proposal that Curtiss race Henri Farman, who was soon scheduled to tour the United States. He also summoned Casey Baldwin to Cape Breton to join him in resuming kite work. Selfridge and McCurdy remained with Curtiss, where McCurdy was charged with leading the design of Aerodrome #4.

The three members remaining in Hammondsport all flew *June Bug*, honing their skills and modifying the aircraft to test proposed innovations for Aerodrome #4. However, as July slipped toward August, McCurdy was working more on his own. Curtiss and Selfridge had another major project with which to contend.

The U.S. Army had decided to enter the aeronautic field, with leadership for the project under the Signal Corps. In soliciting bids for an airship, the Corps had deliberately set standards so high that only one person in the United States had the experience to meet them—Tom Baldwin. Baldwin won the bid outright anyhow, forthrightly planning to build at a loss.

The specified airship would be twice as big as anything that had ever flown in the United States. It would have mechanical pitch control, rather than control by shifting the weight of a shuffling pilot. It needed to fly 25 miles at a stretch. It also would need an impermeable envelope, an unmet requirement that had led to all bids, including Baldwin's, being voided in the first round. By the time of the second solicitation, Baldwin had what he needed—a layer of rubber sandwiched between two layers of silk.

Contract in hand, Baldwin began work on the gasbag and gondola, cheerfully tossing the engine problem to Curtiss. The distance, endurance, and speed requirements called for water cooling, which Curtiss had always avoided because of the added weight. He had been offering water-cooled options for some time, but there is no record of any engines actually being built until this point. Curtiss, Kleckler, and Pfitzner put their heads together, quickly creating a water-cooled straight four, similar to the air-cooled model used on earlier airships.

The entire contraption was shipped to the Ft. Myer army base in Virginia, where it would be assembled for the first time. Curtiss came along to give Baldwin a hand, and the two friends put to work interested army personnel, including Frank Lahm and Benjamin Foulois, both of whom would reach high rank in army aviation. Foulois showed up in immaculate uniform, and a suspicious Curtiss told him he would need some old clothes and a rag if he really wanted to help. He did, and Curtiss was satisfied.

SC-1, as the dirigible became known, epitomized the freewheeling cross-pollination of the various Hammondsport workers. The fabric, reduced to a single ply of silk with the rubber, would be borrowed for Aerodrome #4. The biplane elevator was borrowed *from* plans for Aerodrome #4. The water-cooled straight four provided a testing ground for the water-cooled V-8 planned in #4, and the dirigible propeller was designed by Tom Selfridge.

Curtiss and Baldwin would conduct the acceptance trials because no army man could fly the thing. Baldwin, in the stern, acted as command pilot and operated the rudder. Curtiss, in the bow, acted as flight engineer, operating both the engine and the elevator. This arrangement showed its drawbacks in an early test when the dirigible began to porpoise, bucking through air that had piled up before its bow. Curtiss, bent over his engine to adjust it, could not hear Baldwin, who assumed Curtiss was fiddling with the elevator. The non-stop profanity with which the Captain turned the air blue entertained the crowd, including ranking officers; Washington, D.C., dignitaries; and diplomatic observers. However, it was utterly lost on Curtiss, who, as so often, had ears only for his engine.

"The enemy is in sight," Baldwin roared on one turn over the crowd, again providing entertainment while pointing out the potential of the airship. Curtiss, perhaps more practical and certainly less flamboyant, found that the engine worked so well he actually had little to do. He quietly turned in a terrain sketch he had made with a nail and a piece of paper.

After several days, the tests were completed, culminating in repeated round trips between Ft. Myer and Falls Church (Fig. 5.10). "Come on down," the ecstatic crowd called, excitedly realizing that Baldwin had met all the army requirements as the last leg was finished. "Be careful with her, boys," the pilot told enlisted handlers when he landed. "She doesn't belong to me." The United States had an air force, thanks to Tom Baldwin and Glenn Curtiss. Baldwin lingered long enough to teach Selfridge, Foulois, and Lahm how to fly the airship and to host a party for reporters, in which they all toasted the accomplishment with Pleasant Valley's Great Western champagne. [9, 15, 19, 24, 29–31, 33]

Selfridge stayed on to gain experience on the *SC-1* and to prepare for tests of the Wright Flyer. This was the first time any of the Hammondsport group had seen the Wright machine, which was finally being exposed at least to semipublic scrutiny. "He has no secrets, and no special features," Curtiss wrote Bell—an assessment that probably would have incensed Orville Wright. [3] Orville was also disgusted to find Selfridge on the army's acceptance board, but he was the only man in the service with any knowledge of airplanes.

On September 17, Orville took Selfridge up for required tests involving endurance with a passenger. When a propeller snapped in flight, Selfridge heard the noise and turned to Orville with a concerned glance. The broken chunk sliced a control cable, and as the airplane nosed in, Selfridge said, "Oh! Oh!"—the last words he ever spoke. The aircraft was

*Fig. 5.10   Tom Baldwin (stern) and Curtiss, conducting
army acceptance trials of* SC-1.

destroyed, and Orville Wright was seriously injured. Selfridge died a few hours later, never regaining consciousness after the crash. He was the first man to die in an airplane accident.

Selfridge's interest, knowledge, and enthusiasm had inspired Bell to form the Aerial Experiment Association. He had led design on perhaps the first airplane in the United States outside of the Wright camp. He had been the first U.S. military man to fly, and if logs had been kept in those days, Selfridge's would have shown him piloting *Cygnet*, one or more AEA gliders, *White Wing*, *June Bug*, and *SC-1*—every type you could get into the air in those days, except for free balloons. A West Point graduate and the nephew of a naval hero killed in the Civil War, Selfridge was obviously destined for great things in the army and in aeronautics. In a moment, just as his work was bearing fruit, he was gone.

Naturally, this tragedy shattered all three of the country's main forces in the field—the army, the Wright brothers, and the interlocked Hammondsport-Bell circles. (This latter group was shaken further within the week, when Charles Oliver Jones, erstwhile ornithopter man who had returned to LTA, died as his airship caught fire at an exhibition in Maine.) The bad feeling that was developing upset the hospitalized Orville Wright, who heard that the Bell team, in Washington, D.C., for Selfridge's funeral at Arlington National Cemetery, had taken advantage of the situation to inspect his aircraft closely. Orville's sister Katherine asked an Aero Club official to investigate, and it turned out simply that Bell, who carried a tape in his pocket, had measured some wreckage to help army men who were uncertain whether the pieces would fit in their prepared crates. Selfridge was unmarried, and his father took over his position in the AEA as far as any financial interest was concerned but did not take part in the work. [2, 3, 5, 7, 8, 10, 14, 18–20, 23, 24, 31]

That work was putting *June Bug* through various indignities. The upper wing of the aircraft was cut through to accommodate the tall standing pipes of the radiator for a new water-cooled V-8. Her tail was shortened and reconfigured. Eventually, her landing gear was removed in favor of two canoelike floats. Rechristened *Loon*, she was launched on Keuka Lake for experiments in water flying. These were unsuccessful, apparently resulting not from calculation but from a spirit of stick-floats-on-and-see-if-it-works.

More careful work was going into *Silver Dart*, as McCurdy named Aerodrome #4 from the color of her Baldwin rubberized silk. Built "like a watch" in McCurdy's words, *Silver Dart* was designed and constructed as the crown of the AEA efforts. In addition to the new fabric and the new water-cooled engine, which were intended to extend their flying "from minutes to hours," the aircraft sported a chain drive, unique in the AEA efforts and rare in anything Curtiss built. Again, the aileron area was increased. In place of the single-surface canard elevator of Aerodromes #1 through #3, Aerodrome #4 had a large biplane elevator in the bow, similar to that used on *SC-1*. The horizontal and vertical stabilizers in the tail were removed altogether. McCurdy wanted a machine that steered very sensitively—which meant, of course, that the aircraft had little inherent stability, although the opposing dihedrals were retained.

Silver Dart was test-flown repeatedly in Hammondsport as 1908 turned to 1909. McCurdy found time in the same period to sink *Loon*, unwittingly breaking a float in the dark. "Submarine test most successful," the irreverent pair wired Bell, describing their escapade as a "vaudeville performance by moonlight." His lengthy stay in the Curtiss home was slowly making McCurdy unfit for life and work in Bell's shadow.

Aerodrome #4 was shipped to Cape Breton Island, where McCurdy, on the frozen Bras d'Or, made the first airplane flight in Canada—indeed, in the British Empire—on February 23. As with the earlier flights in Hammondsport, this was a festive public occasion, and the dignified Bell was so excited that he jumped up in his sleigh when McCurdy took off (Fig. 5.11). In the exact moment that *Silver Dart* was landing, two girls skated in front of it. McCurdy turned easily aside, landing elegantly and justifying his insistence on sensitive steering. It was his coming of age in aeronautics. The man who could not be trusted to sit a motorcycle properly, who had wrecked *White Wing* and sunk *Loon*, was showing

Fig. 5.11 McCurdy, in Silver Dart, *conducts the first flight in Canada.*

what he was finally becoming—one of the finest pilots of the pioneer days. He would live to attend the golden anniversary of his flight, the last of Bell's Boys, after a long career of service to Canadian aviation.

Experiments with *Silver Dart* continued, as did tests of tetrahedral kites. However, the work of the Aerial Experiment Association, which had already extended its original charter by six months, was spectacularly concluded. In a year and a half, the group had designed, built, and flown supremely successful airplanes, having for resource virtually no knowledge of other airplane work on either side of the Atlantic Ocean. Bell wanted to hold the group together, and he gathered Baldwin and McCurdy—both his employees—for a midnight meeting on the last day of the charter, hoping to arrange either an extension or a successor corporation. Although it was an occasion for bittersweet nostalgia—especially when thoughts turned to Tom Selfridge—midnight passed, and the Aerial Experiment Association with it. Glenn Curtiss was not there. [1, 2, 3, 5, 6, 19, 31]

✫ ✫ ✫

Curtiss, who was an independent cuss anyway, apparently could see no future either in the AEA designs or in Bell's lumbering approach. He was still doing well in the engine and motorcycle business, and he had a foot in the LTA door through his friend Tom Baldwin. Now he hoped to make a few dollars on airplanes.

Curtiss and Kleckler quickly designed a flying machine that was a dramatic advance on its AEA predecessors, and on the contemporary Baddeck aircraft soon to be created by McCurdy, Baldwin, and Bell. Curtiss #1, originally and informally called *Gold Bug* because of its fabric color, had a far shorter wingspan than the AEA aerodromes. Moreover, the wings eliminated both the taper and opposing dihedral, harking back to the Chanute biplane arrangement used on the hang gliders a year earlier. In place of four triangular wingtip ailerons, *Gold Bug* sported two rectangular ailerons, mounted on the outboard leading struts midway between the wings and overlapping the wingtips (Fig. 5.12). Although engineering was the genesis of this arrangement, the migration of the ailerons also had the happy potential of weakening challenges under the Wright patent, which concerned manipulation of the surface of the wing.

For its powerplant, the new machine used a water-cooled Curtiss four-cylinder inline, descended from the *SC-1* engine. The tricycle landing gear, pusher propeller, pilot controls, rubberized fabric, and box-kite elevator were carried over from previous work. [1, 6, 22]

Curtiss built *Gold Bug* under contract from the Aeronautical Society of New York. The society, a split-off from the Aero Club, paid $5,000 for the airplane, including delivery and flight instruction for two members—the first airplane sale in the Western Hemisphere. Being members of high society, they elegantly rechristened their new toy *Golden Flier*. [31]

Fig. 5.12 Gold Bug/Golden Flier *was a much trimmer, tidier airplane than the AEA predecessors. Note the two interplane ailerons.*

Curtiss and the Aeronautical Society agreed that he should perform a series of exhibitions in New York. The society would venture the risk and reap the benefits from the shows, but Curtiss would be risking the airplane because the society had not technically taken possession of it. On June 26 in the Bronx, 5,000 spectators paid a dollar apiece, signaling new opportunities for anyone crazy enough to take up aerial performing.

Curtiss soon suggested moving operations to the flat ground of Long Island, which he had visited during his motorcycle racing days. He began exhibitions and test flights at Mineola on July 12, flying 15 miles on July 16. On July 17, he took off shortly before 5:30 A.M. to try for the 1909 *Scientific American* trophy.

The minimum requirement for 1909 was a 25-km circular flight, with takeoff and landing within the specified course. The award would be held until the end of the year, with the trophy going to whichever pilot made the longest flight. Curtiss tanked up with 3 gallons of gas and started his laps around three stakes, watched by 3,000 visitors. Charles Manly (Langley's erstwhile assistant and luckless pilot) was course official, and Manly's sister held up a placard with the lap number each time Curtiss passed his starting point. Twelve laps met the minimum, but Curtiss flew for 19, covering 24.7 miles and landing with a half gallon of gas. No one else attempted the trophy, so Curtiss won it two consecutive years.

The delighted Aeronautical Society accepted the aircraft, and Curtiss met his first two students on the following morning. Charles F. Willard made a good flight in two hops, but Alexander Williams overturned the airplane, knocked himself out, broke his arm, and gave up flying—all before noon. It appeared as though the Aeronautical Society was out of business—and out $5,000—on its first day, but Curtiss assured the group that *Golden Flier* could be repaired quickly. [19, 24, 31]

✴ ✴ ✴

An accident of a different sort was waiting for Curtiss in Hammondsport, and this would not be fixed as easily. After taking on the Aeronautical Society contract, Curtiss had formed a new company in conjunction with Augustus Herring, who had been sniffing around the AEA operation for several months.

The jury will probably always be out on Herring, who sometimes seems to have been a serious student and pioneer in aeronautics, while other times seems to have been a flim-flam man on the grand scale. It is possible that he was both.

Herring had worked with both Langley and Chanute during the 1890s, taking a hand in the design, construction, and operation of Chanute's hang gliders. He had produced scientific papers on flight. He had developed a type of hang glider, powered with a compressed-air engine, with which he experimented in the Indiana dunes during the 1890s. On the strength of these experiments, Bell considered him the first man to have flown, and

Herring could display a photograph to verify this claim. The photograph putatively shows Herring nearly clearing (or landing in) a sand dune. To the less charitable, it looks like a photograph of Herring sitting on the sand just beyond the crest of the rise, hanging on *as though* he were in flight.

That was the enigma of Augustus Herring, who was knowledgeable enough—and plausible enough—to convince workers such as Langley, Chanute, Curtiss, Bell, Tom Baldwin, and the Signal Corps, but whose actual accomplishments remain maddeningly difficult to pin down. Even if his handheld contraption gave him a few extra inches as he ran down the beach, he was not flying any more than Hiram Maxim had been half a century earlier, when his much more elaborate behemoth escaped into the air a few inches as it careened down rails.

After Kitty Hawk, Herring had generously offered to give the Wright brothers a two-thirds interest in the airplane, retaining only a one-third share for himself. Herring had contributed nothing to the Wrights' work, although he visited them once in company with Chanute, failing on that trip to fly a glider of his own design. His overweening suggestion was apparently based on chutzpah, on his earlier work, and on the dark hint of prior patents.

These patents—and the suggestion of using gyroscopes to neutralize the Wright's wing-warping patent—excited Curtiss and Tom Baldwin. Herring's hints of strong financial offers from three European countries excited Cortlandt Bishop of the Aero Club, who volunteered to raise capital and keep this paragon in the United States. In the last month of the AEA, a press conference at the Aero Club announced the formation of the Herring-Curtiss Company. Bishop came up with $38,000 from his own funds and two other investors. Curtiss turned over property appraised at more than $82,000: his company (which employed more than 100 employees and had cleared $120,000 in the previous year), all patents, the factory, and even his home. For this, he received $60,000 in cash and mortgages, 160 preferred shares and 400 common shares, the position of vice president and general manager, and a $5,000 annual salary.

Herring, who became vice president and director, also received a $5,000 salary. More significantly, he held $200,000 worth of stock, from a total of $360,000, which gave him a voting majority. In exchange, he put in his shop equipment (which was used only for making aerial toys such as whirligigs, and never left his works in New York City), his patents (which he later admitted under oath had never existed), and, according to estimates by Curtiss biographer C. R. Roseberry, about $650 in cash. [2, 3, 19, 20, 31] Eugene Husting, in a positive appraisal of Herring (few students seem to take a middle ground), identifies $8,500 paid in by Herring's family and associates. [21]

Strains started showing immediately. The *Hammondsport Herald* reported that the company would be called Curtiss-Herring, which it retracted before stating the correct name of Herring-Curtiss. It reported that the motorcycle business was exempted from the merger, then revealed that it was, in fact, included. Herring claimed to be working at a separate location on a prior private project, an airplane for the U.S. Army, of which he wanted Curtiss to have no part. However, he kept kibitzing on *Gold Bug,* Curtiss's similar prior private contract, until Curtiss sharply told him to mind his own business.

Even so, it was as an official of the Herring-Curtiss Company that Curtiss tore into his next project. He had agreed to represent the Aero Club at the Grande Semaine d'Aviation in Reims, France. This would be the first international air meet, and Curtiss was the only U.S. participant. Because the Aeronautical Society refused to release *Golden Flier* (even as a spare), Curtiss needed a new machine, and fast.

This machine was slightly smaller than *Golden Flier,* although it sported a new and improved 50-hp Curtiss V-8. It has been a matter of controversy for decades as to whether the fabric was yellow (gold) or gray. If a contemporary French print is accurate, both colors were used. The passing of an age was demonstrated by the fact that this airplane was given no individual name, although later generations have retroactively called it the *Reims Racer*.

This was a rush job. Curtiss did not fly the machine and gave the engine only a quick test before crating it for shipping. He stopped in New York City long enough to put *Golden Flier* back in order, make a few test flights in the repaired machine, and receive his final payment. Accompanying him to Europe were Tod Shriver (a mechanic borrowed from Captain Baldwin) and Ward Fisher, Curtiss's old swimming and cycling friend from his Rochester days. Fisher was now into motorcycles, and he held the Curtiss agency in Flower City.

Curtiss shocked the French people while he was still on the dock, when his greeters asked where his airplane was. "Right here," he replied, putting his hand on one of four long crates. They could not believe that his aircraft was so small or could be packed so compactly. This miniaturization was highlighted even more when railroad officials agreed to ship the crates as personal luggage. All Curtiss included by way of spare parts was a single propeller; Louis Blériot's builder gave him another, in case he needed it. Blériot had already stunned the world by flying across the English Channel.

The Herring-Curtiss was the only entrant from the United States in the meet, although there were also five European-owned Wright-type airplanes in addition to the 38 entirely European contenders. The former motorcycle racer had set his eyes on the Gordon Bennett

Trophy, sponsored by the eccentric publisher who lived at the time in Paris and who had already established a similar prize for aerostats. With an untested machine and no margin for error, Curtiss passed up the first six days of competition to concentrate on assembling and testing his little racer. He also had several conversations with Cortlandt Bishop, in which they came to the sickening realization that they had each incorrectly believed that the other had investigated Herring's claims.

With his earlier successes on motorcycles and airplanes, his uniqueness as the only non-European contestant, his airplane so unlike any of the others, and his quiet nature fostering an air of mystery, Curtiss fascinated the French. They were thrilled to see that he rolled up his sleeves to work alongside Shriver and Fisher, and their enthusiasm was piqued by his holding back from the early competitions. Excitement crackled when his test flights revealed that his little machine was at once maneuverable and speedy, even setting an unofficial air speed record at 69 km/h (42.87 mph). [1, 2, 19, 22, 31]

Excitement exploded when the aviators learned that the Wright brothers, who had declined to participate in the meet, had purposely selected that week to file suit against Herring-Curtiss, the Aeronautical Society, and Glenn Curtiss personally. In addition to damages and restraint against exhibitions, the brothers demanded that *Golden Flier* be surrendered and destroyed. The Wrights' bad feeling against Curtiss had only been deepened by his association with Herring, whom they had already written off as a cuckoo trying to insert himself into their nest.

In addition to feeling ill will against what they saw as bad sportsmanship, the fliers at Reims recognized that the Wright brothers considered all airplanes to be in violation of their patents. They worried that the Curtiss suit was only the beginning, but, as Curtiss reported home, "No one thinks there is any infringement." [2, 5, 7, 8, 20, 31, 34]

Gordon Bennett contestants were allowed fly at their own discretion within a time frame that Saturday, with test laps allowed. At one end of the course, Curtiss ran into turbulence that was so bad he feared for his life, but was startled to learn that the test flight had been his best time yet. Racing his mind over the conundrum, Curtiss reasoned that in calm air, a relative vacuum opened behind the aircraft, giving the pusher propeller less thrust. In air that was turbulent but windless, on the other hand, no such vacuum would form. If so, did that mean that there would always be "fresh" air, and did that then mean that the prop would always be biting well? Curtiss threw himself back onto the seat and signaled that he was ready.

Seeing how speedy Louis Blériot's monoplane was—the Frenchman had ordered a new 80-hp V-8 specifically to meet Curtiss's challenge—Shriver had advised Curtiss to win the race on the turns, similar to the way he so often had done on motorcycle tracks. Four red-and-white pylons marked a rectangular 10-km (6.3-mi) course, which pilots had to circle twice. Curtiss climbed to 500 ft, then dove for the starting line to pick up speed. Turbulence at one end—which he now regarded as a friend—bounced him off his seat, but he wedged his feet (despite an ankle sprained earlier in the week) and kept on flying. Spectators gasped in shock as he peeled pylon after pylon. No one, including Curtiss, had ever seen flying like this. He landed with the official world air speed record at 46.5 mph.

Despite his success, Curtiss's reasoning was probably wrong. It is more likely that his increased speed came from a reduction of wingtip vortices in turbulent air. His experiential approach had again stood him in good stead. But other contestants, including Blériot, had still to fly.

Curtiss stewed for almost seven hours until Blériot, who had been having engine trouble, took his laps at the last possible moment. The Curtiss contingent gave up hope with a sigh as Blériot's first lap beat Curtiss's time. But the Frenchman landed, all remained silent. After a few moments, Cortlandt Bishop sprinted for the judge's stand, then came racing back. The "Star-Spangled Banner" rang out from the bandstand, and the American flag was hauled up the pole. Blériot's final time had fallen behind by six seconds. Curtiss had won.

American spectators set up a roar, and the French joined in instantly. Blériot rushed to pump Curtiss's hand. The U.S. ambassador presented the stunned Hammondsporter to Mrs. Theodore Roosevelt and her children. (Her son, Quentin, would be killed in France as a U.S. pilot in 1918.) The French acclaimed Curtiss "le premier aviateur du monde," and neighbors back home in Hammondsport went wild with their own celebration. [19, 31, 34]

On the next (and final) day, Curtiss tried two races, losing to Blériot in the 10-km (6.3-mi) dash. Blériot wrecked his machine in the Prix de la Vitesse (30 km [18.8 mi]), leaving Curtiss as the only serious contender. Following these major victories and a quick-start prize, Curtiss was also honored with French pilot's license Number 2 (Blériot was first, of course). The French Aero Club named its new balloon after him, he suffered through a formal dinner for 500 people at the U.S. Embassy, and he was mobbed incessantly everywhere he went in Paris. It was an eerie harbinger of the experience of Lindbergh, another quiet and withdrawn straight arrow, 18 years later. [31] What Captain Baldwin could have made of the opportunity!

Resentment or fear at the lawsuit notwithstanding, the verdict of the aviators was nearly united. The European designs, and the Herring-Curtiss, had been successful. The Wright machines were definitely several steps behind. This stimulated orders back in Hammondsport, although some wariness existed because the legal questions remained unresolved.

Rather than heading for home, Curtiss set off for Brescia, Italy, where Bishop had entered him in the Concour Internationale d'Aviation. This was, of course, Curtiss's first trip outside the United States or Canada, and the two men motored through France, Germany, and Switzerland on their way there.

After his Reims performance, Curtiss was naturally the star of the show at Brescia. Moreover, the competition was not up to the Reims standard, except for Blériot, who was still nursing injuries from the Prix de la Vitesse, in addition to having his best machine wrecked. Curtiss handily won the quick-start competition and the Grand Prix de Brescia speed prize, covering 50 km (31.3 mi) in 49 min 23-1/5 s. He carried his first passenger (Gabriele D'Annunzio, who would later become a star pilot) and impressed King Victor Emmanuel III. When he finally headed for home, after about a month abroad, he had grossed $15,000, turned himself into a world figure, and put the Curtiss airplane firmly on the European map. Most of his winnings he turned over to his wife, giving $500 to an elderly woman in Hammondsport who had helped him during the bicycle days. Lena bought an electric car and got her name in the paper for driving it to Corning, New York, and back.

Curtiss was a little rattled to be met by the combined populations (and bands) of Bath and Hammondsport when he got off the train. After appropriate serenades, a reception, and a quick dinner, the Hammondsport contingent boarded the B&H and returned to their own village, where there were fireworks, more speeches, a triumphal archway, and plenty of free beer. C. C. Jenkins, who had designed the Curtiss trademark, presented a carefully crafted model of the *Reims Racer*. Although always allergic to public speaking, Curtiss relaxed a little before his friends and neighbors, delivering a few gracious words: "The last four weeks have been very eventful [masterful understatement!]. I have met with considerable success and have met many notable people, but on no occasion have I experienced the happiness that I do tonight." He probably meant it, too. If he worried about lingering village disapproval of his father and mother, he was now undoubtedly Glenn Curtiss, his own man, of whom his village warmly approved. [19, 31]

New conflicts with Herring were already poisoning the atmosphere. Herring had pulled off several deals on the strength of Curtiss's European performance, and all of them, tellingly enough, involved show business rather than aeronautics. He had agreed to build a motorless copy of the *Reims Racer* for a vaudeville tour, and he had arranged to display the original machine at Filene's and Wanamaker's department stores in Boston and Philadelphia, respectively.

However, Curtiss had immediate engagements to fly back-to-back exhibitions in New York City and St. Louis, and he wanted *Reims Racer,* or at least its engine. Nothing doing, Herring told him—the department stores had contracted for the very machine, and that was what they were going to get. (This was a nice commitment to authenticity, considering some of Herring's other arrangements.) Curtiss went to New York with new construction that was later uncolorfully designated the *Hudson-Fulton Machine,* after the celebration for which it was scheduled. He had built up a float on the undercarriage, in case it was necessary to ditch in the harbor. (This did not create a seaplane; it simply added a safety device.) However, he had to be satisfied with one of the four-cylinder inlines, and that was, to his mind, not satisfactory at all. To make matters worse, Wilbur Wright was also on the bill.

The two men spoke two or three times during the exhibition and even exchanged information about flying conditions. Wright complimented Curtiss on his European success. However in the only meet at which they ever appeared together, Wright far outshone Curtiss, who was unhappy with his engine, his field, and the weather, in addition to being pressed for time because of his St. Louis date. He made only a few unimpressive flights, whereas Wilbur Wright performed superbly in his first U.S. appearance. [1, 6, 8, 31]

The St. Louis meet, at which Baldwin also presented an airship, went much better, but when they arrived in Chicago for new exhibitions, gusty winds allowed only a few short hops. At Chicago, Curtiss met Charley Hamilton, a balloonist who had broken off his tour of Asia after reading about the Reims meet. He had returned to the United States expressly to join Curtiss. Because Curtiss had been on the road almost continuously from July through September, he clearly needed other fliers in his stable, much the way he had needed other motorcycle racers. Curtiss taught Hamilton to fly, and Charley took to airplanes quickly. Worrying about liability for Hamilton's wild streak (on the ground and in the air), Curtiss dropped plans to make him an employee and put him on contract instead. [19, 31]

Legal matters with Herring and the Wrights were now consuming Curtiss's attention. Herring had handled his private Signal Corps contract by making "technical delivery" with a couple of suitcases filled with parts. Granted an extension, he later confessed himself unable to deliver, claiming he had built the promised airplane but wrecked it in a test flight on Long Island, after which he had lost heart and given up on the project. No one else, including his assistant, ever admitted to having seen this airplane or even its wrecked carcass.

Herring voted 2,015 shares out of 3,600 total in the company, but he had only one vote of five on the board of directors. Here Curtiss, Tom Baldwin, and Judge Monroe Wheeler of Bath (the board president) controlled a majority, even in the unlikely case that Herring were ever to gain the support of Cortlandt Bishop. In late 1909 (when the company was scarcely six months old), the board put through several resolutions aimed at limiting Herring. First, Curtiss was granted the right to retain all trophies and prizes he might win. Judge Wheeler pointed out that this was only fair, given the fact that Curtiss, unlike the other stockholders, was risking his own neck.

Next, the board ordered Herring to return patents he had received from Curtiss, to surrender the (nonexistent) patents he had promised the company, to provide a list of his patents and inventions, and to turn over the promised jigs and equipment from his shop in New York City. All these matters, of course, should have been investigated and arranged before agreements were signed. Curtiss (and, for that matter, Bishop) had been extremely naive. Moreover, Curtiss's lawyers, notably Judge Wheeler, had served him incompetently—not for the last time.

With the January annual meeting looming, the board voted in December to seek an injunction requiring the uncooperative Herring to produce his patents and equipment. Herring excused himself from the room, and sometime later, his professedly puzzled attorney went after him. Eventually, the remaining directors realized that neither one was coming back. They had taken off on foot in the dark, rustled up a farmer, cadged an auto ride out of town, and caught the train for New York.

A flurry of lawsuits followed, with Herring asserting that he was being bilked of his rights, that his inventions had been responsible for the success of the company, and that Curtiss had been hired only as a professional driver for the airplanes. With ten days to spare, Herring was enjoined from voting his stock at the annual meeting. The wound was still festering, but at least the company was still in business and effectively in the hands of Curtiss. [16, 31]

Curtiss was simultaneously contesting the Wright lawsuit and, particularly, an injunction issued a week earlier by Judge Hazel, even though the underlying patent question had not yet been adjudicated. Hazel's ruling prohibited Curtiss and associates from flying exhibitions, which were not only a stimulus for sales but were, in fact, the main source of income for the company. Judge Hazel was also central to two other legal events of the opening decade of the twentieth century. He had been the court of first resort in Henry Ford's eventually successful campaign to break the Selden automotive trust (he ruled against Ford). He had also administered the oath of office to Theodore Roosevelt on the assassination of President McKinley. The judge would probably have been happy to forego all three "honors."

Also falling afoul of the Wrights was France's Louis Paulhan, who was served as he came down the gangplank for a U.S. tour. Paulhan and Curtiss, who had met in Reims, both posted bonds against adverse appeal judgments and appeared with other aviators at the Los Angeles International Air Meet in January 1910. Curtiss at last had his Reims machine back and took several speed prizes, while Paulhan won awards for distance and altitude. Curtiss, Hamilton, and Charles Willard wowed the crowd by stunting three Curtiss planes in the air at once. Curtiss also demonstrated to knowledgeable observers several maneuvers that, in his opinion, invalidated claims in the Wright suit. Thousands of spectators trekked to Dominguez Hills for this first air show on the West Coast, again stimulating sales for the Hammondsport company. [34]

With his legal situation dubious and his financial situation desperate, Curtiss decided to roll the dice for double or nothing. It was now 1910, so he would try simultaneously for the third leg of the *Scientific American* trophy and the $10,000 New York *World* prize for a flight between New York City and Albany.

This 150-mile trip could be done in either direction, and it could be done in any type of craft. Tom Baldwin had made an abortive airship attempt at the Hudson-Fulton affair. [15] It was certainly spectacular enough to jump-start Curtiss and his company in the public mind, and he set the shop crew to work on a new machine and a new engine. For now, the craft was unnamed, but Curtiss would retroactively designate it *Hudson Flier.* Some writers have used the name *Albany Flier.* [1, 6]

At Dominguez Hills, Curtiss had flown 53 miles by repeatedly lapping the field. The Hudson River trip would be three times that length, plus presenting constantly changing air and ground conditions. Adequate tanks and a well-running engine could handle fuel and oil consumption; one stop was allowed for refueling, in any event.

The flight would take Curtiss into unpredictable air conditions, in addition to following, through much of its route, a rocky gorge with few fields, if any, suitable for landing. Always conscious of safety, Curtiss prepared for a water landing by rigging a cork-filled canvas float on the lower longeron, with two torpedo tanks slightly outboard the center line. Although he was always interested in the prospect of water flying, this arrangement, similar to the Hudson-Fulton float, did not create a seaplane. It was designed only to give him a few seconds to exit the airframe if necessary, after which he would have to depend on his fine swimming skills. Curtiss made repeated long test flights over Keuka Lake and even practiced ditching in the water. He further tested this machine by joining his growing exhibition team on a tour of the south. On this trip, he gave Lena her first airplane ride. Tom Baldwin also tried out his *Red Devil,* designed with Curtiss's help and contract-built by the Curtiss plant. Captain Tom could see that airship exhibitions were quickly becoming outdated and eagerly entered the airplane age. He prudently took out a Wright license. [1, 6, 15, 31]

As in the motorcycle days, Curtiss studied the course carefully before the big flight, steaming up the Hudson, surveying possible landing sites (very few), checking air currents, consulting ship captains, and befuddling onlookers as he considered whether to fly over or under certain bridges. [31]

The Curtiss party that headed for Albany in late May included Lena, Henry Kleckler, two mechanics, Curtiss Exhibition Company manager Jerome Fanciulli and his wife, and Carl Adams, Glenn's young half-brother. Also on hand was Augustus Post, as official observer for the Aero Club. Weather frustrated them (and the public) for several days, and a Poughkeepsie newspaper wrote, "Curtiss gives us a pain in the neck." But on May 29 (eight days after his thirty-second birthday), Curtiss decided that conditions were right. He took off from Van Rensselaer Island at 7:02 A.M. and headed south, paced by a New York Central special that carried the Hammondsport crowd and the officials. Post kept a careful record of times and landmarks, and at 8:26, Curtiss landed between Poughkeepsie and Camelot.

Kleckler, Curtiss, and the mechanics went over the machine, contenting themselves with tightening a loose wire and unaccountably missing an oil leak, despite obviously excessive consumption. Although the stop had been scheduled, his oil and gas never materialized, and Curtiss filled his tanks with eager donations from automobile drivers who had gathered. Curtiss took off again at 9:26. Four-year-old John Miller and his father walked over from their nearby farm to watch the excitement. Young John, who until that point had been fascinated by steam, decided on the spot to become a pilot. In 2002, after 92 years had passed, he was still flying routinely.

When his supplies turned up missing at Camelot, Curtiss complained that he could have made New York in a single hop, and he stuck to that opinion in his published summary of the flight. In this report, he stated that "of course" only two things could have prevented the flight, "the breaking of some vital part" and bad weather. He had every confidence in engine and airframe, he reported, but worried about air conditions around Storm King, where, in fact, he almost lost the airplane, considerably frightening Lena, who could clearly see its gyrations from the train.

Cadets went wild as he passed over West Point, setting Curtiss to brooding about how simple it would have been to bomb the place. "After I had negotiated the narrow reaches in the Highlands south of Poughkeepsie, I felt pretty sure of success, but the Metropolitan Tower certainly looked good to me when I first caught a glimpse of it far to the south, when soaring over the Tappan Zee." [11, 13] The locomotive engineer let loose a blast on the whistle as train and plane crossed the city line from Yonkers into New York at about 10:30.

Curtiss could tell he was having oil problems. Rather than risk the last 14 miles to Governor's Island, he doubled back and landed on a grassy stretch he had spotted in a well-to-do neighborhood of Harlem, on the northern tip of the city. This caused such a stir that police quickly arrived to organize things. Telephoning the *World,* Curtiss reported his arrival in the city limits, meeting the requirements of the prize. He had landed 3 hours and 22 minutes after first taking to the air.

Tanking up again with eagerly donated gas and oil, at 11:42 A.M. Curtiss negotiated the dangerous downhill takeoff he had gotten himself into and again sped down the river. He passed over Grant's Tomb and circled the Statue of Liberty as ships in harbor cut loose with sirens, whistles, bells, and anything else that would make a noise. News of his progress had been flashing downriver for hours, and the harbor was packed. At noon, he landed on Governor's Island, from which he had made his uninspiring Hudson-Fulton flights (Fig. 5.13). He could easily have ended the day in Harlem—he had already won the prize—but he admitted that he wanted very much to wipe out the stain of his previous visit. [11, 25–27, 31]

General Grant, son of the president, greeted Curtiss. Lena arrived shortly afterward by ferry, and the couple enjoyed a big hug. Although they were generally undemonstrative in

Fig. 5.13 Curtiss was thoroughly satisfied with his performance by the time he landed on Governor's Island. Two underslung torpedo tanks would have assisted the centerline canvas float in the event of a water ditching. This view illustrates the Curtiss control system. The yoke (horizontal piece visible overlapping his right shoulder) engages the ailerons. Pushing or pulling on the wheel adjusts the angle of incidence for the biplane elevator in the nose. Steering the wheel engages the rudder. Notice that the pilot hampers airflow over the radiator.

public, they happily repeated this gesture several times for the cameras. After a luncheon at the Astor, there was a press conference at the Pulitzer Building. Here Curtiss was handed his check for $10,000, which he promptly presented to Lena.

Curtiss had done the same with his Reims winnings. Perhaps the maneuver sheltered funds from Herring, but by any measure, Lena was entitled to a reward. She had worked alongside him, particularly since the time of Carlton's death. Although he traveled with her husband and remained his strongest supporter throughout his racing and exhibition days, she certainly agonized over his injuries and his near-disasters, such as the loss of control that morning at Storm King. Lena had been served with the Wright lawsuit during Curtiss's absence in France. During that same absence, she had had to contend single handedly with Augustus Herring, who showed up one day, demanding to see the books and insisting that *Golden Flier* income belonged to the company.

At a formal dinner on Tuesday night, Curtiss presented the mayor of New York with a letter he had carried from the mayor of Albany. The total flight in three legs was computed at 142.5 miles, of which the longest leg (Albany to Camelot) was 71.3 miles. Although Curtiss had to wait until the end of the year, no other aviator even approached his distance, and the *Scientific American* trophy was retired to him. Altitudes had been as high as 1000 ft, while his airtime was 2 hours and 50 minutes. As Curtiss pointed out, speed estimates were difficult to calculate considering changes of altitude and shifts along the river course, but he figured it to be about 53 mph. By way of comparison, Paulhan had flown 117 miles from London to Manchester but over better ground and at a slower speed. He added another 66 miles on the following day to complete the route, making the two friends from Reims the undisputed distance champions of the day, along with Claude Graham-White, who finished the Manchester race behind Paulhan. [11, 17, 31]

Curtiss was still in deep legal trouble, but he was currently fending off both the Wrights and Herring. His Dominguez Hills flights, and especially the Hudson River flight, had reestablished him as the leading pilot and manufacturer in the United States. His exhibition company was in strong demand. Despite his troubles, he was still very much in the fight, and he got another enthusiastic welcome when he returned home to Hammondsport (Fig. 5.14).

Not content with defensive measures or even continued success in the same vein, Curtiss's busy brain was now consumed with new issues. Airplanes carrying explosives, he had recognized during his flight, could have devastated West Point or New York with impunity. The gigantic, heavily armored, all-big-gun battlewagons, led by *Dreadnought* in Britain and *Michigan* in the United States, were less than ten years old. Curtiss

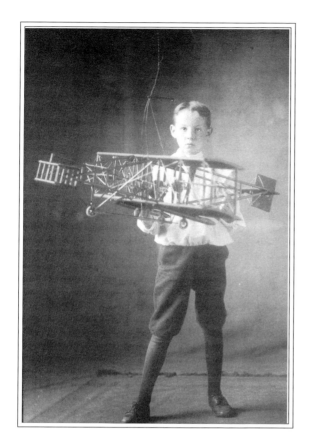

Fig. 5.14 C. C. Jenkins, who had created the Curtiss logo, crafted a superb model of Hudson Flier, *displayed here by son James Jenkins. The model is now in the Curtiss Museum.*

straightforwardly, if unbelievably, asserted, "the days for big warships are numbered." Writing in the *Saturday Evening Post,* he observed that when an airplane costing a few thousand dollars could sink a battleship costing millions of dollars, there would be "some change" in the composition of navies. The following month, he set out floats in the shape of a battleship on Keuka Lake and dropped lead-pipe "bombs," scoring 17 hits and a near miss in 19 attempts. [12]

In his *Post* article and other venues, Curtiss promoted the notion of dedicated flying fields for major cities, with specified corridors between them, and his Albany field eventually became the first municipal airport of the city. He made long overwater flights at Atlantic City and on Lake Erie, meanwhile expanding his exhibition teams, including training and contracting Blanche Stuart Scott, who thus became the first female pilot in the United States. Curtiss announced that he would establish a winter flying school in San Diego, California, and offered to teach any army or navy officers free of charge. He had several ideas that he thought might interest them. [24, 31]

REFERENCES

1. Bowers, Peter M., *Curtiss Aircraft 1907–1947,* Putnam, London, 1979.

2. Boyne, Walter J., *The Smithsonian Book of Flight,* Smithsonian Books, Washington, DC, 1987.

3. Bulletins of the Aerial Experiment Association, I–XXXIX, July 13, 1908 to April 12, 1909. GHCM holds Curtiss's original set, now in three hand-bound volumes.

4. Carpenter, Jack, *Bell & Curtiss: How the Partnership of Alexander Graham Bell and Glenn Hammond Curtiss Led to the Founding of the American Aviation Industry,* Arsdalen, Bosch & Co., San Juan Capistrano, CA, unpublished.

5. ———, *Pendulum: The Story of America's Three Aviation Pioneers: Wilbur Wright, Orville Wright, and Glenn Curtiss, The Henry Ford of Aviation,* Arsdalen, Bosch & Co., Carlisle, MA, 1992.

6. Casey, Louis S., *Curtiss: The Hammondsport Era, 1907–1915,* Crown Publishers, Inc., New York, 1981.

7. Combs, Harry, with Martin Caidin, *Kill Devil Hill: Discovering the Secrets of the Wright Brothers,* Houghton Mifflin Company, Boston, 1979.

8. Crouch, Tom, *The Bishop's Boys: A Life of Wilbur and Orville Wright,* W. W. Norton & Co., New York, 1989.

9. "Curtiss Aero Engines 1909–1914," manuscript (n.d.), GHCM Curtiss Engines Files.

10. "Curtiss Engines," unpublished two-page typescript, GHCM, Kleckler Collection.

11. Curtiss, Glenn H., "Albany-New York," *Aircraft,* iss. I, no. 5, July 1910, p. 177.

12. ———, "The Commercial Side of Aviation: Business Possibilities of the Aeroplane," *The Saturday Evening Post,* 183:14, October 1, 1910.

13. Curtiss, Glenn H., and Augustus Post, *The Curtiss Aviation Book,* Frederick Stokes Company, New York, 1912.

14. "Curtiss Motors," G. H. Curtiss Manufacturing Company, Hammondsport, circa 1907, GHCM Motorcycle Catalogs File.

15. Eklund, Don Dean, "Captain Thomas S. Baldwin: Pioneer American Aeronaut," Ph.D. dissertation, University of Colorado, 1970.

16. Eltscher, Louis R., and Edward M. Young, *Curtiss-Wright: Greatness and Decline,* Twayne Publishers, New York, 1998.

17. Ettington, Raymond C., "The Patent War," Glenn Curtiss Museum, Hammondsport, NY, 2001.

18. Grosvenor, Edwin S., and Morgan Wesson, *Alexander Graham Bell: The Life and Times of the Man Who Invented the Telephone,* Harry N. Abrams, New York, 1997.

19. The *Hammondsport Herald,* published weekly throughout Curtiss's lifetime, includes multitudinous references to Curtiss, his works, and his times. (GHCM holds a microfilmed set.)

20. Howard, Fred, *Orville and Wilbur: A Biography of the Wright Brothers,* Alfred A. Knopf, New York, 1988.

21. Husting, Eugene, "Augustus M. Herring," *World War 1 Aero # 130,* November 1990.

22. Mitchell, Charles R., and Kirk W. House, *Glenn H. Curtiss, Aviation Pioneer,* Arcadia Publishing, Charleston, SC, 2001.

23. Molson, K. M., "Early Curtiss Aircraft Engines," *A.A.H.S. Journal*, Summer 1966, pp. 133–137.

24. Morehouse, Harold E., and Marvel Dyer, *The Flying Pioneers Biographies of Harold Morehouse*, GHCM.

25. "Opening of the Aviation Season," *The Literary Digest,* June 10, 1910.

26. Post, Augustus, "Chronographic Account of Flight" [Curtiss Albany–New York flight], *Aircraft,* iss. I, no, 5, July 1910, pp. 177, 178.

27. ———, "The Evolution of a Flying Man: Incidents in the Experience of Glenn H. Curtiss with Motors and Aeroplanes," *The Century Illustrated Monthly Magazine,* vol. 81, no. 1, November 1910.

28. Prendergast, Curtis [and the eds. of Time-Life Books), *The First Aviators,* Time-Life Books, Alexandria, VA, 1981.

29. Rinek, Larry M., "Curtiss Aviation Engines: An American Success Story."

30. ———, "Glenn H. Curtiss: An Early American Innovator in Aviation and Motorcycle Engines," SAE Paper No. 940571, Society of Automotive Engineers, Warrendale, PA, 1994.

31. Roseberry, C. R., *Glenn Curtiss: Pioneer of Flight,* Doubleday & Company, Garden City, NY, 1972.

32. Thurston, David B., *The World's Most Significant and Magnificent Aircraft: Evolution of the Modern Airplane,* Society of Automotive Engineers, Warrendale, PA, 2000.

33. Untitled typescript table (one page) describing Curtiss aero engines from 1906 to 1911, GHCM Curtiss Engine Files.

U.S. PATENT REFERENCES

34. 821,393 O. & W. Wright, Flying Machine, May 23, 1903–May 22, 1906.

35. 1,011,106 A. G. Bell, F. W. Baldwin, J. A. D. McCurdy, G. H. Curtiss, and T. E. Selfridge, Flying Machine, April 8, 1909–December 5, 1911.

Chapter 6

Close-Up:
The Curtiss Airplane

★ ★ ★

The *Silver Dart* made its first exciting Canadian flights in February 1909, and the AEA expired the following month, primarily because of Curtiss's lack of interest in extending the formal relationship. That summer, he made the first airplane sale in the Americas, before heading to France with the *Reims Racer*.

Glenn Curtiss was in the airplane business, with aircraft of his own design. This fact in itself is startling. He had never seen an airplane before the AEA built its own *Red Wing* in 1908. However, Curtiss #1 (*Gold Bug/Golden Flier*) and its successors were clearly distinct, even to the untutored eye, from the AEA series. They were also highly successful aircraft. [1, 2, 6]

From whence did these aircraft spring? Curtiss and Henry Kleckler were still doing nearly all of their own design work—business had not yet reached the point that called for new hiring. It is true that A. L. Pfitzner joined the staff around this time, working in engine design. He had aeronautic ideas of his own, but he concentrated on building his own monoplane. Although this monoplane stood in splendid isolation from nearly everything else produced in those days, it did not work very well. The same was true of Pfitzner's later designs, a bitter truth that probably contributed to his apparent suicide in Marblehead harbor. [1, 6, 16]

So Pfitzner was not the inspiration for the new Curtiss design. Nor did inspiration flow directly from the work of the AEA because Bell, McCurdy, and Casey Baldwin were contemporaneously building their series of *Baddeck* airplanes. These craft strongly resembled their AEA parents and were not as successful as the Curtiss models. [11]

Was Augustus Herring the inspiration for radical design changes? He certainly gave the impression that that was so, and he was merging his interests with those of Curtiss at the time. Herring was one of the deans of aeronautic experimentation in the United States, along with Chanute. However, Curtiss and Herring were already bickering, each essentially ordering the other to keep his nose of their respective private projects arranged before the merger: Herring's Signal Corps bid and Curtiss's *Gold Bug* order from the Aeronautical Society. For all his successes with gliders, Herring never produced a powered airplane that anyone but he would ever admit to having seen. [16]

Curtiss might have had the opportunity to see the modified Voisin biplane being flown by Henri Farman in the summer of 1908. He was appointed to the Aero Club greeting committee for Farman, although apparently decamping for Fort Myer immediately after the ceremonies. Future Farman biplanes resembled the Curtiss machines in many ways.

Any influence, however, seems to run in the opposite direction. The Voisin biplane depended entirely on the rudder for lateral control (an extremely unsatisfactory arrangement). Farman was interested in the AEA "ailerons" (he supposedly introduced the term to the United States), and shortly began to install ailerons himself. However, his machine (which made only a few short hops) was large and boxy, comparing unfavorably to the AEA machines, at least in American eyes. [15, 16] George H. Guy's article, "Real Navigation of the Air," published in *The American Review of Reviews* and reprinted in *See Them Flying: Houston Peterson's Air-Age Scrapbook, 1909–1910,* quotes "an eminent scientific authority" as saying, "the *June Bug* gives you a much bigger 'sensation' than Farman's machine, for its lines are finer and the tail small and inconspicuous. In flight it resembles a gigantic yellow bird soaring, while Farman's machine suggests a big box-kite. It is under better control, too, for it has movable wingtips, which work to a charm" (Fig. 6.1). [14]

Of course, Curtiss finally got a chance to see the Wright airplane at the army trials in Fort Myer during the previous August and September. Could this be the source of design for the Curtiss airplane, which was so distinct from the AEA machines? Could it, indeed, be the point at which Curtiss finally "stole" a design from the Wright brothers?

The answer is an unsurprising no. Before we can dig into possible sources of inspiration, we need to examine the first true Curtiss airplane and its two main North American contemporaries: the AEA/Baddeck types and the Wright brothers' models.

Gold Bug, Curtiss's immediate successor of the AEA machines, was formed, it is virtually certain, without reference to Herring. Comparing and contrasting *Gold Bug* with *Silver Dart* (the final AEA aerodrome) is very revealing.

First, the dihedral wings (see Figs. 5.6, 5.7, 5.9, and 5.11; compare with Fig. 5.12) were discarded altogether. Upper and lower wings on *Gold Bug* ran straight across (accounting for the airfoil), parallel to each other and bisected perpendicularly by the centerline of the airframe.

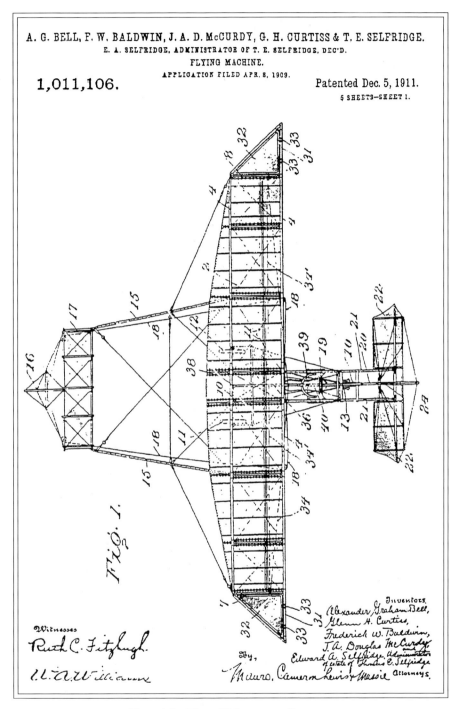

*Fig. 6.1 The AEA patent diagram
(substantially June Bug).*

The wings were essentially rectangular, with a slight overhang on the trailing edge. The AEA tapered wings described a roughly curved trailing edge with pointed wingtips on *Red Wing* and pointed aileron tips on the others. They gave the overall impression of a cape billowing out behind the aircraft. [1, 6]

Perhaps the most breathtaking contrasts were those of size, as detailed in the following table. Because the Wright brothers' airplane presented for 1908 army trials will soon be discussed, these data are included here for convenience. These are approximate figures for the Wright brothers' 1907–1909 machines (around seven, each of which varied somewhat from the others), as reported by Harry Combs and Martin Caidin in *Kill Devil Hill: Discovering the Secret of the Wright Brothers*. [7]

	Silver Dart (1908–1909)	**Gold Bug** (1909)	**Wright** (1907–1909)
Wingspan:	49 ft 1 in.	28 ft 9 in.	41 ft
Wing Area:	420 ft^2	258 ft^2	510 ft^2
Length:	30 ft	30 ft 4 in.	31 ft
Chord:	6 ft, tapering to 4 ft at tips	4 ft 6 in.	6 ft 6 in.
Gap:	6 ft, tapering to 4 ft at tips	4 ft 6 in.	6 ft
Gross Weight:	860 lb	550 lb	800 lb

It is clear that *Gold Bug* was a dramatically more compact airplane, offering advantages in production, storage, shipping, maintenance, and cost. It was also a vastly simpler machine. The number of ailerons was halved, reducing the hardware and rigging required. *Gold Bug* had a straight-four engine, in contrast with *Silver Dart*'s V-8. This, however, was probably a function of the aircraft's purpose as both a training and testing machine for the Aeronautical Society. The succeeding *Reims Racer* returned to the V-8 powerplant. In all these cases, the engines were water-cooled, as production Curtiss aero engines would remain for nearly all their history. *Gold Bug* sported the typical Curtiss direct-drive prop, eschewing the chain drive on *Silver Dart*.

Lines were also simplified, the wide triangular tail of *Silver Dart* giving way to a straight tail, narrowed to align with the nose framework.

Certainly there were also similarities. Both aircraft omitted any stabilizers, except for a small triangular upright in the nose of *Gold Bug*; Peter Bowers, encyclopedist of Curtiss aircraft, describes this as Augustus Herring's sole contribution to the Curtiss airplane. Airfoils on both aircraft were covered only on the upper surface. Both employed the tricycle landing gear, and both used Baldwin's rubberized silk. [1, 6]

As Curtiss went into manufacturing in the United States, Bell, McCurdy, and Casey Baldwin did the same in Canada, conveniently beyond the reach of a Wright patent. The several *Baddeck* series aircraft they produced were along the lines of *Silver Dart*, retaining its configuration (with the addition of horizontal stabilizers) and its relatively huge size. Over-engineering seems to have been a habit of Bell's, at least with respect to aeronautics. Selfridge had once annoyed him by demonstrating that only 41% of the cells in his huge tetrahedral kite were necessary. [11]

The Bell group tried Kirkham engines as well as Curtiss engines in their machines, but the finished products received little encouragement from the Canadian government or from any other potential buyers, so the effort was soon dropped. Clearly, the innovations of the Curtiss #1 were not drawn from Curtiss's colleagues in the Aerial Experiment Association. [11, 14]

Could Curtiss have derived his 1909 innovations from viewing Orville Wright's airplane at Fort Myer in late 1908? If so, his knowledge could scarcely have come from close inspection. While the Wright machine was finally, in a sense, open to public viewing, the AEA crowd would not have been welcome to examine it minutely. They would have had no reason to do so, except for Selfridge, and even his participation in the review process was understandably resented by Orville. Obviously, Selfridge had little opportunity to pass on any trade secrets he hypothetically could have learned.

Curtiss clearly took at least one hard look, because he reported to Bell, "He [Orville Wright] has no secrets, and no special features."[3] Assuming Curtiss was telling the truth, he would not have seen industrial espionage on the Wright Flyer as a profitable activity. Likewise, neither Curtiss, the AEA crowd, nor Tom Baldwin were in constant residence at Fort Myer, even if they had had time for spying while they were there. Curtiss missed the celebration he cosponsored with Captain Tom immediately after their *SC-1* triumph, because he had already hurried to New York City on motorcycle business. On his several trips to Virginia, he kept in touch with Bell and Casey Baldwin (in Baddeck) and McCurdy (in Hammondsport) by telegram. [3, 5, 9, 16, 18]

What was the ill-fated Wright army trial machine of 1908 like? Similar to the forthcoming Curtiss machines, contemporary Wrights had abandoned the early dihedral, presenting two straight planes, stacked directly over-and-under. As would be the case with the new Curtisses, Wright wings were mostly rectangular, although they also had a curve on the trailing corners. [7]

The Wright, Curtiss, and AEA/*Baddeck* machines shared several other similarities. All were pushers, all were fabric-covered, all had a biplane nose elevator, and all had vertical tail rudders. The Wright and Curtiss machines lacked stabilizers (except for the small tri-angular vertical on the Curtiss elevator). *Baddeck* models had stabilizers in the tails. [11]

All employed a single engine, with the Curtiss and Kirkham units being far more efficient than those of the Wrights. The Wright brothers operated two chain-driven counter-rotating props from their engine, whereas the Curtiss and Bell groups used a single prop on the centerline, where they also located the powerplant. The Wright engine was starboard of the centerline, balanced by the weight of the pilot and passenger, if any, to port. The Curtiss and Bell machines were not equipped for carrying passengers at that time. [1, 6, 7, 11]

The Hammondsport and *Baddeck* models were using tricycle landing gear, whereas the Wright brothers were using skids. Two distinctive features of the Wright airplanes were the launching monorail and the assisted takeoff, each of which rendered operations extremely cumbersome. A newspaper article headed "Special to The Record. Dayton, O., July 23," is reprinted in *See Them Flying*. Perhaps with some exaggeration for effect (perhaps in itself exacerbated by my excerpting), the correspondent describes the operation as follows:

> Five men conduct the plane to the monorail track, one pulling at each wingtip, one at each of two detachable wheels like enormous casters, and one supporting the "tail." . . . The plane is placed on the rail . . . A man stands at the tip of one of the wings to keep the nicely balanced machine from tipping . . . Two other men go to the rear, one to each of the big propellers. A [mechanic] goes to the front of the machine, worming himself in between taut piano wires, and begins to test the motor. . . someone else gets under the frame and makes the plane fast to the track by a wire . . . which can be thrown by a trigger. . . . Orville Wright . . . crawls in between the wires and pulls himself up into the little seat. . . . The men at the rear reach up and grasp the outside blades of the propellers. The man at the wingtip grasps the end stay and braces himself like a sprinter . . . The men at the propellers begin to count in unison. . . . At the word "three" they pull down on the propeller blades and "turn over" the motor. . . . Orville . . . nods to the man at the wingtip, whose duty it is to run with the machine to hold it level till it gains momentum. Last he reaches down and pulls the trigger which releases the wire that anchors the airplane. The machine begins to slide down the track,

slowly at first, but with ever increasing speed. Ten—twenty—thirty yards it glides, still clinging to the rail. The runner loosens his hold on the plane and drops behind. Then the forward control planes are tilted upward a few inches. As gracefully and sure as wild swan ever rose from the water . . . the airplane rises from the track and climbs the air. [14]

Wright airplanes did not always require assisted takeoffs; if fitted with wheels, they did not even require launching rails. Wright biographer Tom Crouch [personal communication] explains that conditions at Kitty Hawk and at Huffman Prairie made it desirable to get the aircraft into the air with as short a ground run as possible. Even so, the Wrights at this stage clearly preferred the rail launch, and even the assisted takeoff, which required assembling a derrick to suspend and drop a weight, providing a catapult boost for the aircraft on its rail. It scarcely need be said that by this time, Curtiss would have been appalled by what he would have considered aggressive complication. Most other makers felt the same way. One of the Wrights is supposed to have remarked that it would be easier, as time went on, to find short rails than it would be to find long fields. This truth overlooked the fact that overall operation would remain simpler and more practical by discarding the rails and falling weights and trusting to luck (or, eventually, industry) for the fields.

Both the Curtiss and Bell machines used the control system Curtiss had developed for *June Bug:* steering wheel for rudder, push-pull on wheel for elevator, and shoulder yoke for ailerons. The Wrights had abandoned their original prone-pilot arrangement as far back as 1905 and now used a system of levers for cockpit controls. The Wrights, of course, were still wing warping. [7, 8, 12] The *Baddeck* series carried on the four AEA triangular wingtip ailerons, while the new Curtiss had two rectangular interplane ailerons. [1, 6, 11]

To delve into the controversy a bit: regardless of independent developments, did the Curtiss (and AEA) work infringe on the Wright patent?

The basis of the Wright brothers' work was laid out in their "Flying-Machine" patent 821,393 (March 28, 1903; May 22, 1906). [19] Irrelevant to the question, but certainly of interest, is the fact that success at Kitty Hawk still lay nine months in the future at the time they filed their application. This patent described their work in terms of a glider.

It is, of course, the wing, and not the engine, that flies the airplane (as my friends at the National Soaring Museum frequently emphasize). Wilbur and Orville had already demonstrated their claims with motorless aircraft in flight. This decision to realize their work first on kites and gliders was an example of the Wrights' genius and a cornerstone of their success. The addition (and complication) of a propeller and powerplant, although their goal throughout their long years of labor, would come almost as an afterthought. At any rate, the patent pointed out that the aircraft utilizing these new and useful improvements could be operated "either by the application of mechanical power or by the utilization of the force of gravity."

The Wrights' real success, and their departure from previous experiments, came in establishing a means for controlling the three axes of flight. Some have argued that their systems were not tremendously effective or that they did not yet constitute true three-axis control. [4, 5] Certainly, the work was crude, but the brothers had clearly worked out a means of control, even if it left much to be desired.

Sixteen of their 18 patent claims center on the "airplanes" (wings to us) and their warping features for lateral control. Even claims 13 and 14, describing what we would now call the rudder and elevator, implicitly include this warping feature by stating that the rudder and elevator are installed on a flying machine with airplanes.

The brothers claim [19] movable lateral marginal portions of the airplanes—the famed "wing warping" (Fig. 6.2). These are described, of course, as moving oppositely on each side of the centerline to present differing angles of incidence to the atmosphere, thus "imparting to said airplane a helicoidal warp around an axis transverse to the line of flight." As described, warping takes place at all eight corners (four upper, four lower) of the two superposed and interconnected airplanes. Indeed, the preferred construction twists each entire wing, although the claimants point out that they are not limiting themselves to that arrangement. "[I]t is only necessary to move the lateral marginal portions. . . ."

Even in warping only at the corners, the system required a good deal of hardware. The left front pair (upper and lower), for example, moves together but opposite to the two adjacent corner pairs (left rear and right front). The diagonal corner pair (right rear) moves in concert with left front. Linked with this system is the rudder, which moves simultaneously to abet the lateral movement. In other words, diagonal corner pairs (upper and lower) move simultaneously in the same direction (up or down), while the corners on the opposite diagonal move in opposition and the rudder moves to assist.

The AEA airplanes (after *Red Wing*) employed triangular movable flaps just outboard of each wingtip (a total of four). These panels moved together at each extreme and opposite to those at the other extreme. They had their own framework and operated by pulleys. They had no interconnecting (and moving) standards (struts) as described in the Wright patent, and they did not require interconnected rudder movement. [1, 6, 10, 20] The Wrights' requirement of rudder action would form a subsidiary argument in the drawn-out patent case.

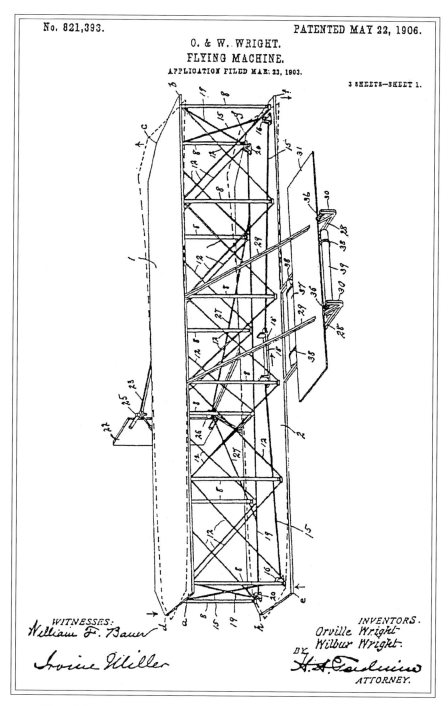

Fig. 6.2 Wing warping, as diagrammed in the Wright patent diagram (substantially the 1902 glider).

The AEA aileron was almost certainly an independent development, and it paralleled work being done in Europe. But did the arrangement infringe on the Wright patent? Was this an example of laterally moving marginal surfaces on the airplane (wing) to create lateral control? [17]

Part of the riposte, of course, would be that these ailerons were not part of the airplane or wing. True, they lay (in AEA #2 through #4) nearly along the plane of the airplane, but they did not form a component of the wing. They were a separate structure, first of all. Additionally, and perhaps more tellingly, they had no airfoil. The ailerons were simply cloth stretched flat over a framework. They contributed no lift at all and hence were not part of the "airplane" (Fig. 6.3). No portion of the true airplane moved in the slightest, either by a complete helicoidal twist or by the shifting of lateral marginal surfaces. Likewise, the straight edge of the aileron did not extend the dihedral of the AEA wing, although it also did not depart radically from that dihedral.

This point was certainly susceptible to argument, particularly before a court (or a public) not well versed in the technical side of aeronautics. The ailerons, the Wrights could argue, were obviously part of the wing—all one had to do was look at them with the naked eye to see it. Not only did they lie (nearly) in the same plane, they even (roughly) followed the leading and trailing edges to their point of intersection. Moreover, they took the place of the (integral, nonmoving, but also triangular) ends of the wings in *Red Wing*.

The point could probably be argued *ad infinitum*, but Curtiss certainly obviated that particular discussion on his #1 (*Gold Bug/Golden Flier*) when he removed the ailerons from the wings altogether (Fig. 6.4). There were now two, rather than four. They no longer lay at all in the plane of the wings, being mounted *interplane*—midway between the upper and lower wings—on the leading struts. Moreover, the ailerons extended outboard of each wingtip and were very small when compared with the total wing surface. No longer did they lie along the wing; no longer did they visually "complete," or even conform to, the wing. Again, they had no airfoil.

The aileron was completely separate from the wing in location, form, and function. Moreover, no portion of the wing (or "airplane") was manipulated or moved in any way. (Ailerons would shortly migrate from the leading struts to the trailing struts.)

This would seem to make the aileron independent of the Wright patent, which rested on manipulating surfaces of the airplanes to create lateral stability. The question then becomes one of how broadly the Wright patent should be interpreted and applied. [17] Orville Wright wrote Curtiss shortly after the *June Bug* triumph, "This patent broadly covers the combination of sustaining surfaces to the right and left of the center of a flying machine adjustable to different angles." [3] Sustaining surfaces in this case would refer to the wings.

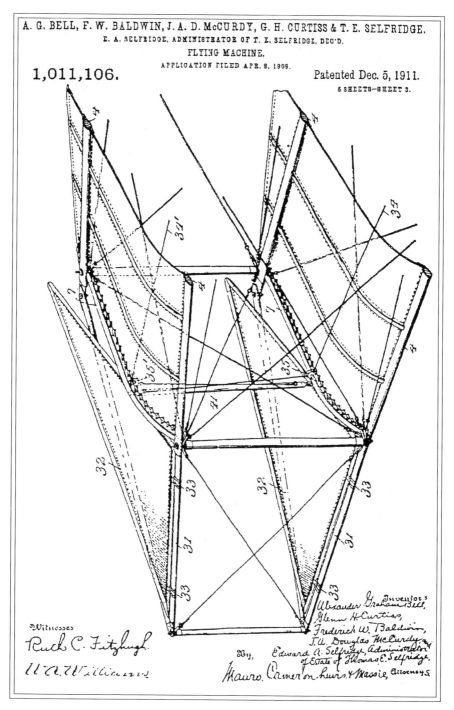

Fig. 6.3 *Ailerons, from the AEA patent diagrams.*
Note the complete lack of camber.

Fig. 6.4 Curtiss in flight with Gold Bug/Golden Flier. *Note the new ailerons: reduced in number from four to two; changed in shape from triangular to rectangular; and, most significantly, separated altogether from the wing to be placed interplane on the leading struts. The light, compact, simplified nature of the Curtiss production airplane is clear here. Note the photographer on the left. He may be taking the photograph found in Fig. 5.12.*

Although, in the Curtiss airplane, there is no manipulation of the surface of the wing, does the patent cover manipulations of other surfaces completely separate and distinct from the wing? This becomes a legal question, rather than a technological or historical question. Having no legal background, I leave that field to others, confining myself here to a few technological and historical observations:

1. The Wright control system, however much it may be criticized for being crude, cumbersome, or inefficient, at last and at minimum established an approach that provided the necessary three-axis control and could, at least in theory, be elaborated further.

2. The AEA "aileron" (to use the term anachronistically) was an independent development, as probably was the slightly earlier development of similar features in Europe. (The purposes of these similar aileron-like features are not always clear.)

3. Bell believed that he had originally proposed the idea of "wingtips," although clearly the entire AEA force contributed to this realization. Bell stated forcefully that he was at the time completely unaware of any work the Wrights had done in this area. He and his patent attorneys both considered the aileron to be among the several AEA features that were new and useful enough to be patented, without infringement on other patents.

4. The aileron and the warping wing applied the same natural principal to create lateral control.

5. The aileron was a more efficient and effective device, as well as being simpler and less expensive.

6. Interplane ailerons, at minimum, were worthy of a separate patent as being a significant advance of the art. [30] They *appear* to exclude themselves from the patent covering movable lateral marginal portions of the airplanes, calling for a legal resolution as to whether this separate patent should owe license to the original patent.

7. Because the question is capable (to say the least) of dispute, Curtiss was certainly justified in defending himself legally. Oddly, some commentators appear to deny him this right, seeming to regard the very fact of his legal defense as in itself somehow reprehensible.

8. The Wright's insistence on remaining with wing warping—which continued until Orville gave up controlling interest during World War I—contributed to a drastic loss of market share and stagnation in design within the company.

9. In view of the Wrights' insistence (never ended throughout their entire period of influence on the company they had founded) on maintaining wing warping in favor of the more effective aileron, it seems a little awkward to view them as having discovered "the aileron principle." The brothers deserve accolades in plenty, but this in particular seems a little excessive.

The genius of the Wright brothers will rightly be acclaimed for centuries. Their painstaking, carefully thought-out work led to the first workable form of powered, controlled, sustained, heavier-than-air flight.

Sadly, they limited themselves and their success by overcommitment to what were essentially dead-end technologies: wing warping and assisted takeoff. Additionally, they neglected further development of the engine.

Linked with this, at least under Orville's leadership after Wilbur's death, was a lack of business acumen. Finally, the Wrights' control system grew so cumbersome that it eventually required two pilots, neither of whom could "change seats" and operate the other's controls without retraining. These factors frittered away the tremendous advantage they might have enjoyed as originators of a new technology. It is also sad that, although they retained many close and loyal friendships, they managed to alienate many early supporters such as Octave Chanute. [7, 8, 12]

At any rate, the Wright brothers' work was not the inspiration for the radical new design embodied in *Golden Flier*. Nor did that inspiration come from Herring, Farman, Pfitzner, Bell, or the other members of the AEA. Curtiss and Henry Kleckler, scarcely a year into their HTA (heavier-than-air) aeronautic experience, had pooled their untutored minds; applied their customary approaches of simplification, weight reduction, and marketability; and produced an impressive new example of a young technology. Elaborations of their new design by themselves and by others (some authorized, many not) would quickly come to dominate North American aviation, much the way the Curtiss company would come to dominate the business side of aviation.

With the Wright brothers being so successful because of slow, steady, incremental research, how could Curtiss be equally (or even more) successful by leaps and bounds? Here, as so often, we can only speculate. Curtiss clearly had an unusual mind. It may be that he was one of those people who can see the finished product globally. A person such as this can frustrate or even frighten coworkers who insist on a linear approach, ensuring that each step rests firmly on its predecessor. However, for the intuitive understanding of some people, step 10 is actually step 2. It is so clear to them that they are bewildered by suggestions that they "invent" eight intermediary steps for testing. Curtiss's mind may have been of this type.

At any rate, the uneducated motorcycle man had transformed himself almost overnight into a cutting-edge creator, manufacturer, and vendor of airplanes. In the process of inventing the airplane anew, he reinvented himself as well.

In the quest of a source for *Golden Flier* and its successors, we probably need look no further than the forgotten stepchild of the Aerial Experiment Association, the hang glider (see Fig. 5.2). Bell's Boys worked with hang gliders for about two months in early 1908 (possibly more than one, possibly a single unit that was repeatedly modified). The glider was built on the Chanute lines. These were well known; indeed, Mathias Arnot, a businessperson in Elmira (45 miles away) had been funding Augustus Herring's work with a Chanute-type glider a decade earlier.

The structure of the Curtiss pusher is essentially that of a Chanute glider, even down to many of the materials. Because Herring had worked with Chanute in the original creation of this type of aircraft, (and probably was largely responsible for the design), he might actually deserve some indirect credit for Curtiss's later work.

Few records were kept on the AEA glider, but one source describes it as having a 25-ft span, 5-ft chord, and 5-ft gap. Laying these figures alongside the corresponding measurements for *Golden Flier* reveals suggestive similarities. [1, 6]

Kleckler told Curtiss biographer C. R. Roseberry that he and Curtiss had both considered the tapered and dihedral wings to be "nonsense." [16] In the Chanute-type biplane, apparently, they had experienced and recognized a simple arrangement that worked well, and they built it readily. Daringly, confidently, and successfully, they "miniaturized" and simplified the airplane, creating a new type of aircraft that first startled and then captured the minds of the U.S. aeronautic world.

REFERENCES

1. Bowers, Peter M., *Curtiss Aircraft 1907–1947,* Putnam, London, 1979.

2. Boyne, Walter J., *The Smithsonian Book of Flight,* Smithsonian Books, Washington, DC, 1987.

3. Bulletins of the Aerial Experiment Association, I–XXXIX, July 13, 1908– April 12, 1909. GHCM holds Mr. Curtiss's original set, now in three hand-bound volumes.

4. Carpenter, Jack, *Bell & Curtiss: How the Partnership of Alexander Graham Bell and Glenn Hammond Curtiss Led to the Founding of the American Aviation Industry,* Arsdalen, Bosch & Co., San Juan Capistrano, CA, unpublished.

5. ———, *Pendulum: The Story of America's Three Aviation Pioneers: Wilbur Wright, Orville Wright, and Glenn Curtiss, The Henry Ford of Aviation,* Arsdalen, Bosch & Co., Carlisle, MA, 1992.

6. Casey, Louis S., *Curtiss: The Hammondsport Era, 1907–1915,* Crown Publishers, New York, 1981.

7. Combs, Harry, with Martin Caidin, *Kill Devil Hill: Discovering the Secrets of the Wright Brothers,* Houghton Mifflin Company, Boston, 1979.

8. Crouch, Tom, *The Bishop's Boys: A Life of Wilbur and Orville Wright,* W.W. Norton & Co., New York, 1989.

9. Eklund, Don Dean, "Captain Thomas S. Baldwin: Pioneer American Aeronaut," Ph.D. dissertation, University of Colorado, 1970.

10. Ettington, Raymond C., "The Patent War," Glenn Curtiss Museum, Hammondsport, NY, 2001.

11. Grosvenor, Edwin S., and Morgan Wesson, *Alexander Graham Bell: The Life and Times of the Man Who Invented the Telephone,* Harry N. Abrams, New York, 1997.

12. Howard, Fred, *Orville and Wilbur: A Biography of the Wright Brothers,* Alfred A. Knopf, New York, 1988.

13. Morehouse, Harold E., and Marvel Dyer, *The Flying Pioneers Biographies of Harold Morehouse,* GHCM.

14. Peterson, Houston [ed.], *See Them Flying: Houston Peterson's Air-Age Scrapbook, 1909–1910,* Richard W. Baron, New York, 1969.

15. Prendergast, Curtis [and the eds. of Time-Life Books], *The First Aviators,* Time-Life Books, Alexandria, VA, 1981.

16. Roseberry, C. R., *Glenn Curtiss: Pioneer of Flight,* Doubleday & Company, Garden City, NY, 1972.

17. Scott, Phil, "Wright v. Curtiss (Parts 1 and 2)," *Air and Space/Smithsonian* 12:1 (April/May 1997) and 12:2 (June/July 1997).

18. Studer, Clara, *Sky Storming Yankee: The Life of Glenn Curtiss,* Stackpole Sons, New York, 1937.

U.S. Patent References

19. 821,393 O. & W. Wright, Flying Machine, May 23, 1903–May 22, 1906.

20. 1,011,106 A. G. Bell, F. W. Baldwin, J. A. D. McCurdy, G. H. Curtiss, and T. E. Selfridge, Flying Machine, April 8, 1909–December 5, 1911.

Chapter 7

Panorama:
Aerial Yachting

✬ ✬ ✬

Military applications, particularly naval applications, were looming large in the mind of Curtiss. So was the bright prospect of military sales. The offer of free instruction for military personnel, although it doubtless had its altruistic and patriotic dimension, was also a shrewd business move. Manufacturers in those days had unique sets of pilot controls, and changing brands required complete retraining—people who tried it on their own often died. Officers trained on Curtiss machines would be useless without Curtiss machines to fly. It was similar to the difference between VHS and Beta, or between Apple and IBM. Once started on a technology, the customer was usually committed to continue.

On November 14, 1910, Curtiss pilot Eugene Ely was aboard the U.S. cruiser *Birmingham* in Norfolk. Revving the engine on *Hudson Flier*, Ely shot down a makeshift flight deck and picked up barely enough speed from his fall to lurch into flight at the moment of striking the water (Fig. 7.1). Confused by fog, he headed out to sea, but he corrected himself and landed safely ashore. For the first time, an airplane had launched from aboard ship.

On January 18, Ely undertook an even trickier proposition in San Francisco. Lifting off from the shore, he landed on yet another makeshift deck aboard the U.S.S. *Pennsylvania*. For the world's first shipboard landing, he used tail hooks, grabbing arrestor ropes tied to sandbags, the progenitor of much more elaborate systems on aircraft carriers today. The airplane was turned around, and Ely took off, safely returning to shore.

Although the U.S. Navy found this maneuver to be very interesting, it made clear to Curtiss that what it really wanted was an aircraft that could use the surface of the sea. Curtiss had been puttering with the concept since *June Bug/Loon* in 1908 and had given it a lot of thought during his Hudson flight. He was also eager to get a foot in the door of the navy, because the U.S. Army had already bought a Wright airplane. [2, 5, 18, 19, 29]

Fig. 7.1   First shipboard launching.

Curtiss had begun work on North Island in San Diego, which he had rented for winter quarters. In addition to clearing brush and chasing away jackrabbits, the Curtiss team had to erect sheds and hangars for their work. Pitching in were the local Aero Club and three army lieutenants—G. E. M. Kelly, Paul Beck, and J. C. Walker—plus naval Lieutenant Theodore G. "Spuds" Ellyson. In addition to teaching these men to fly, Curtiss intended to develop a water-based aircraft. Henri Fabre in France had already taken off from water in 1910, but his design was not practical and was not followed up. Glenn and Lena took time off on New Year's Day to drive an electric Victoria in the Rose Parade. [18, 19]

Fabre had used pontoons in a tricycle arrangement, which presented considerable difficulties in trying to alight safely. Curtiss began by removing the landing gear from one of his pushers and replacing the three wheels with two fore-and-aft floats, the stern one considerably wider. Repeated modifications (Ellyson estimated more than 50) always revealed the same reality—the thing just didn't work. Not only did it fail to get airborne, but, in most configurations, it did not even taxi well. Finally, Curtiss devised a single shallow 12-ft float mounted along the centerline. On January 26, he tried the new arrangement and accidentally took off—quite easily—while avoiding an obstacle. "The effect of that first flight on the men who had worked, waited and watched for it was magical," he wrote (Fig. 7.2). [19] When he tried it several more times, naval vessels observing the activity on North Island cut loose with their whistles.

Fig. 7.2 Curtiss becomes airborne with his tractor seaplane.

Pennsylvania soon returned from San Francisco, its decks again shipshape after removing Ely's ramp. On February 17, Curtiss invited himself out to see Captain Pond. After a short flight, the aircraft was hoisted aboard, the athletic Curtiss clambering up to ride the hook (Fig. 7.3) and reduce stress on his machine. (There is no word about what this did for the stress of the men operating the hoist.) He found some grease for his engine, visited a few minutes, was lowered over the side, and returned to shore. He clearly had the world's first successful water flyer and now set about making it truly practical. [2, 5, 19]

Fig. 7.3 Wings for the fleet. Note the hydroplaning surface at the bow of the float. The wingtip slats also "hydroplane" to a certain extent, forcing upward a tip that has tilted too low toward the water.

A tractor arrangement, with propeller in front, was quickly discarded. Curtiss, who had pulled the cloth windscreen off *White Wing* for his first flight two and a half years earlier, always wanted plenty of visibility. Prop wash is also always a problem in an open aircraft such as this, and the problem is worse when the prop is throwing up water. The propeller went back to the stern where, in Curtiss's opinion, it belonged.

A triplane configuration was tried and scrapped. Retractable landing gear, however, was definitely a keeper (Fig. 7.4). On February 26, Curtiss took off from water, lowered his new wheels, landed on the beach at the Coronado Hotel, and went in for lunch. Having dined, he took off, raised the wheels, and again alighted in the bight by North Island, already talking about future flights across the Atlantic. Winston Churchill had yet to coin the word "seaplane," and the Curtiss men called their new creation a hydroaeroplane, or hydro for short. The amphibious type, with retractable wheels, Curtiss called "Triad," because it could go by land, sea, and air (Fig. 7.5). [1, 2, 5, 16, 18, 19]

Fig. 7.4 Curtiss mechanic Damon Merrill helped to create the retractable landing gear.

Fig. 7.5 Land, sea, and air—the Triad. Later versions discarded the nosewheel and extended the float farther sternward.

Ellyson, on behalf of the U.S. Navy, took delivery of a Triad-type at Hammondsport that summer. He had passed flight training at San Diego to become Naval Aviator #1, receiving all the paperwork and certification available in those days, which amounted to a letter from Glenn Curtiss. His new machine, designated *A-1*, was the first naval aircraft, the navy having avoided dirigibles altogether until that point (Fig. 7.6).

Ellyson set up the first unofficial naval air station at the Curtiss flying field on Keuka Lake (Fig. 7.7). Captain Baldwin had built his dirigible shed and shop at Kingsley Flats, an open field on the edge of the village, years before this time. This space (more or less behind the current high school) then became the airplane field after those makeshift operations at Stony Brook Farm from 1908 to 1909. Because the sheds and hangars had been built along the shoreline, the field was now eminently suited for seaplane operations out one side of the hangars and land plane flights out the other.

This field, by the way, was a popular tourist attraction. A postcard in the Curtiss Museum collection shows a photograph of three aircraft in flight at Keuka Lake. The message reads, "These things are as thick as fleas around here. When you say, 'Isn't it wonderful,' the natives say, 'Well, I suppose it is, when you stop to think about it.'" Perhaps the natives were not as blasé as they liked to appear, but Hammondsport was one of the few places in the world where you could at least fake it with some degree of plausibility. Many photographs show a dozen or more airplanes congregated together at Kingsley Flats.

Ellyson had a detachment of enlisted men and a fellow academy graduate, Lieutenant John Towers, who took flight instruction from Ellyson to become Naval Aviator #3. In addition to taking possession of land plane *A-2* (later passed on to the Marine Corps as its first aircraft), Ellyson, Towers, and their men set about working up their machines and

Fig. 7.6 Curtiss and Ellyson with U.S. Navy A-1. *Hammondsport is in the background.*

*Fig. 7.7   The first air station of the U.S. Navy. Notice how the
landing gear lifts the float off the ground.*

undertaking experiments such as wire launching (Fig. 7.8). [2, 5] Towers, by the way,
would build most of the U.S. Navy aviation establishment and would become a major
architect of Pacific victory in 1941 to 1945. He distinguished himself his first day in
Hammondsport by upchucking a glass of buttermilk over the rail on Glenn Curtiss's porch.
[18, 19]

Fig. 7.8   Navy wire launching experiments at Keuka Lake.

On both land machines and hydros, the big box-kite elevator in the bow had by now been drastically reduced to a single-plane canard, abetted by a negatively acting single-plane tail elevator. Land machines also had a single-plane vertical stabilizer perpendicular to the bow elevator, in addition to the large vertical stabilizer in the tail. On hydros there was no front stabilizer, and the front elevator, mounted to the bow of the float, had become quite small (Fig. 7.6). All that forward outrigger apparatus, so prominent in the days of *June Bug* and *Silver Dart*, was rapidly atrophying into oblivion. (Lou Casey, in a personal communication, reports pioneer pilot Dick Richardson telling him that the front apparatus made the aircraft dangerously unstable.)

By this time, the ailerons had migrated from the leading struts to the trailing struts, and *A-1* was also equipped with a hinged throw-over steering column, meaning the airplane could be piloted from either of two side-by-side seats. Although Curtiss airplanes had become capable of carrying two occupants, passengers generally had had to crouch behind the pilot or sit on a wing with arms and legs wrapped around a strut. Two-seat arrangements, of course, simplified flight instruction considerably. Before this time, a pilot's first "solo" (the term was not yet in use) was often his first time in the air. [2, 5, 18, 19, 29]

In the months following Ellyson's completion of the course in San Diego, pilot certification became more regularized. Acting under the auspices of the Federation Aeronautique Internationale, the U.S. Aero Club established a voluntary licensing program. To receive a license, pilots were required to take off before official observers, fly 5 km (3.1 mi) at a minimum altitude of 50 ft, describe an uninterrupted series of figure eights over a prescribed course, and land within 50 ft of their starting point. Trainees such as Towers took advantage of the program. He became Naval Aviator #3 and U.S. licensed aviator #62.

Because a few dozen pilots had already met or exceeded these requirements, some certificates could be granted without formal testing. The Aero Club elected to honor Glenn Curtiss with American pilot's license #1. [19]

As Orville and Wilbur Wright were both still actively flying at this time, the award raised some controversy and stirred up further bad feeling. The Aero Club felt that Curtiss deserved the honor because he had made the first public flight in the United States. This claim had been made in the past—and disputed. The Wrights pointed out that they had been flying next to the trolley line in Dayton for years, and even the first flight of *Red Wing* had been hailed as the "first public flight." It is a fact that spectators were generally discouraged at the Wright camp, while they were expected and welcomed at AEA work, so the AEA operations could be described as willingly public and the Wright operations as begrudgingly public. The most accurate description would be that Curtiss had flown the first *exhibition* flight in the United States, on July 4, 1908. This was the first time that the public was invited, even urged, to come see an airplane fly (Fig. 7.9).

Fig. 7.9 Curtiss aircraft from 1908 to 1911, as illustrated in the 1912 catalog. It is difficult to keep in focus the fact that all the development has occurred across a span of only three years.

By this time, Curtiss had sold an airplane to the U.S. Army, while the navy was ordering a Wright to add to its Curtiss airplanes. Both services, unfortunately, would soon be plagued by bad feeling and competition between Wright pilots and Curtiss pilots, pointlessly reflecting the corporate controversy still raging. The competitive ill will was exacerbated by the fact that neither group was capable of flying the other's airplanes.

The Curtiss Exhibition Company, with its numerous contract fliers, had become a huge success, easing demands on Curtiss's time. Having rebuilt in the wake of the Herring disaster, he again had a large business to run—he was still making motorcycles and engines, in addition to making and exhibiting airplanes. He also took on custom work, building airplanes to order for clients such as Tom Baldwin, who could see that LTA exhibitions were by now a thing of the past. Curtiss had been trying to ease himself out of personal exhibitions ever since contracting Charley Hamilton back in 1909. [2, 5, 11, 19, 29]

The hydro renewed Curtiss's personal enthusiasm for flying. He had grown up on a large inland lake, and even his youthful sojourns in Rochester and Rock Stream had been in lakeside communities. He was an expert and powerful swimmer. He loved fishing, speedboating, and ice boating, and he would establish every one of his future homes close to water. Curtiss returned enthusiastically to exhibition flying.

In addition to the safety factor of being able to alight in water, seaplanes had another advantage. There were few landing fields in those days. Pilots made do with what they could spot from the air, but finding a level field that did not have a barbed-wire fence, a cornfield, or a herd of cows was problematic. For that matter, any pilot trying to land or take off in those days was likely to attract a crowd of spectators, none of whom understood the length of field required for landing or takeoff. Apparently thinking that airplanes landed like balloons, they would charge the machine long before it could come to a stop.

Flat water surfaces were easier to find than flat land surfaces. Many knowledgeable observers concluded that seaplanes would become the standard type of aircraft, with land planes as the exception. The huge numbers of land planes produced for World War I helped to determine the balance, of course, but in 1911, Curtiss was awarded the first Collier Trophy for the year's most significant contribution to the science of aeronautics. The basis of the award was the hydroaeroplane. [19]

The Imperial German Navy ordered two hydros, and the Imperial Japanese Navy sent three lieutenants for flight training; Lieutenant Nakajima later founded the first private airplane factory in Japan. Nakajima airplanes and Curtiss airplanes fought each other across Asia and the Pacific during World War II, and Nakajima was minister of munitions at the time of surrender.

Inspired by his own pleasure in the hydro, Curtiss began to create a new market. Until this time, most airplane sales had been for military or exhibition use, with a trickle of orders for experimental purposes (A. P. Warner of Warner Instruments in Beloit had made the first private airplane purchase, back in 1909, for this reason). Now Curtiss promoted directly to the wealthy sportsman, touting the hydro as combining the pleasures of boating with the thrill of flying. The stream of private owners, and private students in the flying schools—now established at Hammondsport, San Diego, and Miami—began to grow.

William B. Atwater and his wife, Lillian, met Curtiss on a westbound train during their honeymoon. Atwater operated a livery stable, and his wife was the widow of Senator Tom Platt; they had decided to try flying. Curtiss recruited them to his own school, and both learned to fly, although Bill Atwater was the official, tuition-paying student. Lillian Atwater narrowly missed either fame or ignominy when she tried Curtiss's latest sporting brainstorm, capturing birds in flight by means of a net on an outrigger. She made a great try, but the pelican shot past her head through the struts and almost fouled the propeller. The idea was quietly dropped by unanimous consent. Bill Atwater later did some exhibition flying in the Far East, but their airplane seems to have been the first one ever purchased primarily for pleasure. [17, 18, 19]

Successful and spectacular though the hydro was, Curtiss was not satisfied. He longed for a more seaworthy aircraft, which called, it seemed to him, not for a float but a hull. Early experiments tried building up the float with a sort of superstructure to shield the pilot. These met, at best, with indifferent success. They increased weight, aerodynamic drag, and, worse yet, hydrodynamic drag. The vessels were "glued" to the water.

Curtiss tackled the problem in his accustomed way, through observation, experience, and experimentation. He operated the new machines himself, and he raced alongside in a speedboat while others operated them. By the summer of 1912, he had reasoned his way into a method for "ungluing" the hull. Following an unsuccessful attempt in which Curtiss rode the chase boat, he directed Henry Kleckler to nail several blocks of wood to the underside of the hull. These broke up the flow, and the flying boat became airborne.

Curtiss and his team had already put a break into the underside of the hull, which tapered upward from a point about midway down the length. Now this break became a full step, patented in # 1,210,374 (October 18, 1915–December 26, 1916) [13, 25] and since then called the "Curtiss step." Similar arrangements are found today on speedboats and pontoons, as well as hulled aircraft, which Curtiss now busily began manufacturing and promoting. Two upright pipes behind the step communicated outside air pressure to the underside of the hull, likewise promoting "ungluing." [13]

That year of 1912 was a turning point for Curtiss. The flying boat had more military and sporting potential than had the hydro, which presaged an upturn in business, particularly because both seaplanes had clearly been Curtiss products from start to finish. Curtiss won the second Collier Trophy for inventing the flying boat, and he published *The Curtiss Aviation Book*, which was ghostwritten by Augustus Post. Post was educated and cultured, with numerous publications to his credit, while Curtiss was an eighth-grade graduate who looked on his own writing skills very negatively. He would have been better off tackling the *Aviation Book* on his own. Post's flowery style contrasts sharply with the direct, forceful, and lucid style of Curtiss's own writing. *The Curtiss Aviation Book,* although very interesting in parts, was obviously a slapdash proposition, riddled with inaccuracies including wildly incorrect dates. However, it preserves several interesting anecdotes and contains essays by other Curtiss aviators. The book was dedicated to Mabel Bell, whose husband wisely shied away from any involvement with it. [9, 19]

After 1912, Curtiss finally discontinued manufacturing motorcycles under the Curtiss name, although he remained in partnership with Tank Waters to manufacture the Marvel motorcycle for perhaps two more years. The Marvel had a clean, attractive design that marketed itself partly by stressing exclusive use of the Model G, Curtiss's last single-cylinder engine, which developed 4.5 hp.

The airplane business had become the main undertaking of the company, and Curtiss had not raced on two wheels in five years. His businesses were always very personal, and development was languishing under his neglect (Fig. 7.10). Furthermore, Curtiss and Waters had always concentrated on light, belt-driven motorcycles. Americans increasingly wanted bigger, more powerful motorcycles that could be "ridden by farmhands and repaired by blacksmiths," in the words of Ed Youngblood, president of the American Motorcyclist Association. [22, 24]

There was also considerable shrinkage in the motorcycle business (as had already occurred with bicycles) because automobiles were becoming more common. At the turn of the century, consumers had a choice among three powered personal-transportation options: the motorcycle, the quadricycle, and the automobile. (Auto owners had the additional options of steam power, electric power, or internal combustion.) The quad, a sort of overgrown go-cart or scaled-down auto, died out quickly. Motorcycles survived but rapidly became, in the main, a supplement to the auto, rather than a direct alternative. Internal combustion, of course, became the preferred source of power, a decision finally sealed by the U.S. government during World War I, when it invested heavily in gasoline-powered automobiles, trucks, and tractors.

While Curtiss was inventing the flying boat on Keuka Lake in the summer of 1912, he probably kept one ear cocked to the house on the hill, where, on June 16, Glenn Curtiss, Jr.

Fig. 7.10   The Curtiss plant in 1911, as illustrated in the "Curtiss Aeroplanes"
catalog— compare this with the view in Fig. 4-10! In addition to the facilities
being more extensive, a truck has replaced the horse-drawn dray. The three-
story structure in the foreground is the Curtiss home; all that survives is its
cupola, or "sky parlor," which is now in the Curtiss Museum. In 1935,
Hammondsport built the Glenn Curtiss Memorial School
(now a middle school) on the site.

was born. It was ten years since the death of Carlton. Glenn Junior was perfectly healthy, and the family's joy is not difficult to imagine.

Curtiss had been so enthusiastic about the hydro that he had resumed exhibition flying in 1911. But he wrapped that up in August of the same year, taking Billy Sunday for a ride off the waters of Winona Lake, Indiana. Although he continued test flying for years, after baby Glenn's birth, Curtiss never made another exhibition flight until shortly before his own death in 1930. The races, the record trials, the exhibition tours, on motorcycles and in aeroplanes, had all taken place between the death of Carlton in 1902 and the birth of Glenn Junior in 1912. Curtiss was now 34 years old, a world-famous man, the founder and operator of a good-sized business. There were probably many reasons why he gave up exhibitions. However, it seems likely that his quest for speed and fame, and the sensationally public courting of danger, were impelled in part by the loss of his infant son. In some way that others will never understand—and which he perhaps could not, or would not, have articulated—the birth of baby Glenn filled a void that had been opened a decade earlier. [19]

By the summer of 1913, Curtiss had a production flying boat, the Model E (or E-wing). Probably no two were exactly alike, but in general terms, these were two-place side-by-side biplane pushers with V-8 engines and interwing ailerons. The bow by now was free from any encumbrance by control surfaces or stabilizers. The land model had also evolved by this time into the "headless" pusher, marking Curtiss's cleanest designs of the period. Stories abound about the inspiration for removing the head, including several stories that a hydro pilot, sometimes said to be Curtiss, was thrown through the front apparatus and injured during a crash. Other stories assert that a landplane pilot (again variously identified) accidentally broke off his front gear. Being committed almost immediately to an exhibition flight, he flew anyhow, discovering to his surprise that the airplane flew better without its head. Entertaining though these stories may be, the bow gear actually had been atrophying since 1910.

Pusher engines, especially those mounted high as in flying boats, were very dangerous in crashes, and a sardonic joke of the day asserted, "A Curtiss pusher pilot is always the first at the scene of an accident." A single large strut supporting the engine ran diagonally into the cockpit of the flying boat. This strut was named for Lt. Louis E. Goodier, who had, in fact, survived a crash. A few years of experience revealed the awkward truth that the Goodier strut did no good whatsoever, and it was replaced by two diagonal struts, each running from a lower front corner of the engine. Although adequate, even this arrangement highlighted some of the design drawbacks with pushers. [1, 2, 5, 8, 13, 19]

There is a flying reproduction of Jack Vilas's 1913 Model E boat in the Curtiss Museum collection, and experience shows that the Goodier strut was a nuisance while entering or exiting the cockpit. However, the cockpit itself was a significant advance. It might have had an open cockpit, but previous Curtiss aircraft had not had even that luxury—the pilot simply sat out in space, straddling a bench in the early days and occupying a chairlike seat later. The cockpit's concession to comfort (at once made possible by the hull and necessary by operating from water) opened the door to Curtiss's latest marketing scheme—aerial yachting.

Harold McCormick, son of Cyrus and vice president of International Harvester, was among the first who journeyed to Hammondsport in quest of a flying boat. Even before there was any production to speak of, McCormick wanted a custom job—a tractor configuration capable of carrying five people. McCormick used his flying boat for commuting along Lake Michigan from his North Shore home to his office in Chicago. Henry Ford bought a flying boat and presented it to Eileen Dahlinger, whom most people regarded as his paramour.

Another Chicago man, Logan A. Vilas, strolled into the plant in early 1913, asking Curtiss, after few preliminaries, to build him a flying boat. "Happy Jack" Vilas (he hated the name Logan, although he passed it on through the family) had had one airplane ride, with Max Lillie in a Wright machine. When a bemused Curtiss asked Jack whether he was certain that he would enjoy flying, Vilas replied that he actually was not certain, but he was determined to try it and see. Curtiss pointed out that a deposit was customary when placing an order. Jack Vilas fished through his pockets, came up with a $1,500 check, and passed it to Curtiss, asking, "Will this do?"

It would, so Vilas checked into Lulu Mott's boardinghouse (which had become the prestige establishment of the village, putting up all the top aviators) and walked down to the lake in the morning to get in line for lessons. Vilas surmised that cash was in short supply around the Curtiss plant, which was still groaning under the Wright and Herring litigations. Vilas was an heir to the New York Air Brake Corporation. According to contemporary newspapers, he was "struggling along" on $30,000 a year.

On rainy days, Vilas took a direct hand in designing and building his own flying boat, christened "*L.A.V.*" Aviation magazines of the day called it "the giddiest thing," enthusing over the beautiful dove-gray corduroy upholstery. *L.A.V.* was a trifle larger and heavier than other Model E boats, and her upper wingtips folded down, slightly reducing, or at least interrupting, the sail area as protection against winds while at rest. The airplane had one of the new 60–70 hp V-8 engines, predecessor to the famous OX series. Vilas's excitement on the day of delivery was quickly dashed when neither he nor his instructor, Doc Wildman, could coax the thing off the water.

Frustrated to tears, Vilas telephoned Glenn Curtiss at the plant, complaining, "That flying boat you sold me won't work!" Curtiss motored down, looked things over, slipped into the cockpit without making any adjustments, taxied out, and took off without difficulty, leaving Vilas (and everyone else) openmouthed on shore. "I learned then," Vilas said, "that there is a difference in pilots." (Fig. 7.11)

Vilas soon got the hang of flying, and Curtiss asked whether he would allow his boat to be shown at the Hotel Astor in New York City, where Vilas was bound with his new plaything. Vilas agreed, if Curtiss would pay for the shipping, and Curtiss threw in a special Nile-green paint job plus nickel finishing. When workers hoisted the hull up the hotel's exterior to the rooftop restaurant, Vilas had to leave the area, unable to watch. However, all went well, and he was soon thrilling the city by flying about the harbor and Long Island Sound, frequently using the Westchester Country Club as his base.

Fig. 7.11 Jack Vilas at Hammondsport with
L.A.V., *before the special paint job.*

Vilas was generous about giving rides, although a female reporter annoyed him by demanding an exciting flight. Determined to show her a thing or two, Vilas shoved the wheel forward to put the airplane into a steep dive. He was shocked to find that he could not pull up when he wanted; the reporter had grabbed the wheel column and refused to let go.

Fighting both his passenger and his dive, Vilas barely managed to haul the wheel back far enough (and soon enough) to avoid a crash into the harbor. Glenn Curtiss, who had come down from Hammondsport to watch Vilas fly, pulled the younger man aside, demanding to know what had happened, as soon as he staggered out of the cockpit.

Vilas freely admitted what he had done, whereupon Curtiss gave him a scathing lecture, strictly charging Jack never to take an unnecessary risk, particularly with the life of a passenger. While his anger and his earnestness were perfectly clear to Vilas, Curtiss had kept his voice low. Turning aside, he summoned a bewildered mechanic and loudly directed him to tighten a particular wire, announcing that this "defect" had been the cause of the problem.

Vilas was not employed by or contracted to Curtiss, operating a Curtiss-owned airplane, or flying on Curtiss's behalf. However, Curtiss, who always remained passionately committed to safe practices, clearly felt a responsibility to intervene when lives were at hazard. This was only one of several recorded instances in which Curtiss privately reamed out a pilot, before contriving some mechanical excuse to disguise misbehavior as a technical problem.

Vilas took Curtiss's admonitions to heart and quickly developed a reputation as "a lovely man to fly with." However, he ignored Curtiss when the Hammondsport man suggested that his proposed flight across Lake Michigan was "not advisable at this time." Vilas realized that Curtiss was gently telling him that he did not have enough experience for such a feat, but he set off on July 1 anyhow. He had had his flying boat for only a month.

"I was temporarily deaf and my head rang with the noise of the motor," Vilas wrote, "but I was content, and having been the first person to fly across Lake Michigan, I was happy." Vilas flew around Chicago, around his summer camp in Wisconsin (where he spotted forest fires from the air), and around the Thousand Islands, where he raced against a speedboat. In all these venues, of course, he was an enthusiastic Curtiss booster, stimulating sales and flying school enrollments.

Vilas took his young lady up for a ride and proposed to her, circling higher and higher until she finally said yes—perhaps the ultimate manifestation of the flying sportsman. He bought a larger Model F Flying Boat (*L.A.V. II*) the following year to accommodate his wife and their baby daughter, who later became a pilot herself. The hull of the E-boat survived and is currently in the Curtiss Museum, on long-term loan from the Smithsonian. Jack Vilas, who piloted until he was 83 years old, offered on his last flight to show his current wife how to recover from a stall. (Hazel declined the offer.) He personified the essence of aerial yachting when he told a reporter in 1913, "It's more fun than I have had for $6,500 in years." [2, 5, 13, 16, 17, 19, 23]

For Curtiss, of course, it was more than fun. It was business. But of what did the business consist?

Curtiss had long since jettisoned the bicycles, sewing machines, auto dealerships, apple press, and perhaps even the vineyard. He gave up motorcycle manufacturing in 1912, although there continued to be some lingering business in parts and engines. His Marvel motorcycle partnership with Tank Waters existed, but it was a separate proposition. If Marvel was still manufacturing, it did provide steady sales for the Model G engine. However, Marvel was only a sideline at best, although perhaps it hedged bets and sheltered assets against adverse court decisions involving Augustus Herring or Orville Wright. (Wilbur had died in 1912.) The Curtiss business was airplanes. [11, 19]

For the general public, the most obvious part of the business was the Curtiss Exhibition Company. With numerous contract fliers, the Exhibition Company booked dates at state fairs, air meets, community celebrations, and other gatherings. Tens of thousands of Americans saw their first airplane at one of these exhibitions, perhaps piloted by Lincoln Beachey, Beckwith Havens, Lanny Callan, or Blanche Stuart Scott. Besides the considerable income that the exhibitions generated, they also stimulated business for other branches of the enterprise.

Curtiss Flying Schools (sometimes called Curtiss Schools of Aviation) operated seasonally at Hammondsport, San Diego, and Miami; later operations would also appear on Long Island and at Newport News. In addition to providing their own income stream, the schools stimulated airplane sales and served as a recruiting ground for new instructors and exhibitors. Some eager pilots never got the hang of it, however. In such cases, Curtiss, if he was at hand, would refund the student's money and gently send him home.

The schools also provided early flying service activity, charging for rides or for photographic flights and similar activities. Probably these flights were often undertaken for publicity value or simply as a lark, especially if young women were involved. Flying was a great way to meet women in those days.

These schools also became prototype airfields and seaplane havens. The financial arrangements made by outside owners are unclear. However, these primitive setups were a faint foreshadowing of fixed-base operations and commercial airports.

Manufacturing was the theoretical heart of the enterprise, although there were periods in which the Exhibition Company brought in the lion's share of the income. Who were Curtiss's customers? Where could a person sell an airplane in those days?

Some construction was for "own use" as demonstrators and as school machines. Contract fliers could buy their own machines over time. Independent exhibitors, or exhibitors for competing companies, also provided a market. If they wished, they could additionally contract "mechanicians" from Curtiss. There was occasional custom work, as when Lawrence Sperry wanted a flying boat for gyroscope experiments.

As the hydro and the flying boat came into service, there were increasing sales for pleasure use, obviously targeted at the wealthy. There were occasional sales for what we would term business use, as when a western rancher bought an airplane for traveling around his vast holdings more quickly than he could do on horseback. Curtiss directly exported all over the world, but he also licensed Louis Paulhan in France to manufacture and sell Curtiss-type machines.

Curtiss always recognized that it was not enough to simply design and manufacture an airplane—he also had to sell it. He has sometimes been called the Architect of American Aviation because of his promotion of what we would now call infrastructure—flying fields, competitions, flying schools, flying services, and exhibitions. He aimed at creating a setting in which the customer could buy and use an airplane. With the advent of the flying boat, U.S. airplanes were on the verge of actually becoming useful in terms of passengers or cargo.

In marketing airplanes, Curtiss naturally began with his spectacular personal accomplishments and the record of his machines—an early example of celebrity marketing, although in this case the connection between celebrity and product was valid. He listed the many satisfied users of Curtiss machines and stressed the safety features of the aircraft. Also important was the customer support system of mechanics and spare parts. [1, 11]

Airplanes rarely flew from city to city back then, so shipping was a major issue. Curtiss advertisements featured the small size and weight of the airplanes. Curtiss airplanes were designed to break down and reassemble with relative ease. Moreover, they were designed specifically with shipping in mind. Many components, such as wing sections, were packed in 5-ft crates, making them eligible for flat rate on the railroads. This approach was electrifying at a time when many airplanes had to be shipped complete, requiring a special end-loading boxcar. When Curtiss's catalog pointed out that pilots could ship his airplane from New York to Chicago for $25, or his competitor's for $250, prospective buyers took notice. [8]

In addition to complete aircraft, there was also a steady business in parts, and especially in engines. Established customers wanted replacements or upgrades, and there was a great vogue for building your own Curtiss-type airplane, a practice encouraged by the aviation magazines, which serialized lengthy how-to articles. Curtiss never seems to have impeded this activity, and some feel that there were as many Curtiss "home-builts" around as there were factory products. The land-based Curtiss pusher (including its unofficial copies) was the most common type of airplane in the United States before World War I. Builders of other types often wanted Curtiss engines, and there was additional demand for engines in other applications, such as automobiles and speedboats.

To promote this extensive business, Curtiss counted on the support of unofficial boosters such as Jack Vilas, Harold McCormick, J. A. D. McCurdy, and other satisfied customers. Not content with resting on their good will, he issued a "Curtiss Aeroplanes" catalog and a supplemental "Aerial Yachting" booklet. He advertised heavily in the leading aviation magazines. His sales department aggressively supplied the world's press with information, new releases, and photographs. Curtiss maintained an extensive network of agents, demonstrators, and sales people in the United States and Europe, supplementing their efforts with frequent road trips of his own on both continents. [1, 23]

During this period C. P. Rudd, who was a partner in Marvel with Curtiss and Waters, remarked that the nations of the world had become too mature ever to fight each other again. "We will always have war," was Curtiss's laconic reply, and sad events proved him far too right. [20]

Then, as now, the military was a major customer for the aeronautic industry. Airplanes are expensive, and Curtiss's concentration on military sales and wealthy sportsmen showed a good deal of insight into where the money was, as well as where the potential uses were.

His star customer was, of course, the U.S. Navy. Although the navy bought from other manufacturers as well, such as Martin and Wright, naval brass maintained a close relationship with Curtiss, bought his machines in (relatively) large numbers, and turned to him for experimental work, such as a hybrid hydro/flying boat designed to run up on the beach and discharge Marines. In 1913, Jack Towers awed everyone by getting four hydros and a flying boat (all Curtisses) into the air at once during maneuvers at Guantanamo. He further demonstrated that from the air he could spot a submarine submerged at 60 ft. The submarine was commanded by Lt. Chester P. Nimitz, and the event presaged decades of prickly relations between the two men. Towers convinced any lingering skeptics when he spotted the "enemy" fleet from the air, without being detected himself. He warned his own commanders in the mock battle; they sortied their destroyer force and sprang upon the unsuspecting attackers. [18]

The army bought both land planes and seaplanes, although not in the numbers that the navy demanded. Foreign powers weighed in with what amounted to sample orders—a couple of hydros for the Japanese navy, a flying boat for the German Kaiser's fleet, and a flying boat for the Ottoman navy (the first aircraft in the Turkish military). The Italian navy placed a heftier order, taking several Model F flying boats configured as two-place tandems rather than two-place side-by-sides; the Turkish unit came from this line. [1, 2, 5, 8]

Imperial Russia was a significant customer and even wooed Curtiss to set up a plant in that country—an offer he considered seriously in the wake of adverse rulings in the Wright suit. [19] The czar's navy bought numerous hydros and flying boats, most of which were deployed with the Black Sea fleet (Fig. 7.12). Assiduous maneuvers with these machines, and with other aircraft of European make, meant that the czarist navy was the only belligerent to enter World War I with a tested doctrine for the use of aircraft.

Curtiss's military business, at least with respect to land planes, was perilously threatened by Grover Loening in 1914. Loening had received the country's first master's degree in aeronautics, and he had worked as Orville Wright's assistant. He liked Curtiss personally and admired him as an aviator, but he deprecated Curtiss's engineering talents when he

Fig. 7.12   Curtiss hydro in Russian service on the Black Sea.

found in conversation that Curtiss did not know the square footage of the tail surfaces on the airplane he was flying at the time. Curtiss also impressed him as a promoter, but Loening despised the Curtiss publicity, which he considered untrustworthy.

Loening thought more highly of Wright as an engineer but recognized his obsession with the Curtiss lawsuit and his lack of business drive. Wisely seeing no future in the Wright Aeronautical Corporation, Loening took a newly created civil service job as Aeronautical Engineer for the Signal Corps. The Signal Corps was in a panic, having recently lost eight out of fourteen pilots in crashes. After a little study, Loening condemned every one of the army's Wright and Curtiss pushers. This nearly put the army out of the flying business for the time being and certainly cut off both Wright and Curtiss at the knees. [15, 17, 19]

Glenn Martin and Curtiss both had tractor airplanes in early development stages, and these were rushed forward. Curtiss, recognizing that design was getting beyond him and his staff, had already imported B. Douglas Thomas, a Sopwith engineer he had met on a trip to Great Britain. Thomas blended his own work with some features of an existing Curtiss tractor to create in quick succession the Model J, the Model N, and the Model JN. This latter machine, a two-place tandem tail-dragger, became the famed Curtiss *Jenny* (Fig. 7.13). Army and navy both took it on as a trainer, and *Jennys* made the first U.S. Army flights in an actual operation, unsuccessfully chasing Pancho Villa around Mexico. [2, 5, 18–20]

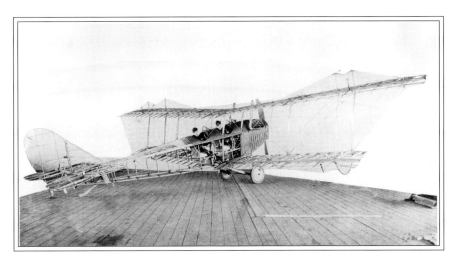

Fig. 7.13 The Curtiss Jenny.

✶ ✶ ✶

The *Jenny* was an exciting new product. The flying boat was doing wonders with both civil and military buyers around the world. The flying schools were packing in men and women who would soon be big names in the field of aeronautics. The Wright lawsuit was going badly, but appeals were in process, as was the search for technical exceptions to the patent. Both these efforts were abetted by attorneys for Henry Ford, who saw parallels between Curtiss's situation and his own eight-year battle with the Association of Licensed Automobile Manufacturers. The Curtiss plant was busy, and Hammondsport crackled with excitement. [4, 6, 7, 11, 12, 19]

As if that were not enough, down at Kingsley Flats, the Curtiss team was assembling Langley's old 1903 *Buzzard*, which had been shipped from its ignominious storage at the Smithsonian.

Lincoln Beachey, a former Curtiss pilot, had offered to reproduce Langley's aerodrome and prove it could fly. Beachey then left for a tour of Europe, but Curtiss proposed taking on the job himself. Bell, Walcott, and other Smithsonian officials were interested in rehabilitating the memory of their old friend and mentor. They decided to restore the original, so they sent the crated pieces to Hammondsport, igniting an explosion of controversy that echoes to this day. [2–7, 11, 12, 17, 19, 21]

Because "prior art" could theoretically weaken the Wright patent, many observers, vociferously led by Orville Wright, stormed that the Smithsonian was intervening in a lawsuit between citizens on behalf of one side. It seems unlikely that Smithsonian officials were surreptitiously trying to support the Curtiss case. However, as later became clear, they were certainly ready to trumpet Langley's fame at the expense of the Wrights'.

What did Curtiss have in mind? As always, he was so closemouthed that it is hard to say; at least he was happy to pocket the $2,000 fee from the Smithsonian. Walter Johnson stated years later that Langley's machine at one point was crated for shipment to Buffalo, New York, for demonstration in the patent case, but that this trip was called off at the last minute because of a legal compromise. It is difficult to see how a demonstration flight could have helped Curtiss's case, but they may have been optimistic about the prospects anyhow. Curtiss at the time made another odd aircraft, Goupil's *Duck*, which had been designed but never built prior to the Wrights' first flight. This creation was specifically aimed at demonstrating prior art.

So, some such scheme might have been a partial motivation, although the *Langley* (as it came to be called) apparently never entered the legal case. Smithsonian officials were certainly open to criticism for their pro-*Langley* (if not pro-Curtiss) bias. Curtiss could scarcely be criticized if he had attempted to use objective information about the *Langley* to defend himself in court (which he did not, anyhow).

Because the modified *Langley* flew repeatedly from 1914 to 1915, controversy continues to rage over the nature and extent of those modifications. From the outset, Curtiss decided to eschew Langley's catapult and launch the craft as a seaplane. This required modification from the start, although these modifications would clearly make it *harder* to get airborne rather than easier. They added weight and drag while sacrificing the assisted takeoff. On top of all that, Langley's old assistant, Charles Manly, had been unable to get the engine up to its original output, although Curtiss improved its ignition.

Manly supervised the engine restoration, while Dr. A. F. Zahm oversaw the entire project on behalf of the Smithsonian. Both men repeatedly asserted, with Curtiss and Kleckler, that they made only those modifications necessary for the seaplane configuration, plus repair of broken parts. Curtiss even used the original engine when he took the weird contraption off the water on May 28 for 150 ft of flight before the usual enthusiastic crowd. Bell wired Curtiss, "Congratulations on your vindication of Langley's drome. This is really the crowning achievement of your career, at least so far." [19]

Because Curtiss was clearly an interested party to his own defense at law, any assertions that he or Kleckler made would be open to question in court—but the matter never entered court. Manly and Zahm could be suspected of being mendacious in honor of Langley's memory; Tom Crouch has also demonstrated several ways in which each benefited financially from future relations with Curtiss, opening the question as to whether their testimony could have been tainted.

It is theoretically possible, of course, that there was *inadvertent* adjusting of Langley's machine. If his configuration had been a little bit off, Curtiss staff could conceivably have assembled the thing "right" in light of their own superior experience. However, Zahm and Manly insisted that Langley's written descriptions had been followed minutely, and the aircraft was at any rate vastly different from anything the Curtiss team—or anyone apart from Manly—had ever seen.

Because the Smithsonian had also commissioned Curtiss to test the tandem arrangement of the *Langley*, the aircraft now went through another series of modifications, including an up-to-date Curtiss engine. It flew repeatedly from water and ice at Keuka Lake (but not elsewhere at any time), piloted in turn by Lanny Callan, Gink Doherty, and Walter Johnson. Beginning in 1918, it was exhibited at the Smithsonian. While the museum label admitted that it had first flown in 1914, it also described the aerodrome as "the first man-carrying aeroplane in the history of the world capable of sustained free flight." This quite reasonably incensed Orville Wright, who sent the 1903 Wright *Flier* to the British Museum and circulated a list of modifications made on *Langley*. [4, 6, 7, 10, 14, 19]

The label's assertion was, of course, puerile and irrelevant. Each person is capable of many things, but if someone does not actually do something of which he or she is capable, that person certainly does not get any credit—or blame, as the case may be.

What do we actually know about the affair, which continues to stir up controversy almost a century later?

The reproduction project was first aired by Lincoln Beachey, before being picked up by Curtiss.

The proposal and decision to restore rather than reproduce came from the Smithsonian. It also ordered additional tests and paid Curtiss $2,000 for the work. It is possible that Bell and Walcott covered this fee themselves.

Langley, piloted by Curtiss, made its first flight on May 28, 1914. Curtiss, Kleckler, Manly, and Zahm all insisted that it was in its original configuration, except for repairs, the seaplane gear, and the weakened engine. Their assertions have been strongly contested. Grover Loening stated that the installation of seaplane gear "incidentally" corrected an original defect by stiffening the wings. [15] Apparently, the Hammondsport team also omitted leading-edge wing extensions, resulting in a cleaner wing with better aerodynamics. [21]

Langley underwent further modifications and further flights, from water and from ice, under several pilots, including Doc Wildman, Lanny Callan, Walter Johnson, and Gink Doherty, during the course of a year (Fig. 7.14). All agreed that the craft was difficult to turn. Flights as long as 10 miles were claimed. In one flight, Doherty claimed to have

*Fig. 7.14 Langley's aerodrome in flight,
with Gink Doherty as pilot.*

flown her 10 miles into the lee of Keuka Bluff because winds prevented him from turning the airplane. He stated that he alighted on the water, turned around, and flew back 10 miles.

Langley never entered the Wright-Curtiss legal case.

The original Smithsonian label contained a fatuous statement at which Orville Wright rightly took strong offense.

Orville Wright's list of modifications was cumulative; it failed to distinguish modifications made for the original flight from modifications made during succeeding months when the machine was used as a test bed. [19]

The fact that Langley's machine may have been "capable" of flight has no bearing on the fact that it spectacularly failed to fly even one foot in 1903. Moreover, the original craft included no practical provisions for landing. [6, 7, 14, 15]

It is evident that Langley's aircraft, *with modifications* (and with experienced pilots) could fly. Spectacular though his failures were, he seems at least to have been on the track of success and perhaps could have reached it with further experimentation. Maybe he was not so far off the mark as the public assumed. This speculative nod to Langley does not in the slightest detract from or obscure the Wrights' tremendous achievement of that year. They flew. Langley (or Manly) did not.

And as if the *Langley* excitement weren't enough, even seen-it-all Hammondsport was agog at Curtiss's other big project for the summer. Ten and a half years after Kitty Hawk, three and a half years after creating the hydro, two years after the birth of the flying boat, Glenn Curtiss was building an airplane to cross the Atlantic.

This was flying boat *America*, financed by Rodman Wanamaker, whose department store had exhibited *Reims Racer* following the airplane's European victories. At stake was a £10,000 prize from British press baron Lord Northcliffe, and the effort was completely Anglo-American.

B. Douglas Thomas, a British subject now living in Hammondsport and working for Curtiss, was leading the design. Curtiss, who was overseeing the entire project, also contributed to design; if usual practices were followed, so did any other Curtiss employee who had something to contribute. The aircraft was built in the Curtiss plant.

John Cyril Porte also helped in the design and would serve as command pilot. Porte was an inactive Royal Navy lieutenant, handsome (we know this not only from his pictures but from the testimony of Hammondsport maidens), and a natty dresser. Jack Towers from the U.S. Navy would be Porte's copilot, and Wanamaker would provide backing.

Construction and planning kept the village bubbling. *America* was big. It was a closed-cabin flying boat, and by some reports, the first twin-engine airplane in the United States—and certainly the first from Curtiss. Progress was well along when the navy yanked Towers from the project. The navy had been dubious about a serving officer being involved in a monetary prize effort, but its immediate interest was the U.S. occupation of Vera Cruz, Mexico. Towers received orders to support the intervention with his airplanes. One of the Curtiss flying boats took ground fire while scouting, marking the first combat flight in the U.S. military.

Porte suddenly needed a partner, and George E. A. Hallett suggested to Curtiss that he consider a different approach. Curtiss had hired Hallett on his first trip to San Diego, where both had pitched in on creation of the hydro. Hallett's mechanical brilliance made him a valued member of the Curtiss team, and now he suggested that Porte did not really need another pilot; what he needed was a good mechanic who could take a trick at the wheel. So Hallett, rather than Towers, stood beside Curtiss and Porte on June 22 as 16-year-old Katherine Masson christened *America* with Great Western champagne. (No one had scored the bottle, and Porte had to lend a hand breaking it.)

Porte and Hallett planned to fly several stages, stopping in Newfoundland and the Azores before reaching Europe. During the summer, key personnel such as Lanny Callan went out on station to prepare for reception, resupply, and repairs. Everyone was delighted with the performance of *America*, and no one at the time had any doubts about her ability to fly the distance, although Hallett decades later concluded that they probably would have failed due to carburetor icing. What was frustrating the team at the time was an even more obvious, and seemingly insurmountable, problem.

The two engines (new 90-hp OX models) did the job competently in normal flight, but they could not get *America* off the water with the full load of fuel needed for the crossing (Fig. 7.15). After toying with the hydrodynamics and weight reduction for a while, the team turned to a third engine, mounted high on the centerline. This worked. It got *America* airborne, but once aloft, the third engine was merely a nuisance. No one wanted to chance an Atlantic odyssey with such a detriment. If they ran the engine, not only was it unnecessary but it reduced the fuel store. If they did not run it, the drag problem was even worse. They studied simply feathering the prop throughout the trip and even desperately considered ways to jettison the thing in flight. [2, 6, 18, 19]

In the end, it did not matter. The problem was still unsolved when Porte rushed home to England abruptly. Curtiss recalled his men from their far-flung stations. They dismantled *America*, and the craft made its Atlantic crossing in crates. When the craft arrived in Great Britain, Porte had her reassembled and then put her to work, hunting submarines.

Fig. 7.15 Porte, Curtiss, and Hallett checking out America.

Far from linking hands across the sea in friendship, *America* was now a pawn in a war about which no one had even dreamed merely a few weeks earlier, on the day her keel hit the waters of Keuka Lake.

REFERENCES

1.   "Aerial Yachting," The Curtiss Aeroplane Company, Hammondsport, NY, circa 1913.

2.   Bowers, Peter M., *Curtiss Aircraft 1907–1947,* Putnam, London, 1979.

3.   Boyne, Walter J., *The Smithsonian Book of Flight,* Smithsonian Books, Washington, DC, 1987.

4.   Carpenter, Jack, *Pendulum: The Story of America's Three Aviation Pioneers: Wilbur Wright, Orville Wright, and Glenn Curtiss, The Henry Ford of Aviation,* Arsdalen, Bosch & Co., Carlisle, MA, 1992.

5.   Casey, Louis S., *Curtiss: The Hammondsport Era, 1907–1915,* Crown Publishers, New York, 1981.

6.   Combs, Harry, with Martin Caidin, *Kill Devil Hill: Discovering the Secrets of the Wright Brothers,* Houghton Mifflin Company, Boston, 1979.

7.   Crouch, Tom, *The Bishop's Boys: A Life of Wilbur and Orville Wright,* W. W. Norton & Co., New York, 1989.

8.   "Curtiss Aeroplanes," The Curtiss Aeroplane Company, Hammondsport, NY, 1911–1912.

9.   Curtiss, Glenn H., and Augustus Post, *The Curtiss Aviation Book,* Frederick Stokes Company, New York, 1912.

10.   ———, "Little Known Facts About Little Known People—As Observed and Told to Me—R. C. Written for Glenn H. Curtiss Jr. by His Aunt Rutha 1952," manuscript in GHCM Curtiss Family File.

11.   Eltscher, Louis R., and Edward M. Young, *Curtiss-Wright: Greatness and Decline,* Twayne Publishers, New York, 1998.

12.   The *Hammondsport Herald,* published weekly throughout Curtiss's lifetime, includes multitudinous references to Curtiss, his works, and his times. (Curtiss Museum holds a microfilmed set.)

13. House, Kirk, "A New Curtiss E-Boat," *World War I Aero*, 1997.

14. Howard, Fred, *Orville and Wilbur: A Biography of the Wright Brothers*, Alfred A. Knopf, New York, 1988.

15. Loening, Grover C., *Takeoff Into Greatness*, Putnam, New York, 1968.

16. Mitchell, Charles R., and Kirk W. House, *Glenn H. Curtiss, Aviation Pioneer*, Arcadia Publishing, Charleston, SC, 2001.

17. Morehouse, Harold E., and Marvel Dyer, *The Flying Pioneers Biographies of Harold Morehouse*, GHCM.

18. Reynolds, Clark G., *Admiral John H. Towers: The Struggle for Naval Air Supremacy*, Naval Institute Press, Annapolis, MD, 1991.

19. Roseberry, C. R., *Glenn Curtiss: Pioneer of Flight*, Doubleday & Company, Garden City, NY, 1972.

20. Rudd, Clarence P., to Rosa Lee Nudd, October 3, 1959, manuscript, GHCM Yorkers Collection.

21. Shulman, Seth, *Unlocking the Sky: The Forgotten Story of Glenn Curtiss & The Birth of the Airplane*, HarperCollins, New York, 2002.

22. Stein, Geoffrey N., *The Motorcycle Industry in New York State: A Concise Encyclopedia of Inventors, Builders, and Manufacturers*, The University of the State of New York, Albany, NY, 2001.

23. Vilas, Jack (Logan A.), *My Life—To My Children*, privately published, 1934. Photocopy excerpts in GHCM 4-520, Vilas biographical files.

24. Youngblood, Ed, "Introduction," *The Encyclopedia of the Motorcycle*, by Hugo Wilson, Dorling Kindersley, London, 1995.

U.S. Patent References

25. 1,210,374 G. H. Curtiss, Hull for Flying Boats, October 13, 1913–December 26, 1916.

Chapter 8

Close-Up:
The Curtiss Seaplanes

To alight on the sea; to arise from it; to be upon it or above it at will; to command equally the adjacent shore, and move hither and thither over both as the fancy listeth, is surely magnificent sport. And such indeed will be the new sport of Water-Flying—a mere outline of the possibilities of which is sufficient to thrill those who love vast open spaces, and yearn for the physical freedom which comes of the open sea.

Henry A. Wise-Wood [1]
Member of the Aero Club

My hydro is handier than a polo pony, it is faster than a racing automobile, it is cleaner than any powerboat, it is steadier than any yacht. It can skim on the surface like a swallow or swim and soar like a gull. It can spread at my feet all afternoon the golden panorama of the bay, and bring me back at twilight with its nose nestling safely against the beach. Yet, with all its poetry, it is a practical conveyance. I propose to use one of mine at Raquette Lake this summer, for flying to and from the station.

Robert Collier [1]
President of the Aero Club
and proprietor of *Collier's Weekly*

★ ★ ★

"Curtiss Aeroplanes," a 28-page catalog issued in 1912, provides a good view of the hydro and the land plane, at the time the flying boat experiments were at last succeeding. [4]

Two hydro models were offered: the D-8 "exhibition type" at $5,500 and the E-8-75 "'triad' passenger-carrying hydroaeroplane" at $6,000. Each price was for the correspondingly numbered land plane, plus $500 for the "hydro attachment," which could also be obtained separately for the same amount. Six land models were available, and the hydro equipment was "Interchangeable with Wheel Running Gear on all machines." In case the customer did not know what he would be getting in those days when few people had seen an airplane, the catalog specified that the attachment was "for rising from and alighting on the water."

Thus, the first commercial hydros reflected several of Curtiss's passions: standardization, interchangeability, and hybridization. His enthusiasm for small sizes and for compact shipping also carried over to the hydro. [4]

The D series, available in three land variations, was described as the "Curtiss Standard Biplane," as used by the Curtiss Exhibition Team. Model suffixes reflected the three engine options, the only variations apart from resultant differences in speed and weight.

All the D models had a 33-ft 4-in. wingspan. Length from front to rear control was 25 ft 9 in., and height to the highest point (in land configuration) was 7 ft 5-1/2 in. Model D4 sported a four-cylinder inline engine cranking 40 hp. With Curtiss's V-8, 60-hp water-cooled engine, the D-8 weighed 650 lb ready for flight with land gear. The D-8-75, with 15 more hp, weighed an extra 50 lb. They were advertised at 60 and 70 mph, respectively (Fig. 8.1).

The E series airplanes were advertised as military, cross-country, and weight-carrying types. They were a little bigger than the D versions; a Model E had a 35-ft 4-in. wingspan and 8 ft of height, while retaining the same overall length. Increased wing area meant increased lifting surface. As with the D series, the three E models differed only in powerplant, and their suffixes reflected this.

The float gear weighed 125 lb, although there was a slight offset from removing the so-called regular chassis—a longeron, three wheels, and the attachment hardware. "This can be done," the catalog assured readers, "in two hours by two competent mechanics." In addition to the float, hydros were equipped with dual control or throw-over control, allowing pilots to take a break during long flights (Fig. 8.2). [4]

The float, as described in patent 1,203,550, granted October 31, 1916, was 1 ft deep, 2 ft wide, and 16 ft in length. (The patent referred to the float as "a single watertight boat.") Even so, Curtiss "preferred" constructing it with internal partitions to contain any leakage. [10] Leakage in a float had caused the sinking of *June Bug/Loon* back in 1909. [9]

The top and bottom of the float were flat and parallel. They were joined by flat sides, parallel to each other but perpendicular to the top and bottom ("in abruptly turned chine edges"). The prow inclined upward in a curving sweep, while the stern swept downward

Fig. 8.1 Bill Atwater in San Diego with a Curtiss hydro, minus any land gear. This would be a version of the Model D-8. Note the cambered, Chanute-type biplane wings with minimal airfoil. Ailerons are on the trailing struts, and their opposing action can be seen. There is still no vertical stabilizer in the tail—that entire upright surface is the rudder. The severe economy of a Curtiss airplane is evident here. Seated at left rear is Atwater's wife, Lillian, also a pilot. They were the first people to buy airplanes for private pleasure use.

with an opposite curve. The flat bottom and rising bow formed hydroplaning surfaces, according to Curtiss (Figs. 7.2 and 8.1).

"In accordance with the laws of the hydroplane," the application continued, the center of hydroplane lift lay aft of the front edge of the planing surface at a distance about one-third the length of the entire planing surface. This point Curtiss placed beneath the leading edge of the wings, so that the center of "aeroplane lift" lay even further aft. At speed, the central float would rise in the water, reducing resistance and increasing speed even further. Raising the elevators tilted the aircraft slightly upward, increasing the angle of incidence on the wing and thereby increasing aeronautic lift. With relatively little hydrodynamic drag, the craft became airborne. The bow hydroplane also caused the bow to rise upon alighting in the water, protecting against nosedives below the surface.

All of this was predicated on keeping the wingtips out of the water, which could be tricky with a centerline float, especially when under way or in choppy water. Curtiss provided a

Fig. 8.2 Mr. and Mrs. W. A. Davis in San Diego, at dual controls of a Curtiss hydro. Control cables running through small disks on the hubs of the steering wheels impart some mechanical advantage; this feature is entirely missing on most Curtiss aircraft, in which the cable runs along the circumference of the wheel. The push-pull rod for elevator control runs only to the left-seat wheel, although the copilot would have been able to add his or her muscle power. The shoulder yoke can be seen, with the formal flying attire of the day. Note the large chronometer on Mr. Davis's wrist. Wristwatches for men would not become commonplace until World War I.

torpedo tank below each lower wingtip, with a slat extension trailing into the water when at rest (Fig. 8.1). This arrangement formed an automatic stabilizer. The slats barely touched the water in level surface running. If either wingtip drooped, hydrodynamic lift forced it up again. In later models, the slats were often extended from an accordion-type arrangement, rather than using tanks.

The hydroaeroplane patent also described the new retractable landing gear. On each side, diagonals (one pivoted to the fore, and the other to the aft, of the structural framework of the aircraft) descended to the axle of the wheel. A long hand lever operating on a rack bar closed a knuckle on the forward diagonal, scissoring it to draw the wheel upward and forward, eliminating its hydrodynamic drag and even reducing its aerodynamic drag. The pilot reversed the operation when approaching shore on water. Drag and weight together latched the knuckle into place. Because the lower portion of the wheels extended beyond the float, wheels engaged when the water was shallow enough for them to touch bottom. As the aircraft rolled onto the beach, the float kept a few inches of clearance, reducing drag and preventing damage. Likewise, the pilot would drop the wheels if descending directly to land at the end of a flight (Figs. 7.4 to 7.7). [10]

Hydros were equipped with throw-over wheel columns, a patented Curtiss innovation that allowed two occupants to take turns piloting. The pilot handled the wheel, leaned into the shoulder yoke, and operated ignition and throttle with foot pedals. The catalog pointed out that this allowed the pilot to keep one hand free for using field glasses, making sketches, or any other purpose that might occur to him. Of course, one hand could be kept free only for as long as the aircraft was stable, straight, and steady in cooperative weather. Even so, the Curtiss *could* be operated with a hand free, while many other controls *required* two hands or even two pilots. A double-wheeled arrangement would soon simplify transferring control during flight (Fig. 8.2).

Curtiss airplanes for land or sea in those days were somewhat reductionist, as can be seen in photographs. For all its extensive breadth and length, there was not much actually "there." The two-wing planes bound open space, interrupted by struts and wires. Ailerons trailed the outboard trailing struts. Sitting in space, midway between planes and midway between wingtips, was the completely uncovered engine with radiator and pusher prop (Fig. 8.1).

Two pairs of upper and lower diagonal bamboo booms each met to anchor the tail, consisting of a rudder, horizontal stabilizer, and elevators (no vertical stabilizer or fin). Again, the framework created by the booms was completely open. Two diagonal braces of laminated wood descended from the engine to the nosewheel (or float). Perched on these braces was the pilot's seat, shoulder yoke at his back and wheel column rising between his legs. The pilot had no shielding or shrouding. [2–6]

Some models, including most of the hydros, had a small nose elevator. This was mounted on the upper bow of the float in the hydros. In land models, the elevator was installed on front booms, and may or may not have included a small vertical stabilizer. (Few seaplanes had one.) The land plane had a single centerline longeron joining rear axle to nosewheel and anchoring the braces for the diagonals on which the pilot sat. In the hydro, of course, wheels and longeron were replaced by the single float, which also supported the diagonals. None of the wheels or braces had any sort of shoes, shrouds, streamlining, or airfoil.

The only covered surfaces in the entire contraption were the wing planes, the ailerons, the horizontal stabilizer, the rudder, the pilot's seat, the elevators, sketchy horizontal stabilizers in the tail, and the small vertical stabilizer forward, if present. The Curtiss airplane was essentially a pair of wing planes, some control surfaces, a powerplant, and some landing gear. Even the pilot's seat appeared to be a begrudging concession. [2–4]

All of these features created an airplane that was compact and straightforward, a fact blazoned forth by the Curtiss catalog. Long-distance flying was still a rarity, and aviators, especially exhibition pilots, depended on railroads to get from one place to another. "Any Curtiss aeroplane may be 'knocked-down' and put on a truck within one hour. . . . It may be assembled, set up, and ready for flight within two hours of arriving on the flying field." Curtiss claimed that all competing manufacturers required at least four or five hours for each operation.

Almost as significantly, "The Curtiss aeroplane can be shipped as ordinary express; will go into a side door of any express car, and the cost of shipment is but one-fifth that of any other aeroplane. Practically all other aeroplanes require a special car [for end loading the wing structure, still mostly erected], at five times the cost of shipping a Curtiss." The catalog backed this up by explaining that "other aeroplanes" could be shipped from New York to Chicago for $250. The cost for shipping a Curtiss between the same two points was $27.50. This was accomplished in part by seeing that as many crates as possible measured 4 ft 11 in., qualifying them for the 5-ft flat rate on the railroads. All of these figures, by the way, no doubt apply to the land plane. The large hydro float would have complicated matters somewhat. [4]

This, of course, evokes memories of Curtiss landing in France with *Reims Racer*. This extensive (though speedy) knockdown also meant that damaged sections could be delivered and replaced quickly and cheaply; indeed, it was even practical to carry spares on tour. While all of this would be worthwhile to any user, it particularly appealed to exhibition pilots and the military. The company claimed that 80% of the exhibition flying done in 1910 and 1911 had been accomplished in Curtiss aircraft, although it is difficult to confirm how this calculation was made. The company also figured that in 1911, pilots working directly for Curtiss had flown enough distance in exhibitions to surpass the circumference of the earth. One may cavil at the grounds of the calculation (330 hr of exhibition at 60 mph), but it certainly would have totaled a very impressive distance. [4]

The catalog included two photographs of Lincoln Beachey in his "headless" pusher (Fig. 8.3). Beachey's acrobatic model had no front gear at all—the only thing in front of the pilot was the nosewheel. As the catalog makes no offering of this type, it seems to have been considered a specialty custom item at press time. [4] This headless type would soon be in production. However, the birth of *Jenny* was near, and the headless Curtiss pusher would be the last in a line of direct descent from *Gold Bug/Golden Flier* (Curtiss #1) or even from the 1908 *Red Wing*, *White Wing*, and *June Bug*.

The flying boat, finally successful in 1912 and sold commercially by 1913, came just too late to make the catalog. Wheels, whether fixed or retractable, were eliminated altogether.

Fig. 8.3 Beachey stunting in a "headless" pusher, regarded initially as a specialized acrobatic aircraft.

This is, in fact, a boat with wings and not a land craft at all. The hull provides all the flotation and makes no provision for landing anyplace other than on water. The engine is a pusher, with obvious advantages for a watercraft, although Harold McCormick ordered a specialty five-seat tractor version. Tail feathers, mounted on the narrow stern of the boat, compose horizontal stabilizers, a small vertical stabilizer, elevators, and a large rudder. There is no forward gear. Small panels flanking the engines at right angles to the upper wing were optimistically expected to prevent skidding. [1–3]

At last, a Curtiss airplane had a cockpit, albeit an open one. The pilot and passenger shared a bench, separated at the centerline by the "Goodier Strut," which was designed to keep the engine from collapsing onto them in a crash (Fig. 8.4). Naval Lt. Louis E. Goodier survived such a crash, lending his name to the strut. When aviators finally concluded that this strut did no good whatsoever, Curtiss replaced it with *two* struts, each leading from a forward front corner of the engine (Fig. 8.5).

Using many references, including the original hull (on loan from the National Air and Space Museum), Curtiss Museum volunteers in the late 1990s created a flying reproduction of Jack Vilas's 1913 Model E boat. The Vilas boat is a little bigger than most of its sisters, but experience clearly demonstrated that the heavy strut makes entering and exiting the cramped cockpit extremely awkward. It would be even more awkward on the

Fig. 8.4 Gink Doherty in a Curtiss flying boat, showing the strut on which so many hopes were vainly placed.

Fig. 8.5 Lanny Callan with the more effective double struts.

surface of the water. Cranking the pusher prop is clearly not an option on a seaplane, and early flying-boat pilots had to brace themselves on the seat or gunwale to turn a hand crank.

This first generation of flying boats had the same wings as the Model E land plane. In fact, some early listings describe them as "E-Wing Flying Boats." Some students have questioned whether the Model E designation was ever formally applied to flying boats. [3] (It would certainly seem awkward with the same designation already in use for a land plane.) However, a Curtiss Flying Boat manufacturer's plate in the Curtiss Museum collection, in the space for "Model," is clearly incised with a capital "E" and no qualifications.

What with added weight and drag from the hull, the more spacious Model E wings, with their greater lifting power, were clearly more practical than the D types. The 40-ft upper wing structures comprised seven sections of framework, while the 31-ft lower wings required five. The center section of the lower wing lay directly atop the hull, rather than interrupting the wing.

Working outboard from the center sections, corresponding sections on the same plane were identical; each of these pairs, however, differed from the others. Each section was independently covered with Goodrich rubberized fabric, permitting easy assembly, disassembly, replacement, and repair. The upper wing plane extended beyond the lower plane. In the Vilas boat, upper wingtips could be dropped to approximately a 45° angle when the aircraft was at rest, to reduce wind resistance.

Sitka spruce was used for the wing sections, with ash for the leading edge and the rear spar. Ribs and spars were laminated. Sheet metal reinforcing plates were used at each joint. Vertical wing struts were made of ash. These were placed at leading and trailing points where wing sections meet; sections were joined together by the hardware that also set the struts in place.

The hull was 28 ft 9 in. long. Lengthwise chines were made of spruce. Spruce, of course, has many other applications, particularly in boatbuilding. However, spruce workers had their own draft classification during World War I, and this was no doubt because air power had so quickly vaulted into a vital position in the war effort.

Forming an internal structure within the hull were a series of rectangular frames, each made of clear pine with ash gussets at the corners, the whole glued and riveted together. Frames placed at the stress points were all ash, for added strength, and again were reinforced at each corner. All nails and rivets were made of copper. The boat was further separated into six watertight compartments. A copper tube led from each compartment to a bilge pump beneath the pilot's seat.

Lengthwise cedar planking covered the whole, except for the section forward of the step, where planking was laid in a herringbone pattern. This section naturally suffered the most wear, so the herringbone was covered with fabric and then overlaid with another layer of cedar planks, this time lain lengthwise. Planking was glued, nailed, and riveted. Internal planking was applied only in the cockpit. Spruce battens were used behind blanking joints throughout, and, of course, the wood was varnished.

The forward part of the cockpit was protected (to some extent) by a small wooden windscreen. A piano-type hinge allowed pilot and passenger to drop this forward, affording them access and egress over the nose without stepping into the water. (The passenger would find this relatively simple, but the pilot would need to clamber over the steering wheel.) The underside of the windscreen and the upper side of the forward deck were each covered with rough mats to improve footing.

Controls were of the standard Curtiss type, which led to an interesting observation. Admiral Clyde Robbins (U.S.C.G.-Ret.) and Carl Ericsson each flew the Curtiss Museum's reproduction of the Vilas boat for test flights in 1998. Ericsson, who had had considerable experience with Curtiss controls (but none with seaplanes) at Old Rhinebeck Aerodrome, performed the exhibition flights in 1999. He reported considerable difficulty turning the wheel to operate the huge rudder during flight. There are no hydraulics, of course, and the control cable runs through a groove on the circumference of the wheel, affording no mechanical advantage. Curtiss workshop volunteers crafted a half-diameter wheel affixed to the full-size wheel, running control cable through the smaller wheel to create a 2:1 mechanical advantage. Ericsson was delighted with this arrangement, but early pilots seem rarely to have used anything of the sort. They simply bulled their way through the sky by sheer muscle power.

In the cockpit, pilot and passenger sat side-by-side on a bench seat with a straight back, seat and back each running the full beam of the craft. (Jack Vilas installed bucket seats on the bench, upholstered with dove-gray corduroy.) A hatch centrally located in the upper back of the seat led into a compartment holding anchor, lanterns, fire extinguisher, and other emergency supplies. This compartment also meant that, for the first time, a Curtiss airplane could conveniently carry a small amount of luggage or cargo. By the following year, large Curtiss flying boats would be carrying respectable weights of bombs as they hunted German U-boats. [8]

A supporting member ran the length of this compartment. Here also were found two copper tubes, each placed abaft the step, communicating between the underwater space behind the step and the open air above the hull. These served to vent the space behind the step, preventing a vacuum buildup.

This famed step was, of course, key to the creation of a flying boat. [13] Curtiss was aware of hydroplaning principles. He had demonstrated this in creating the floatplane, and he had had access to information from hydroplaning endeavors going back to the Aerial Experiment Association. The AEA *Bulletin* reported these in detail, and Curtiss still retained his copy, hand-bound into three volumes.

Water flying had frustrated Curtiss and McCurdy as far back as their 1909 experiments with *June Bug/Loon*. Curtiss finally became successful with his hydroaeroplane in early 1911, but a more seaworthy hulled aircraft eluded him.

Weight, hydrodynamic drag, and surface tension all make it difficult for the hull to break free from its "seal" with the water. Curtiss recognized this factor, and he constructed several unsuccessful hulls with a break. The step did not yet exist, but the angle of the bottom of the hull changed along its length, creating three sections: the upswept prow, a straight section inclined downward away from the bow, and another straight section inclined upward toward the stern. Regardless, it did not work.

Curtiss was not limited to his own ingenuity in tackling the problem. His own workers, including Henry "make-it-happen" Kleckler, were involved, plus naval officers assigned to Hammondsport for expressly this purpose. Even so, it was Curtiss, probably the least qualified formally, who finally came up with the solution.

In keeping with his usual practice of emphasizing observation and experimentation over modeling and calculation, Curtiss took to pacing the (non) flying boat in a speedboat, often accompanied by naval constructor Holden Richardson. After one run, he gathered his colleagues around him, according to Kleckler, who was extensively interviewed, late in life, by Curtiss biographer C. R. Roseberry. Suppose, Curtiss suggested, that they tried to break the flow and the suction by putting a jog into the underside of the hull? [9]

This procedure is exactly the one described by Ellyson a year earlier, during the time they were creating the hydro. Curtiss solicited opinions and put his own ideas into the mix for evaluation. The group would decide which ideas to try, although, Ellyson noted, Curtiss's ideas were usually the best.

And so it proved in this case. The others agreed that they might as well try it—perhaps everyone was fresh out of other ideas by this time. Kleckler sawed off some blocks of wood and had them fastened to the underside of the hull. "As soon as that was done," he told Roseberry, "they found they could rise up on top of the water and take off like a flying dog." The flying boat was born, as abruptly as the hydro had been born 18 months earlier (Fig. 8.6).

Fig. 8.6 An early flying boat, with understated step. Elevators are now entirely in the tail, which also features vertical and horizontal stabilizers in addition to the rudder.

This step (and the later standpipes) allowed the hull forward of the step to act as a hydroplane. Getting up onto the step at speed brought the tail out of the water, further reducing hydrodynamic drag. Curtiss patented this step (colloquially named after him) as part of his overall flying boat patent (Fig. 8.7). [13] To this day, it is a standard feature in amphibious aircraft and in pontoons, a fact that would doubtless make Curtiss proud. With his passion for going faster, it would probably make him happy to know that his step is even a standard feature on speedboats.

Curtiss well deserves his reputation as the father of water flying. Apart from practical and mercantile considerations, Curtiss was also driven by his own enthusiasm for water—an enthusiasm that lead him to establish all of his homes (in Hammondsport, San Diego, Buffalo, Long Island, and the Miami area) close to large bodies of water.

His particular enjoyment of Keuka Lake also was no doubt a factor. From an early age, he had been swimming, fishing, boating, skating, and ice boating on its waters. In addition, Keuka Lake was traditionally the heartland of Finger Lakes boatbuilding. There was a long tradition in the craft, a good understanding of its techniques, needs, and opportunities, plus a body of experienced workers from which to draw. With so many construction methods and materials in common, there was a good deal of crossover in those days. Two Early Bird pilots, Charles A. Herrmann and Ralph M. Brown, later created Penn Yan Boats at the foot of the lake, a company that endured prolifically until 2001. [7] Not far from Hammondsport in Curtiss's day was the company of Sutherland Boat and Coach—still building boats in these early years of the twenty-first century, a hundred years and five generations later.

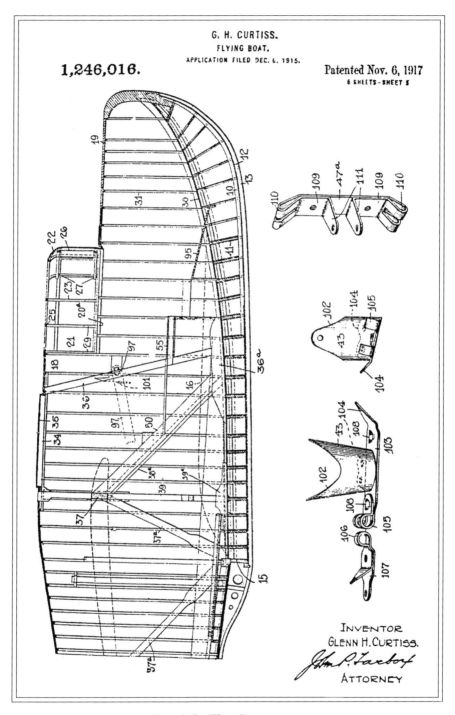

G. H. CURTISS.
FLYING BOAT.
APPLICATION FILED DEC. 6. 1915.

1,246,016.

Patented Nov. 6, 1917

6 SHEETS—SHEET 5

INVENTOR
GLENN H. CURTISS.

ATTORNEY

*Fig. 8.7 The Curtiss step
(feature 15 in this patent diagram).
For other Curtiss seaplane patents, see Refs. 10–17.*

REFERENCES

1. "Aerial Yachting," The Curtiss Aeroplane Company, Hammondsport, NY, circa 1913.

2. Bowers, Peter M., *Curtiss Aircraft 1907–1947,* Putnam, London, 1979.

3. Casey, Louis S., *Curtiss: The Hammondsport Era, 1907–1915,* Crown Publishers, New York, 1981.

4. "Curtiss Aeroplanes," The Curtiss Aeroplane Company, Hammondsport, NY, 1911–1912.

5. Mitchell, Charles R., and Kirk W. House, *Flying High: Pioneer Women in American Aviation,* Arcadia Publishing, Charleston, SC, 2001.

6. ———, *Glenn H. Curtiss, Aviation Pioneer,* Arcadia Publishing, Charleston, SC, 2001.

7. Morehouse, Harold E., and Marvel Dyer, *The Flying Pioneers Biographies of Harold Morehouse,* GHCM.

8. Reynolds, Clark G., *Admiral John H. Towers: The Struggle for Naval Air Supremacy,* Naval Institute Press, Annapolis, MD, 1991.

9. Roseberry, C. R., *Glenn Curtiss: Pioneer of Flight,* Doubleday & Company, Garden City, NY, 1972.

U.S. PATENT REFERENCES

10. 1,203,550 G. H. Curtiss, Hydroaeroplane, October 31, 1916.

11. 1,210,374 G. H. Curtiss, Hull for Flying Boats, October 13, 1913–December 26, 1916.

12. 1,246,014 G. H. Curtiss, Hydroplane Boat, January 21, 1915–November 6, 1917.

13. 1,246,016 G. H. Curtiss, Flying Boat, December 6, 1915–November 6, 1917.

14. 1,246,019 G. H. Curtiss, Flying Boat Hull, February 26, 1917–November 6, 1917.

15. 1,256,878 G. H. Curtiss, Hydroaeroplane Boat, December 11, 1914–February 19, 1918.

16. 1,306,749 G. H. Curtiss, Twin Float Hydroaeroplane, August 12, 1916–June 17, 1919.

17. 1,316,277 G. H. Curtiss, Cruising Hydroaeroplane, July 1, 1916–September 16, 1919.

Chapter 9

Panorama:
The Great War

✯ ✯ ✯

Six days after 16-year-old Katherine Masson helped to smash a champagne bottle on the bow of *America* (Fig. 9.1), 19-year-old Gavrilo Princip smashed the life from Archduke Franz Ferdinand and his wife, and, indeed, from an entire civilization.

The United States watched in fascinated horror as the Great War blazed hotter and wider. This was not the quick, decisive victory of the Spanish-American War, the Franco-Prussian War, or the Russo-Japanese War. It was not the on-again-off-again conflict of the Balkan Wars, which had immediately preceded it. This war was a throwback to the industrial mass horrors of the American Civil War, made even more massive by the stupendous advances of the intervening half-century. It swallowed Europe and entangled the rest of the world, as the wars of Napoleon had done a hundred years earlier.

The United States was not considered a great power in those days—certainly not on the same level as Britain, Germany, France, or Russia. However, what the country lacked in political or military clout, it made up for in agricultural and industrial production. As it became painfully clear that the troops would not be home for Christmas—already tens of thousands would never be home at all—it also became clear that the European nations would turn to the United States and, to a lesser extent, Canada, both safe behind the Atlantic moat, for supplies of war. The Royal Navy ensured that few of these supplies would reach the Central Powers.

Airplanes had proven their value in the opening weeks of the war when a French aviator discovered an open flank among German forces improvising on their strategic plan. Joffre, Foch, and Gallienni parleyed that information into victory at the Marne, bringing the German advance to a halt and thereby saving the campaign, the capital, and, very likely, the war. Among their requirements, Britain and France needed airplanes, and they needed U.S. factories to pour them out.

Fig. 9.1 Porte, Hallett, and Katherine Masson christening America. *Curtiss is mostly hidden between Hallett and Masson.*

However, where were these factories? The Wright Company was languishing under President Orville Wright's insistence on sticking to increasingly outmoded designs. The Burgess Company, in Marblehead, Massachusetts, was a significant manufacturer, but many of its products were licensed from Wright and thus partook of the limitations of that company. [15]

Glenn Martin was making modern airplanes, on a small scale, in Los Angeles. Orville Wright left his company in 1915, and new directors engineered the Wright-Martin merger the following year, adding capital to Martin's work and again making Wright competitive in airframes. However, a disenchanted Martin separated himself in 1917. [4, 5, 11, 15]

The Thomas Brothers in Hammondsport's neighboring village of Bath were doing well enough on a prewar scale. They soon moved operations to Ithaca, where they could tap into a larger workforce and more infrastructure. Entering a partnership with the Morse Chain Company, the brothers made Thomas-Morse the country's fourth-largest airplane manufacturer by 1918. While certainly distinctive enough, the honor is tempered by the research of Peter M. Bowers. He points out that the U.S. government issued millions of dollars in aviation orders on the declaration of war in 1917, and only six of the sixteen companies receiving contracts had made as many as ten airplanes. [1, 15]

Although Glenn Martin had a few fine designs, only Glenn Curtiss was poised in 1914 to quickly produce airplanes in fairly large numbers. The Curtiss *Jenny* and the two-place flying boats were already in production (hydros were not wanted in quantity), and *America* made an excellent prototype for a line of larger boats. *Jenny* could never withstand combat against European models, but she was admirably suited for a trainer, and air forces suddenly envisioned thousands of pilots. Britain ordered a staggering 250 *Jennys* and all the flying boats Curtiss could grind out; these latter craft would be used for training, scouting, and submarine patrols. They were the only U.S. designs used in World War I combat service. [1, 9, 19, 23]

At this time, Curtiss finally cleared out all vestiges of the motorcycle business, desperate for factory space. Tank Waters declined Curtiss's offer to come into the airplane business, whereupon Curtiss gave him his share of the Marvel motorcycle company "for old time's sake." As an old man, Waters observed that if he had accepted Curtiss's offer, he would by that time be either dead or a millionaire. [22] The light machines in which they had specialized were no longer commanding a large share of the market, so even Waters gave up production after 1914, returning to his original business of parts and supplies.

Even after clearing the motorcycle and small-engine work, Curtiss would never be able to meet his orders in Hammondsport, a village of 1,000 inhabitants at the end of a one-track short line. In Buffalo, more than 100 miles northwest, he found the infrastructure he needed. In addition to a large, skilled industrial labor force—with housing and other amenities—Buffalo offered factory space. It had ample electric power from Niagara Falls, whereas electricity in Hammondsport ran only part-time; the Curtiss plant generated its own electricity. The Niagara River would serve for testing seaplanes the way Keuka Lake had. Buffalo was also a hub for transport by highway, rail, canal, and even seagoing vessels. These connections were vital not only for bringing in supplies and labor but for shipping finished products, particularly to Canada and Great Britain.

Curtiss started by renting an empty factory. On March 10, 1915, he commenced building a new 110,000-ft^2 plant. This facility turned out its first complete aircraft two months and five days later. Before long, Curtiss added three more factories in the city, which now became his corporate headquarters. The North Elmwood plant, with 71 acres under one roof, was the largest airplane factory in the world. Many of Curtiss's key staff, such as Harry Genung and Henry Kleckler, also moved at this time. Moreover, Jack McCurdy simultaneously established a subsidiary Canadian company in Toronto. [9, 19]

In 1901, Glenn Curtiss had taken time out from his bike shop, harness business, and acetylene lamps to cobble together his first motorcycle. Fourteen years later, he was, almost overnight, a highly successful businessperson. That trip to the Pan-Am had certainly paid off for Curtiss—and indirectly for Buffalo. The exposition had lost money, but it had now brought in a major manufacturer, and other companies would follow in his wake. There were 18,000 employees during World War I. The Curtiss presence became so pervasive during World War II that the local Curtiss installations employed one person for every 28 residents of Buffalo (Fig. 9.2). The Pan-Am had paid off at last.

Fig. 9.2 One of several Curtiss plants in Buffalo.

While the Curtiss Aeroplane Company was relocating in Buffalo, the Curtiss Motor Company carried on in the original Hammondsport plant. This facility was now relatively "small potatoes" in the Curtiss empire, although at its peak, it employed two or three times the population of the village. Hammondsport was shifted over exclusively to engine production, and demand eventually grew so great that the entire output was used for export alone. A truck met the DL&W train in Bath twice a day, offloading engines.

Hammondsport was simultaneously coining money and staggering under weight of the Curtiss plant, which had almost become a cuckoo in the nest (Fig. 9.3). Between 2,000 and 3,000 people now worked there. Curtiss built several new homes on what is now Curtiss Avenue, but their addition did little to alleviate the housing shortage. The hotels and boardinghouses were crammed full, and so were rooms let out in private houses. The larger village of Bath, 8 miles away, was packed as tightly; five buses a day (from White and from Studebaker) ran between the towns, not to mention rail traffic on the B&H. The *Herald* reported that eight men, unable to secure rooms, were driving by auto 16 miles every day from Avoca to work at the plant. [1, 10]

*Fig. 9.3   The time clock room at Hammondsport gives some hint of
how large the operation had become in a very short period.*

Aileen Arnold McKinney, who had been Henry Kleckler's secretary, reported in 1996 that
the buses kept shovels behind the back seat. When the buses became stuck in snow, all
the passengers, including young girls with dresses and low boots, had to get out and dig
the bus free. She also related that when the bus came over the hill from Bath, passengers
could hear the airplane engines 5 miles away. Part of her job was to go up and down the
hillside where OX engines ran on test stands, checking serial numbers. "I was very young
at the time," she always made clear, and she found that work very trying.

Thus, Hammondsport at this time was noisy, smelly, smoky, and overrun with hundreds of
workers (overwhelmingly men), few of them with families because no family accommo-
dations could be found. The *Herald* pointed out that allowing Sunday movies (a big issue
at the time) would provide a diversion for the off-duty Curtiss men, who otherwise had
nothing to do but wander the streets looking for something to engage their interest. [9]

A British mission maintained itself at Hammondsport, as did U.S. naval officers, one of
whom reportedly brought his wife, the future Duchess of Windsor. (Aileen McKinney said
that few people ever really saw her, because she kept different hours from the
townsfolk.) Foreign officials, big businessmen, and top-flight engineers constantly trooped
to town, which seemed to impress the town fathers not a whit. Most of the streets
remained unpaved, the Civil War statue in the intersection of Lake and Main was the butt

of repeated car crashes, and the village board spurned a proposal to number the houses. Presumably all the natives knew where they were going anyhow. [9]

In the summer of 1914, Curtiss had been test flying *Langley, America,* and the new tractor machines. Those flights appear to have ended his career as an aviator, seven years after it started in one of Baldwin's dirigibles and six years after his first airplane flight in *White Wing.* While it is certainly true that at this early stage many firsts and many records were up for grabs, Curtiss's *curriculum vitae* was breathtakingly impressive. That record obviously reflected his personal piloting skills and his technological successes, not to mention his promotional acumen. It also reflected quiet, but very considerable, courage.

Until this point, Curtiss had lived a good deal of his life on the shop floor or in the control seat of a speedy vehicle. Even when the war started, he would often drop into Kleckler's office, pull out a drawer in Aileen Arnold's desk, prop up his feet in the drawer, and shoot the breeze. Aileen told him he shouldn't do that in the presence of a lady, but Curtiss smiled and kept on doing it anyway.

Now the business was far too big for that, and Curtiss's life would never be the same. With the bulk of the work going on in Buffalo, he and Lena rented a house and made that city their main home, at least for the duration. The Hammondsport place, where he had grown up with his grandmother, had been surrounded by an unsightly conglomeration of industrial structures over the years. Now the factory took over the house, and the Curtisses rented another home for their visits. Hammondsporters were nervous about all this attention to Buffalo, but for the time being, business was booming. [9, 10, 19]

Despite his dramatic successes in business, Curtiss still had only an eighth-grade education. He possessed neither the training nor the temperament to run a huge corporate empire. Recognizing the need for new management and new mass-production techniques, Curtiss sold controlling interest to William Morris Imbrie & Company at the end of 1915. In January 1916, the two main companies were combined as the Curtiss Aeroplane and Motor Corporation, with Curtiss as president. Under the new umbrella were the Canadian division, the Exhibition Company (which also operated the flying schools, now at Hammondsport, San Diego, Miami, and Buffalo), and the Atlantic Coast Aeronautical Station (test flights and flying school, under Captain Baldwin) at Newport News. A month later, Curtiss bought out Starling Burgess in Marblehead for his production facilities; Burgess became a Curtiss director. [9, 10, 15, 19]

Jack Vilas had surmised that cash was in short supply for the Curtiss operation when he turned over a $1,500 check in 1913. Now, in 1916, Glenn Curtiss received $2.3 million in cash and $4.5 million in stock. Lena's mother had been desperately worried when the young couple married, seeing in Curtiss a nice boy with no particular prospects. Presumably she felt better by now. [9, 19]

☆ ☆ ☆

What was the company selling during this time? First, engines were selling in large numbers, mostly the 90-hp V2 OX series (Fig. 9.4) and the 100-hp OXX, but also the more powerful V and V2 lines. All of these were water-cooled V-8 designs. [1, 6, 9, 10, 16–19]

There were orders in the thousands for the Model JN land-based tractor. Curtiss personally did not care for tractors—he wanted to see everything in front of him as he flew. However, he recognized that these were the wave of the future, and he recognized that neither he nor his men were up to creating a truly competitive design. He had imported B. Douglas Thomas, a young Sopwith engineer, to take the lead on this project, and Thomas's work evolved into the Model JN, sometimes nicknamed *Jane* before history and legend settled on the appellation *Jenny* (Fig. 9.5).

Jenny was light-years ahead of the Curtiss pusher. With two tandem cockpits, it was well suited for a trainer, and the British and Canadian governments snapped it up. Production finally ran to more than 7,000, of which 1,360 were made under license by other manufacturers. The explosive growth of the industry can be discerned by remembering that Curtiss had made the first airplane sale in the United States, building *Gold Bug/Golden Flier* for the Aero Club, five years before the war began.

The U.S. Army had used *Jennys* for its fruitless pursuit of Pancho Villa but found the airplanes unsuited to high desert conditions. Curtiss accordingly developed the Model R,

Fig. 9.4 A Curtiss OX-5 engine on the test stand.

Fig. 9.5 Wartime Jenny *production.*

which has been described as a scaled-up *Jenny*. The United States and Great Britain both demanded these for patrol work.

A second offshoot of *Jenny* was the Model N, a virtually identical aircraft with a single central float rather than land gear (Fig. 9.6). The U.S. Navy took hundreds of these (many made in Marblehead) for trainers.

Navies and armies both wanted the small two-place flying boats (Models F and MF) as trainers. Belligerents wanted larger boats for naval scouting and for submarine patrols. Great Britain concentrated on the various H-series machines, follow-on designs from the original *America.* Russia placed a large order for K-boats, most of which arrived in unsatisfactory condition, touching off litigation that continued until almost 1950. [1, 3, 9, 10, 14, 16, 19]

Britain and Canada were Curtiss's prime customers during this period. Russia and Italy were also good customers, with smaller orders going to Spain, New South Wales, and an increasingly nervous United States. Curtiss missions in several of these countries, especially Russia, Britain, and Italy, provided for sales, support, training, and assembly. Domestic civilian business also continued into 1917, although clearly it was dwarfed by military orders. Ruth Law startled everyone in 1916 by flying her obsolete Curtiss pusher nonstop from Chicago to Hornell, New York (near Hammondsport), a 600-mile trip to establish the world women's distance record and the absolute U.S. record. Katherine Stinson broke Ruth Law's mark and then bested herself in the *Stinson Special,* a custom job from Curtiss.

Fig. 9.6   Model N series.

As a sideline, Curtiss brought into existence two airplanes that had been designed but never built. He wanted in the one case to prove that it *could* fly, and in the other to prove that it *could not.* Both projects were inspired by patent suits.

With a series of adverse rulings in the Wright suit, Curtiss seemed at the end of his rope until lawyers for Henry Ford entered the case. Ford saw Curtiss's situation as similar to his own eight-year battle to break the Selden trust of the Association of Licensed Automobile Manufacturers. Selden had designed and patented an automobile but never built it—a vital difference from the case of the Wright brothers. Selden, a Rochester attorney, had foreseen the coming age of the automobile and preemptively filed a patent, extending its lifetime by repeated technical amendments. When manufacturers actually began making autos, Selden was ready with a smile, a patent, and an open hand. The makers quickly bought him out, paid him royalties, and restricted admission into the patent pool. Ford was denied entry in 1903 because his operation was not considered stable enough.

Ford manufactured anyhow, indemnified every buyer against possible adverse rulings, and lost all the battles but the last one, finally breaking the trust in 1911. To deepen the parallel, the Selden-Ford case and the Wright-Curtiss case were each initially argued in Buffalo before Judge Hazel (who had also sworn in Theodore Roosevelt upon McKinley's death). Hazel interpreted each patent as broadly as possible, ruling against Ford and Curtiss. Cynics pointed out that because the judge had training in neither law nor technology, the broad interpretation relieved him from a great deal of study.

However, the cases were far from identical. Ford's attorneys observed that the lawsuit on the Wright wing-warping patent, now ruled to cover ailerons, specified simultaneous opposite warps. If Curtiss made the aileron movements independent of each other, the case would have to start all over again. Curtiss eagerly complied.

Earlier in the war, Great Britain had bought rights to the Wright and Curtiss patents for a total of $95,000. In 1917, Congress appropriated $1 million for a similar approach in the United States, but the manufacturers forestalled them by forming a patent pool. Under this arrangement, Curtiss Aeroplane and Wright Aeronautical eventually received $1 million apiece, which certainly raised eyebrows during postwar investigations. The patent suit was neutralized for the duration, although it would be revived when the war ended. Augustus Herring reared his head again at this lucrative time, charging that Herring-Curtiss had never been properly extinguished and that the other directors had conspired against him. Curtiss was in no mood to compromise with Herring, and the case would still be in court after both men's deaths. [1, 9, 16, 19]

Not content with the technical loophole in the Wright case, Curtiss also recurred to the notion of "prior art" that had arisen, apparently without result, during the *Langley* tests. He had the Buffalo plant build Alexander Goupil's airplane, designs for which Goupil had published in 1884, but never built for want of a powerplant. Although not absolutely the first to propose three-axis control (*sine qua non* for practical flight), Goupil appears to have been the first to describe a workable implementation.

Goupil described and diagrammed a vertical tail rudder, a horizontal tail elevator, and two horizontal regulators, each mounted in the same horizontal plane outboard the fuselage, below and a little forward of the monoplane wings. These regulators functioned primarily as ailerons, although they could also be used to abet the effect of the elevators. Goupil also sketchily described control devices by which the "voyager" could operate these surfaces.

The proposed aircraft was startlingly modern. Goupil specified a forward tractor propeller and presented the concept as having a closed fuselage for both engine and pilot. Lift was provided by a high monoplane gull wing. Goupil, a mining engineer, had become interested in gulls during one of his expeditions. It seemed that the only real problems with his design were the landing gear (four skids or skates) and the pesky powerplant problem. Goupil addressed this in 1908, the year before his death, by publishing a book on jet propulsion.

There does not seem to be any evidence that later workers assimilated Goup prior art could theoretically weaken the Wright patent. In 1916, Curtiss charged N. W. Dalton with building Goupil's machine and testing it.

Dalton, a Hammondsport neighbor of Curtiss, had entered aeronautical engineering apparently with little or no preparation; Curtiss, of course, had none at all, while Kirkham and Kleckler had only sketchy training. Nevertheless, Dalton tackled the project quite ably and may have been the man who "discovered" Goupil and proposed the attempt.

Goupil's sketches had not really been construction drawings, but they were detailed enough for Dalton to follow them closely. He used the same wire, wood, and fabric technology to which the company was accustomed, and ensured that it was structurally sound. The powerplant was a 100-hp Curtiss OXX; a celluloid windshield gave the pilot visibility from his cabin. After designing and building the aircraft in Buffalo, Dalton shipped it to Hammondsport for testing. No one trusted Goupil's proposed skids, so workers installed the old seaplane gear that they had made two years earlier for *Langley*.

By now, this odd creation was being known as Goupil's *Duck* or Dalton's *Duck*. She was an odd duck indeed, large and gull-winged. Hammondsport had become used to strange sights in the past 15 years of living with Glenn Curtiss, but the spectacle of this thing being trundled through the streets from the plant to the lakeside flying field certainly took the prize. Pilots managed to haul the plane off the water several times in repeated tests, but only barely. The *Duck* was quite heavy, particularly with the *Langley* floats. The Curtiss folk seem to have had an inexplicable knee-jerk reaction to try almost everything as a seaplane, which only complicated their tasks.

Giving up on the floats, Dalton shipped *Duck* to Newport News and refitted her with conventional land gear as a tail-dragger. This made all the difference in the world, and Vic Carlstrom flew the aircraft quite nicely, even describing complete turns, at the beginning of 1917. After this, *Duck* was hangared and forgotten as the United States entered the war and the government engineered an aircraft patent pool, obviating the court case at least for the duration. [1, 5, 19]

Curtiss was also undergoing legal challenges from Albert S. Janin, who claimed to have invented and patented the flying boat prior to Curtiss. In an interesting twist of fate, Janin filed his patent application on the same day Curtiss made his first successful off-water flight in San Diego. [23]

As in the case of Selden, there had been no working model. The most significant aspect of Janin's patent was a pair of floats mounted slightly outboard of the "hull-like body portion." These could be adjusted, he claimed, the better to trim or balance the craft in its progress through the water.

Curtiss built a machine to the specifications called for in Janin's patent, using his own successful flying boat components at all points not covered in the patent. The resulting machine would not fly under any coaxing. There is even a photograph, no doubt satisfying to the Curtiss team, of the craft completely driven under water except for its wings and its vertical stabilizer. The patent court finally and decisively ruled in Curtiss's favor in 1921.

This project was so obscure that even Curtiss Museum curator Merrill Stickler, whose great-uncle had worked for Curtiss, was not familiar with it. During the 1970s, he circulated photographs of the Janin patent boat to scholars and pioneer aviators, asking for help with identification. All of them drew blanks, including C. Roy Keys, who had supervised flying boat construction in Buffalo during World War I, later rising to corporate vice president and general manager. Keys commented, "[W]ithout a step I do not believe it would likely get off with the little chop shown. . . ." Keys also joined the others in expressing mystification over Janin's small side floats, saying that their only plausible purpose would be to impart stability if the craft were running without wings. He added, "[T]he hull shown would be quite unstable even with those splash boards," thus dismissing their entire purpose in Janin's creation. [12]

Grover Loening rather tellingly stated, "I imagine it did not last very long, as it looks like rather a wild design, and therefore would only be a negative contribution to the art. The bow is so short with relation to the thrust line that I doubt very much if it ever got off." [13]

Ever fascinated with hybrids, Curtiss developed two abortive contraptions in 1917. Lunching with Coast Guard officers aboard U.S.C.G.S. *Onondaga,* he proposed a "flying lifeboat" that could alight in the sea, retrieve distressed swimmers or mariners, jettison its wings, and cruise to safety. This luncheon is considered to be the birth of Coast Guard aviation, although the resulting Model BT proved completely unworkable. [1]

At the February Pan-American Aeronautic Exposition, Curtiss unveiled the Autoplane. The "fuselage" was a custom-made auto body carrying an operator and two passengers in lavishly upholstered splendor. It sported two full wing planes and one short set, all imported from the contemporary Model L triplane. A Curtiss OXX powered the pusher propeller; tail and wings could be removed for road operation with the same engine driving the wheels. By some reports, this contraption made a few straightaway hops at Newport News before being shelved, probably with a sigh of relief, when the United States declared war in April (Fig. 9.7). [1]

Fig. 9.7   On the eve of war, Curtiss exhibited the autoplane along with a Jenny *and one of the two-place flying boats.*

Demand skyrocketed as the United States placed $640 million in aviation orders. Recognizing that he needed more help and expertise than he had at his command, Curtiss proposed the merger with Willys-Overland, which agreed to buy controlling interest. Glenn Curtiss became chairman of the board, while John N. Willys came in as president to apply automotive mass-production methods. Unfortunately, this proved far more challenging than anyone anticipated. Making a wood-and-fabric airplane continued to be almost a craft and would remain so throughout the war. The huge production runs are all the more impressive in light of this awkward truth.

Cost overruns, production bottlenecks, idle hands, unsatisfactory designs—all would plague the Curtiss operation throughout the war. Much of this was inevitable, given the gigantic growth that occurred virtually overnight, depending for management, labor, and design on people utterly without experience in a new technology that was still imperfectly understood. There was also considerable confusion on the part of governments, whose demands changed rapidly with changes in technology and in military doctrine. Moreover, the company had to depend on licensees and subcontractors—most, again, inexperienced in aviation—that were spread from Rhode Island to California.

That being the case, the firm's achievements are all the more impressive. In 21 months, Curtiss delivered more than 5,000 complete airplanes and 5,000 additional engines to the U.S. government *alone.* Some 3,500 of these were *Jennys,* and 500 more were the closely related N-9, plus almost 200 of the follow-on Model R. There were also more than 1,000 flying boats, including nearly 700 of the HS series, which had been carefully designed to reflect British antisubmarine doctrine. The U.S. and British flying boats tended to be similar, reflecting the close relations among Curtiss, J. C. Porte, and Jack Towers (Fig. 9.8). It appears that 95% of U.S. and Canadian military pilots in World War I logged training time on Curtiss *Jennys,* Curtiss flying boats, or both. [1, 9, 10, 19]

Great Britain, Canada, Russia, France, and Italy were also significant buyers, although the Russian market naturally collapsed after the October Revolution. Total production of *Jennys* ran to more than 7,000 (including those made under license). The stock of OX engines was not used up until 1930. Curtiss also made European designs under license, although this program proved to be less successful than everyone had hoped when the

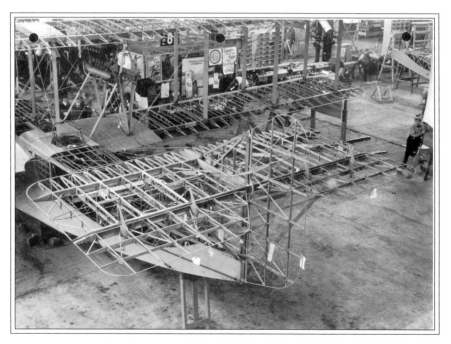

Fig. 9.8   *British Felixstowe-type (F-5-L) flying boat being built under license. A Liberty V-12 engine has already been mounted.*

United States entered the war. On the other hand, with new designs such as Kirkham's *Wasp*, they had finally caught up to European standards.

Despite the disasters and the frustrations, the achievements of the company in a new field represented a production miracle. It has been estimated that after the war, Curtiss had 75% of the aeronautical business in the United States.

✮ ✮ ✮

Curtiss and John Willys were friends, but Curtiss and his old hands did not fit well with the new management regime, and all parties recognized this fact. Shifting to Long Island at the end of 1917, Curtiss established the Curtiss Engineering Corporation, to which the parent company owned 51% of the stock, with Curtiss as president (Fig. 9.9). With Curtiss in this new skunk works and corporate leadership in Buffalo, each kept out of the other's hair. [1, 7–9]

The new facility at Garden City was a state-of-the-art operation, including the world's largest wind tunnel. This became the research, design, and prototype center for the company, with Curtiss overseeing the work of employees such as Henry Kleckler and

Fig. 9.9   Curtiss Engineering Corporation.

Charles Kirkham. The Kirkham-designed *Wasp* brought together several innovative features. The fuselage was a monocoque of laminated wood. The wing arrangement was a triplane—one of the rare occasions in which this was used in a Curtiss aircraft. The engine was a six-cylinder inline, again sponsored by Kirkham. This was a significant departure from the O-OX-OXX-V-V2 series that traced its ancestry to the air-cooled V-8 used at Ormond Beach—indeed, back to the original single-cylinder motorcycle engine. *Wasp* set world records for both altitude and speed.

Garden City also played a key role in Curtiss's greatest technological advance of the Great War period. Navy officials called in Curtiss, told him they wanted an airplane to cross the Atlantic, and asked him whether it could really be done. "Of course it can," he replied without hesitation, and he returned to Buffalo with Kleckler and William L. Gilmore, another of his engineers.

Three days later, they were back in Washington, D.C., with preliminary designs. Curtiss called for a (relatively) short hull and a tail mounted on booms. This at once reduced weight and allowed for a tail gun. The tail could be jettisoned, if necessary (harking back to the abortive Coast Guard BT), for extended surface operation. The aircraft could be constructed with either three engines or five, although Curtiss recommended three. The craft would carry a crew of six and have a wingspan of 126 ft—16 ft longer than that of a Boeing 737. [16, 19]

This was in September 1917. Specifications were quickly agreed upon, navy men were sent to Buffalo to work with the Curtiss engineers, and a contract for four units was signed in December. Work shifted to the new Garden City facility, although the project was so massive that some construction was done in Buffalo or by subcontractors. The first hull was shipped from Buffalo to Long Island via the New York State Barge Canal.

With key work taking place on Long Island, the navy designated NAS Rockaway Point as a base for the giant seaplanes, which by now were designated NC for Navy-Curtiss. Indeed, the navy referred to them as though NC were a ship class and each aircraft a commissioned vessel, denominating them *NC-1*, *NC-2*, and so forth. Contemporaries often called them "Nancy" boats, but the usage died out when they left service.

NC-1 performed perfectly for its first test flight on October 1, but the war ended abruptly scarcely a month later; the unfinished *NC-2* was canceled, along with unstarted *3* and *4*. However, *America*-project veteran Jack Towers convinced Assistant Secretary Franklin D. Roosevelt that the boats should be completed and the Atlantic crossing attempted. The two men badgered the civilian and military establishments and finally won approval. The three remaining boats would be completed and an Atlantic mission scheduled with Towers in command. They would take advantage of the 1914 *America* plan by following almost exactly the same route. [9, 16, 19]

The NC saga deserves a book of its own, and Curtiss's involvement was only peripheral (although highly honored) after the initial design and construction. Suffice to say that *NC-1*, *NC-3,* and *NC-4* staged from Rockaway to Newfoundland, then jumped off for the long hop to the Azores. Naval vessels were stationed every 50 miles along the way as guides. With heavy fog and radio troubles, the three aircraft lost contact with each other and with surface vessels, and soon could no longer be certain of their courses or positions.

Albert Read brought *NC-4* into Horta in the Azores. Towers in *NC-3* and Marc Mitscher in *NC-1* separately descended to the surface of the sea, hoping for better navigational fixes. Neither one could get airborne again.

NC-1 was taken by tow, but the craft suffered so much damage that it had to be sunk by gunfire. *NC-3*, on the other hand, had vanished, and there was no radio contact. After two days, the airplane was feared lost, when suddenly Towers appeared outside his destination of Ponta Delgada in the Azores, having taxied more than 200 miles in 52 hr, declining assistance from other naval vessels in harbor to bring in *NC-3* under her own power with all hands safe. It was a magnificent feat of seamanship, but Navy Secretary Daniels mortified the entire service by ordering Towers to stay on the beach and recover while Read and his crew went on alone in *NC-4*. Not even the protests of the local Senior Naval Officer could move him, and Towers gnashed his teeth as Putty Read completed the first Atlantic crossing, flying on first to Lisbon and then to Southampton (Fig. 9.10). It was 15-1/2 years after Kitty Hawk, and not quite seven years since Glenn Curtiss had had Henry Kleckler nail blocks of wood to the underside of their experimental flying boat on Keuka Lake. [1, 2, 10, 16, 19–21, 26]

Fig. 9.10 NC-4 in Lisbon harbor on May 27, 1919.

REFERENCES

1. Bowers, Peter M., *Curtiss Aircraft 1907–1947,* Putnam, London, 1979.

2. Boyne, Walter J., *The Smithsonian Book of Flight,* Smithsonian Books, Washington, DC, 1987.

3. Casey, Louis S., *Curtiss: The Hammondsport Era, 1907–1915,* Crown Publishers, New York, 1981.

4. Combs, Harry, with Martin Caidin, *Kill Devil Hill: Discovering the Secrets of the Wright Brothers,* Houghton Mifflin Company, Boston, 1979.

5. Crouch, Tom, *The Bishop's Boys: A Life of Wilbur and Orville Wright,* W. W. Norton & Co., New York, 1989.

6. "Curtiss Aero Engines 1909–1914," manuscript (n.d.), GHCM Curtiss Engines Files.

7. "The Curtiss Aeroplane and Motor Corporation," *The Aircraft Year Book 1919,* Doubleday, Page and Company for the Manufacturers Aircraft Association, New York, 1919.

8. "Curtiss Aeroplane and Motor Corp.; Curtiss Engineering Corp.; The Burgess Company" *Aircraft Year Book 1920,* Doubleday, Page and Company for the Manufacturers Aircraft Association, New York, 1920.

9. Eltscher, Louis R., and Edward M. Young, *Curtiss-Wright: Greatness and Decline,* Twayne Publishers, New York, 1998.

10. The *Hammondsport Herald,* published weekly throughout Curtiss's lifetime, includes multitudinous references to Curtiss, his works, and his times. (Curtiss Museum holds a microfilmed set.)

11. Howard, Fred, *Orville and Wilbur: A Biography of the Wright Brothers,* Alfred A. Knopf, New York, 1988.

12. Keys, C. Roy, to Merrill Stickler, manuscript, July 31, 1974, GHCM Janin Patent Boat File.

13. Loening, Grover C., to Merrill Stickler, typescript, September 8, 1974, GHCM Janin Patent Boat File.

14. Mitchell, Charles R., and Kirk W. House, *Glenn H. Curtiss, Aviation Pioneer,* Arcadia Publishing, Charleston, SC, 2001.

15. Morehouse, Harold E., and Marvel Dyer, *The Flying Pioneers Biographies of Harold Morehouse*, GHCM.

16. Reynolds, Clark G., *Admiral John H. Towers: The Struggle for Naval Air Supremacy,* Naval Institute Press, Annapolis, MD, 1991.

17. Rinek, Larry M., "Curtiss Aviation Engines: An American Success Story."

18. ———, "Glenn H. Curtiss: An Early American Innovator in Aviation and Motorcycle Engines," SAE Paper No. 940571, Society of Automotive Engineers, Warrendale, PA, 1994.

19. Roseberry, C. R., *Glenn Curtiss: Pioneer of Flight,* Doubleday & Company, Garden City, NY, 1972.

20. Studer, Clara, *Sky Storming Yankee: The Life of Glenn Curtiss,* Stackpole Sons, New York, 1937.

21. Thurston, David B., *The World's Most Significant and Magnificent Aircraft: Evolution of the Modern Airplane,* Society of Automotive Engineers, Warrendale, PA, 2000.

22. Waters, C. Leonard, to Nancy Hutches, undated typescript, GHCM Yorkers Collection.

U.S. Patent Reference

23. 1,312,910 A. S. Janin, Aeroplane Structure, July 31, 1913–August 12, 1919.

Chapter 10

Close-Up:
Curtiss at Work

✶ ✶ ✶

If you worked for, or with, Glenn Curtiss, you probably were at various times excited, bewildered, frustrated, honored, and awed—often on the same shift.

In 1959, Clarence P. Rudd wrote seven pages of dense script recollecting Curtiss for a Hammondsport school class. Rudd, one of the key men in the motorcycle side of the business, thought highly of Curtiss, but he was no hagiographer. He came to Hammondsport in 1907 to run the Erie motorcycle shop for Tank Waters and remained until 1913. Although Rudd was closer to Waters and on his payroll most of the time, Curtiss was "G. H." to those who worked with him. Rudd worked closely enough with Curtiss, and knew him well enough, to offer some incisive insight.

Rudd repeatedly expressed appreciation for examples of Curtiss's own insight, often contrasting with his own shortsightedness. The earliest example he gives is of Curtiss barking orders and stopping the crowd of watchers from rushing to Casey Baldwin's aid at the 1907 *Red Wing* crash. Curtiss admonished his colleagues that approaching in a group could break the ice and "drop Casey, entangled in the wreckage, into the water." During a 1910 discussion, seemingly on possible military markets for the airplane, Rudd asserted that mankind had become so civilized as to make war outmoded. Half a century later, he vividly recalled the single sentence Curtiss spoke in reply: "We will always have war." Events, of course, proved Curtiss to be right, although Rudd still expressed the hope that time would eventually prove him wrong.

Curtiss outguessed Rudd in several business insights. Correctly predicting that motorcycle demand would drop off badly, he also predicted "the eventual passing of the two-wheeler as an important means of transportation." At the same time, "He foresaw a great future for the airplane, a vision that I didn't share." By 1913, Rudd had left Curtiss and was living in Los Angeles. Curtiss "decided the time was ripe to begin building 'planes on the west coast as he foresaw a future for such a plant. As usual, I didn't share his vision."

Even so, Rudd joined Glenn and Lena to incorporate the Curtiss Company of California. This venture withered before it could really bloom because of gigantic war orders pouring in to the eastern plant, seeming to validate Rudd's pessimism. However, as Rudd admitted in 1959, "Today this coast from Seattle to San Diego is the world's greatest plane building area, thereby confirming his vision [and] judgment."

Rudd likewise had a chance to observe Curtiss's insight in more immediate technical matters, most notably following Hugh Robinson's hydro crash in France about 1911. A cameraperson had captured the event on film, and the newsreel eventually worked its way to Hammondsport for the five-cent weekly showing in the town hall (now Chamber of Commerce office on Sheathar Street). An operator cranked the projector by hand, Rudd recalled, with a pianist in the corner playing appropriate mood music.

It struck Curtiss that if someone were to crank the projector very slowly, he and his colleagues could study the crash carefully and possibly determine the cause of the crash. "This was done, being possibly one of the earliest uses of the motion picture for such a purpose." Perhaps Curtiss should be considered the father of the instant replay. Unfortunately, Rudd mentions nothing of their observations or conclusions. Being from the motorcycle side of the business, it is possible that he was not involved with the actual study.

The idea of the slow-motion study may have sparked from Curtiss's habit of using cameras to record experiments, another example of how he could combine meticulous work with impulsive ideation. We've seen that Alexander Graham Bell may have influenced this approach, although Curtiss's own youthful career as an Eastman employee and as a photographer certainly fixed in his mind the power of pictures. This episode also paints an engaging picture of Curtiss, the world-renowned daredevil, inventor, and businessman, taking in movies with his neighbors at the makeshift little weekend theater at their town hall.

The experiments that Curtiss recorded with his camera were a vital part of his life and work, although the disruption they caused could be extremely frustrating to employees. Whenever Curtiss came up with new ideas, and this was nearly constantly, he wanted to try them out immediately. If these experiments required employees or plant facilities, they could wreak havoc on allocations and schedules.

Curtiss's mother boarded in the same Buffalo rooming house as Rudd's parents, and they knew her as "a fine woman" of "artistic aspirations" but very impractical and with no capacity to plan or budget.

> I esteemed Glenn as a man of character—modest, gentle, tolerant, [and] considerate of others—but I should be less than honest if I didn't add that I also saw something of his impractical mother in him. His was an active, inquiring mind that leaped about [and] it was not easy to pin him down to a firm decision. Experimental work always took precedence in the shop even though it disrupted the normal production schedule, [and] his plans could change with disconcerting ease.

It is worth remembering that Rudd worked in the Tank Waters shop, not the Curtiss shop, although there was a formal linkage after the creation of Marvel in 1909. Apparently, Glenn's talent for disruption affected neighboring plants in addition to his own.

Rudd experienced this directly when the Curtiss company developed "an entirely new motorcycle engine with superior performance characteristics [the Model G]. For some reason this was turned over to me for road testing although I was still on Waters's payroll."

Rudd had experienced this freewheeling approach, impatient with or incognizant of boundaries, immediately upon arriving in Hammondsport when the AEA period was getting under way in 1907. He explained to the students, "It should not be supposed that the airplane was 'invented' in its entirety by any one individual. All great breakthroughs in the field of science are preceded by years of study [and] experimentation by many individuals."

After summarizing the development of airplanes to 1907, Rudd described some of his experiences in that year and in the following *annus mirabilis*. In one barn, he was given a glimpse of an ultimately unsuccessful "orthopter" (presumably Gammeter's ornithopter). He was well informed about, and may have seen, J. Newton Williams's helicopter experiments. He had as an upstairs tenant in the Waters shop Charles Oliver Jones, who was cutting and sewing fabric panels for his dirigible.

He knew "Cap" Baldwin, understanding his continued passion for airships even during the days when he was flying exhibitions in his heavier-than-air *Red Devil*. He knew that Baldwin had drawn on his extensive experience with fabrics to suggest a useful dope for the AEA members. He had watched as Baldwin and Curtiss "pooled their knowledge [and] built [and] flew the first dirigible purchased by the U.S. Army." Rudd had watched the second flight of *Red Wing* and on one occasion helped Alexander Graham Bell fly a tetrahedral kite. [13]

All this while, and even in the future, Rudd's feet stayed firmly on the ground in the motorcycle business, without any formal connections to Curtiss or any other aviator. The atmosphere at Hammondsport was wide open, with independent experimenters and

Curtiss staff freely exchanging ideas, often added to by knowledgeable local bystanders such as Nelson Dalton or C. P. Rudd. AEA nonmembers, such as J. Newton Williams, contributed technical articles to the AEA *Bulletin.* [2] When the AEA experiments added Selfridge, McCurdy, Bell, Casey Baldwin, and Bell staff to the mix, the yeast fermented vigorously.

This same approach with its freewheeling exchanges was evident during hydro development in San Diego. Several groups were involved: Curtiss and his men from Hammondsport; new hires, such as George E. A. Hallet; the local Aero Club; and four military officers (three army and one navy). All evidence is that they worked as a single team, with everyone's ideas getting an equal hearing and a careful evaluation. Spuds Ellyson wrote:

> It was not Curtiss, the genius and inventor, whom we knew. It was 'G. H.,' a comrade and chum, who made us feel that we were all working together, and that our ideas and advice were really of some value. It was never a case of 'do this' or 'do that,' to his amateur or to his regular mechanics, but always, 'What do you think of making this change?' He was always willing to listen to any argument but generally managed to convince you that his plan was best. I could write volumes on Curtiss, the man. [12]

This practice of having ideas test themselves against each other still prevailed in 1913, when Curtiss would gather his student pilots, such as Jack Vilas, into the plant every Sunday night. Here he appointed two captains who then chose sides, after which Curtiss would assign a debate topic: biplane versus monoplane, air-cooled versus water-cooled, or other interesting controversies. [28] Curtiss himself may or may not have gained much fresh insight from these debates of neophyte students, but the students themselves were certainly forced to grapple with the issues and their own understandings of them.

This collegiality, with its free exchange of ideas to be tested and tried, is often held up today as an ideal of engineering. It makes difficult the tracking of Curtiss's ideas. Impatient of restraints, possessed of a quick and active mind, able to leapfrog far past others in his understanding, it may have been impossible for Curtiss to look at something *without* getting ideas from it. He may well have been genuinely unable to say where his ideas had come from and how they had developed. It is easy to speculate that such an approach could lead to accusations of patent infringement. Certainly, Curtiss would have been impatient of patent restrictions, particularly if in his own mind he was several generations past the starting point.

The ideas, at any rate, kept coming. Rudd relates that Curtiss, having once been "persuaded to go to the theater," told his companion midway through the performance, "Let's get out of here, I've got an idea." [13] Glenn Junior related that during the Florida years, his father would appear at the beginning of one of Lena's parties, greet everyone, ensure that the party was going well, and then vanish up the spiral staircase to his office and whatever project he was working on at the moment. Blanche Scott described Curtiss as being a very kind man, apparently with no thoughts for anything except the airplane. Of course, his thoughts ranged much further than that, but the fact is that he was constantly generating new ideas. It would be fascinating to examine Curtiss with modern diagnostic tools for attention disorders.

This leads to the frequently agitated question of exactly how much work Curtiss did in developing his own ideas and projects, in contrast with how much was done by his staff or colleagues. Grover Loening was once appalled on asking Curtiss the tail surface area of the airplane they were inspecting, an airplane Curtiss was about to fly for an exhibition. Curtiss did not know but added that if there were a problem, the boys in the shop would set it right. Loening, knowing that Orville Wright would have had the exact figure in his head, concluded that Curtiss did not design his own airplanes, except in the most general sense. [9]

There was certainly some truth to Loening's conclusion. Rudd wrote, "I really never knew how capable Curtiss was as a craftsman when working with wood [and] metal, since after 1907 his ideas were entrusted to his right hand man, Henry Kleckler, [and] others to be put into tangible form." [13]

Unfortunately, it was only around 1907 that people started paying enough attention to Curtiss to begin recording observations about his development and design work. Certainly in the earlier motorcycle days, he was much closer to the design and engineering process.

Or was he? After the death of Curtiss, Charles Kirkham strongly suggested that he himself had been responsible for the early Curtiss motorcycle engine and its development. [8] It is a fact that Curtiss used the Kirkham foundry for his early engines, beginning around 1902 and ending around 1905, when he brought founding into his own shop. It is also a fact that the *Herald* reported in 1903 that the two friends were taking Benbow, the aeronaut, an engine that "they" had built for him. Kirkham also had more engineering training than did Curtiss, although this consisted mainly of a correspondence course. [7, 11]

Chronology is often a little fuzzy from the days when these men were very young and quite unknown, but Curtiss engine development began in 1901–1902, and production was subcontracted to the Kirkham shop around that time. Kirkham told C. R. Roseberry

(Curtiss's biographer) that he himself was not associated with his father's shop and had not met Glenn Curtiss at the time. It appears that he was not even living in the area just then. Kirkham, after his own engineering business petered out, became a highly successful Curtiss engineer around the time of World War I, after which he set up his own consulting firm. [7, 8, 11]

It was certainly impossible to describe a clear track of idea and product development in the Curtiss operation. Most of the information we have comes from the later period, beginning around 1907, and most of it is in the form of reminiscences. What we do know comports well with what Rudd described: Curtiss developed original ideas and sketches, which he turned over to Kleckler (or someone similar to Kleckler), who refined the design and turned it into hardware. Curtiss then doctored this before turning it back to Kleckler and others, who in turn would take it to production.

While this would form a sort of "critical path" description of events, again we need to remember that work in the Curtiss organization (especially in these early and middle days) was highly collegial. It is likely that at every one of these stages, everyone was looking over everyone else's shoulder and contributing to the process.

The tale of designs being sketched on the workshop walls (and the corollary tale of the hapless new worker who took the initiative to whitewash one night) is persistent and probably has a good deal of truth in it. Glenn Junior is one of many who passed the story on, and so did Jack Towers. However, it was also true that the company developed blueprints, took out patents, employed a wind tunnel at least by 1911, and created models for testing. Henry Kleckler's notebooks include pages of standard values, minute weights, and other engineering details. Even so, engineering at Curtiss in these early-to-middle days remained "heavy-handed," to use Lou Casey's phrase [personal communication], leaning on experimentation probably more than was most efficient.

When Curtiss set up the Curtiss Engineering Corporation in 1916–1917, it was a remarkable center of aeronautic research and development. The facility included three wind tunnels, one reportedly the largest in the world. There were labs for metallurgy and doping. The model shops were extensive. There were facilities to produce prototypes, both for Curtiss and for other customers such as the U.S. Navy. When Curtiss had the means and opportunity, he created a center for truly advanced work, far beyond the sketch-it-out-on-the-wall approach of the Hammondsport era. It is easy to suppose that these facilities were everything Curtiss had dreamed of having (and thus understood was needed) back in the days when he was knocking together airplanes in a motorcycle factory.

Another aspect of Curtiss's work forms a truly curious picture. Curtiss took his V-8 motorcycle to Ormond Beach, his 10-mile world record motorcycle to the same venue, his

Reims Racer to France, and his Hudson-Fulton machine to New York City, all without prior testing. The same was true in the case of *SC-1,* although that was really Captain Baldwin's project. All these machines were actually impressive successes, with the exception of the Hudson-Fulton (which Herring had presumably overseen while Curtiss was in France).

In the case of the V-8, the 10-mile motorcycle, and *Reims Racer*, Curtiss made his own decision to go ahead without testing, and in the case of *SC-1,* he likely contributed to the decision. Was this chutzpah? Confidence? A keen ability to evaluate his own work? Addiction to risk-taking behavior? Merely poor organization? We probably will never know, but it is an aspect of Curtiss's working style that his colleagues must have found nerve-wracking.

In a matter relating to the open collegiality, Rudd observed Curtiss's willingness to open his work, at nearly any stage, for all to see.

> Inventors are notoriously secretive, being afraid that someone may steal their ideas. Prof. Langley was brusque [and] unpopular with reporters. Wright brothers sought out a remote sandpit at Kitty Hawk to experiment [and] were also very reticent.
>
> Curtiss, however, sought publicity. Very early he had learned its value in selling motorcycles [and] that carried over into aviation. I recall a half-hearted attempt at secrecy during the building of the first flying boat, but once revealed, the welcome mat was out for any who might spread the news. [13]

Walter Johnson and Harry Wehman confiscated (and replaced) a roll of film from Lorin Wright, brother to Orville and Wilbur, who was in town under an assumed name, observing work on the *Langley*. Judging from the photographs that have survived and from the crowds shown mobbing the work, Lorin must have been the only one who lost his film. He had already been allowed to wander in and out of the hangars, manually operating the control surfaces. Even after their confrontation over the film, Wehman (who was sticking with Lorin to keep an eye on him) obligingly demonstrated more of the operations of the aircraft. [3, 4, 12, 14]

Contrary to legend, Curtiss (or his company) often charged for use of their patents and occasionally sued to block improper use by others. In general, however, Curtiss's practices carried out a philosophy he had enunciated during one discussion of infringement—that the firm might as well go after the business, rather than going after patent protection.

He seems to have been willing to trust to competition in the marketplace for generating and preserving his revenue.

This leads us to an often overlooked reality. Although Curtiss was an experimenter, an inventor, an engineer, a daredevil, and a publicist, he was also a businessperson. Unlike some of his famed contemporaries and predecessors, such as Henry Ford and Alexander Graham Bell, Curtiss was a businessperson first, who fell into inventing later. He knew perfectly well that it was not sufficient to create a product; he also had to sell it. Likewise, he understood that sales of different products influenced the revenue stream differently. In the discussion with Rudd on the future of the motorcycle business, as we have seen, Curtiss correctly predicted that the motorcycle business would flag, while correctly predicting that the airplane business would soar. However, he also pointed out to Rudd that he could sell a motorcycle engine for $75, whereas a V-8 aero engine would bring in $3,000. [13]

We must remember that through those breathtaking years in which Curtiss was developing engines, racing motorcycles, supporting lighter-than-air work, directing experiments for the AEA, winning the speed prize in France, flying the Hudson, inventing the hydroaeroplane, inventing the flying boat, shifting to modern tractor designs, and expanding the business exponentially and transforming it for total-war production, Curtiss meantime was directly running his own company (companies, to be formally correct). [6, 10, 12]

He did this through the first half of World War I, when he sold controlling interest and moved up to become chairman of the board. However, he almost immediately created the Curtiss Engineering Corporation, with himself as president, placing himself again at the direct head of a significant firm. Those who sniff at Curtiss's supposed distance from the drawing board often overlook what Curtiss *was* doing—running a major industrial concern. [5, 6, 12]

Curtiss as an innovator, entrepreneur, and corporate leader parallels in many ways Walt Disney:

- Each took a field that already existed in primitive form and rapidly shoved forward both its technology and its business.

- Each did this with little or no formal training for his work, at considerable personal financial risk, and with little or no outside financial backing at first.

- Each gathered and inspired other pioneers, many with superior formal qualifications, to expand and further the work.

- Each continued to generate new ideas, getting the development process under way before entrusting it to others.

- Each encouraged the ideas of others to flourish and take center stage.

- Each spent more effort as time passed with the work of idea creation, inspiration, oversight, and direction, always taking care to ensure that the drive was forward.

- Each kept in close touch with the work as it progressed, and each remained fully responsible for the results.

- Each was remembered with excitement and awe by his coworkers long after his death.

- Each saw his techniques, procedures, and innovations adopted as the standard within his field.

- Each saw his work grow into a major business, as well as a major corporation; indeed, each was largely responsible for creating his entire field of business or industry, and dominated that field for many years.

- Each had subordinates who broke away, deeming that "the boss" was getting too much credit for the subordinate's own work, only to be unable to approach the success of "the boss" once on their own.

- Each was eager to see that the finished work was marketable, but each meantime hoped that his work was contributing something of enduring value to society.

- Each made dramatic public presentations of his work in the early days of the business, creating a personality on whom the public could focus.

- Each created a company and a product directly bearing the original creator's name.

- As a final and amusing parallel, each had a trademark that resembled an autograph but was not.

Curtiss seems to have been remembered more fondly than Disney, many of whose key staff, while greatly admiring his genius, found him extremely abrasive and difficult to work with. Curtiss was also probably more generous to those who had contributed to his success.

However, the fact remains that it is no more sensible to sniff at Curtiss for not directly designing his own tail surfaces than it would be to sniff at Walt Disney for not drawing all his own pictures.

How can we sum up Curtiss at work? First, we must specify which work we are discussing: His technological work? His corporate work? His entrepreneurial and marketing work? His daredevil publicity work? As ever, Curtiss is hard to pin down (Fig. 10.1).

For a book such as this one, our key interest is presumably in his technological work. Here he was a prolific creator of ideas and often used his own ideation as starting points. At the same time, he kept up with developments in his field(s), often adopting new developments or using them to spark more ideas of his own.

He worked largely by leading teams. He gathered and inspired groups of extremely talented men, many of them more skilled than he at many aspects of the work. He worked directly with them as "G. H.," sleeves rolled up, ears and mind open to everyone else's ideas.

Fig. 10.1 "G. H."

He originated ideas and concepts, putting them to the test of a freewheeling, collegial examination. He also tended to test ideas, especially in the early days, by experimentation, rather than by calculation or modeling. To make these ideas practical, he turned them over to his teams, continuing to work with the finished product before turning it over for production. He went into production with careful attention to marketing.

While committed to standardization and interchangeability (enhancing manufacture, repair, maintenance, replacement, shipping, and profitability), he subjected his products to continuous modification, innovation, and improvement. If the modifications often seem modest and difficult to discern, it is often because the product was already so refined in its original iteration.

Curtiss may have been what Arthur M. Squires described as a "maestro of technology," able at once to keep the entire enterprise in mind, on task, and moving forward, and able also to work side-by-side with the fellows on the line in the graveyard shift to find out what is going on—and what is needed—at that level. [2] Many people can do one or the other. Many can do both. Being able to do both simultaneously and successfully marks a rare and impressive individual.

REFERENCES

1. Bowser, Hal, "Maestros of Technology: An Interview with Arthur M. Squires," *American Heritage of Invention and Technology*, vol. 3, no. 1, Summer 1987, pp. 24-30.

2. *Bulletins* of the Aerial Experiment Association, I-XXXIX, July 31, 1908– April 12, 1909. GHCM holds Curtiss's original set, now in three hand-bound volumes.

3. Combs, Harry, with Martin Caidin, *Kill Devil Hill: Discovering the Secrets of the Wright Brothers,* Houghton Mifflin Company, Boston, 1979.

4. Crouch, Tom, *The Bishop's Boys: A Life of Wilbur and Orville Wright,* W. W. Norton & Co., New York, 1989.

5. "Curtiss Aeroplane and Motor Corp.; Curtiss Engineering Corp.; The Burgess Company," *Aircraft Year Book 1920,* Manufacturers Aircraft Association, New York, 1970.

6. Eltscher, Louis R., and Edward M. Young, *Curtiss-Wright: Greatness and Decline,* Twayne Publishers, New York, 1998.

7.   The *Hammondsport Herald,* published weekly throughout Curtiss's lifetime, includes multitudinous references to Curtiss, his works, and his times. (Curtiss Museum holds a microfilmed set.)

8.   Kirkham, Charles, "Brief, Updated Autobiography by Charles Kirkham," GHCM typescript in Kirkham Biographical Files.

9.   Loening, Grover C., *Takeoff into Greatness,* Putnam, New York, 1968.

10. Mitchell, Charles R., and Kirk W. House, *Glenn H. Curtiss, Aviation Pioneer,* Arcadia Publishing, Charleston, SC, 2001.

11. Morehouse, Harold E., and Marvel Dyer, *The Flying Pioneers Biographies of Harold Morehouse,* GHCM.

12. Roseberry, C. R., *Glenn Curtiss: Pioneer of Flight,* Doubleday & Company, Garden City, NY, 1972.

13. Rudd, Clarence P., to Rosa Lee Nudd, October 3, 1959, manuscript, GHCM Yorkers Collection.

14. Shulman, Seth, *Unlocking the Sky: The Forgotten Story of Glenn Curtiss & The Birth of the Airplane,* HarperCollins, New York, 2002.

15. Vilas, Jack, *My Life—To My Children,* privately published, 1934. GHCM Vilas Biographical Files 4-520.

Chapter 11

Panorama:
On the Road Again

★ ★ ★

World War I ended so abruptly that it caught the Allies off base and gave rise in Germany to the false legend of the "Stab in the Back." Because the 1917 revolutions and the new Bolshevik regime had knocked Russia out of the fighting, Germany finally had the one-front conflict it had counted on for victory four years earlier. Hindenberg and Ludendorff, by now virtually military dictators, massed their forces on the Western Front. In the spring of 1918, they unleashed their greatest offensive, determined to crush the Allies before the bulk of U.S. troops could be brought into the action.

It almost worked. All along the front, nearly static since 1914, Allied troops reeled backward as jubilantly advancing Germans ate up mile after mile of France. The desperate governments elevated General Foch as Supreme Commander. General Pershing, who had been threatening to withhold his troops if the numerous but inexperienced Americans were not deployed together under his command, appeared at Foch's headquarters, saying, "Everything is yours. Use it as you will." The first units of U.S. troops had been training in France for almost a year because the British and French considered them to be unready for combat. Now Americans were inducted, thrown into uniform, packed aboard troopships, and marched into frontline trenches, all in the space of five weeks.

At last the line held. Pershing got his U.S. sector of front, under his command. Urged on by British General Haig, Foch began his own counterattack. "Everybody fights," he growled, and everyone did. Through summer and fall the Allies—U.S., British, French, Belgian, Canadian, Imperial, and colonial troops—pounded the Germans back. The Ottoman and Austro-Hungarian empires collapsed. The Kaiser's fleet mutinied. Units at the front began deserting, striking, and falling apart. Hindenberg informed a shocked government (which he had judiciously shielded from the facts) that the army was on the point of evaporation and the war was over. He demanded his own country's surrender. Kaiser Wilhelm abdicated and fled to Holland, whose hospitality he would abuse by welcoming

Hitler's troops 22 years later. Aristocrats and military men having failed and fled, the onus of surrender was thrust upon a new civilian republic. World War I had ended as abruptly as it had begun.

In Marblehead, the former Burgess production plant, now a Curtiss facility, burned to the ground four days before Armistice. It was a perfect metaphor for the U.S. aeronautic business, of which Curtiss now controlled about 75%. However, the pie instantly became much smaller. Not only were massive orders quickly canceled, but the Allies now had tremendous overstocks, much of which would no doubt soon make their way into civilian markets.

Curtiss clearly no longer needed 18,000 employees. The original Hammondsport plant closed for inventory on December 31, 1918. To the horror of the town, it never reopened. As if losing 2,500 jobs in a town of 1,100 was not bad enough, on July 1 the Prohibition amendment went into effect, crippling the grape-growing and winemaking businesses of the region. Hammondsport was clearly small, inconveniently located, and outdated. But soon all the Curtiss facilities closed, with the exception of the main plant in Buffalo (now oversized) and the Engineering Corporation in Garden City. [1, 5–8, 10]

As for Glenn Curtiss, where did he stand on Armistice Day in 1918? To put it in simplest terms, he was 40 years old and a multimillionaire. Although his stock was certain to fall and his income to decline, he remained a wealthy man. In ten years, he had made himself one of the most famous men in the world and one of the most successful businessmen in the United States. He was a young man. He did not need more money, nor did he need to make a name for himself. From now on, he could do whatever he liked—if only he could figure out what that was.

No one dreamed, of course, that he had fewer than twelve years to live.

Although the San Diego operation had certainly been worthwhile, it had not worked out as a main base for winter operations. Located about as far from Hammondsport as it was possible to get in the 48 states, the lengthy train journey took its toll on the restless Curtiss. On one trip, he got off the train in Kansas, bought a car, and drove the rest of the way. In addition to the loss of his personal time, the distance from the nerve center of the business was awkward, especially as war orders boomed and new plants were opened. [7, 10]

Curtiss had placed another warm-weather base in Miami Beach, where he expected to find men of wealth and influence whose interest in the business could bear fruit beyond their possible enrollment as student pilots. In the winter of 1916–1917, Glenn and Lena set up house at the nearby Royal Palm Hotel.

Twenty years earlier, most of the lower two-thirds of Florida had been sparsely populated scrub. Henry M. Flagler (who, by an odd coincidence, might have lived in Hammondsport as a small boy) drove his Florida East Coast Railroad down the seaboard as the nineteenth century waned. More convenient transport was spawning an ever-growing wave of settlement and exploitation.

Curtiss liked what he saw in Florida. Winter was far more pleasant than it had been in western New York. All the flat land provided a fine setting for the school and other flying operations. Travel and communications with New York, Washington, or Buffalo were more convenient than they had been from San Diego. He had access to men of wealth and influence, but in an hour, he could be out in that scrub land west of the city, indulging in the outdoor life he had always enjoyed (Fig. 11.1).

Meeting cattle rancher James M. Bright, Curtiss borrowed land to move his school (now contracted to train army pilots). He soon turned over this new location for U.S. Marine pilot training, opened another site nearby, and started the operation that eventually grew into Miami International Airport. Always in love with water, he developed a flat-bottomed vessel powered by an air propeller to traverse the shallow bodies of water in the region. His new creation, *Miss Miami,* set an unofficial world water speed record at 66 mph on April 25, 1917 (Fig. 11.2). It was a sign of the times that Curtiss himself was hundreds of miles away on that day, managing the business in support of total war. During 1917–1918, he bought out Bright's brother to become a partner in the huge ranch. When Curtiss could spare time from business, he rode horseback over the vast acreage, visited with the Seminoles, camped, and hunted. [10, 12, 13]

Fig. 11.1 Curtiss sent this photograph to Damon Merrill, labeling it "Bandit Camp."

Fig. 11.2 The Miss Miami.

When the war ended, the aviation business dwindled dramatically. Military orders plummeted, but the company quickly countered with several civilian products, some conversions, some refits, and some new creations. With many men in many nations having trained as pilots during the war, manufacturers fervently assumed (or at least hoped) that these men would want to continue flying after the war.

The Curtiss *Seagull* flying boat was a conversion of the military Model MF trainer—a three-seat open-cockpit pusher biplane. Sales were disappointing. There was also the dramatically futuristic *Oriole* (Fig. 11.3). Equipped with either the 150-hp C-6 (originally K-6) inline or the familiar 90-hp OX-5, the *Oriole* (similar to the *Seagull*) boasted an electric self-starter. This open-cockpit three-passenger tractor land plane featured a remarkably clean streamlined fuselage, actually a tube of laminated wood.

Designers used the same type of fuselage on the Curtiss *Eagle,* an eight-passenger closed-cabin trimotor designed as an intercity airliner. *Oriole* was a breathtaking advance, *Eagle* a delightfully (if relatively) comfortable ride, and *Seagull* a reliable, tested competitor.

All three quailed in the marketplace, however, because of government surplus. Indeed, the Curtiss company competed with itself, buying up *Jennys* and reconditioning them for resale. The company followed the same practice with the similar J-1 from Standard, reissuing these with OX-5 powerplants. The decision to recondition had taken much study, much negotiation, and much soul-searching. However, the company concluded that it was going to be done. If it were to be done, officers reasoned, it might as well be done properly,

Fig. 11.3 Most later makers of three-place biplanes used the Oriole *as their pattern.*

and Curtiss might as well reap the financial benefits. Moreover, poorly done reconditioning would lead to failures and deaths, which could only hurt the industry.

All of this made perfect sense, but it devastated sales of the more expensive (but clearly superior) *Oriole*. Even so, Curtiss aggressively created a web of agents, dealers, and distributors across the United States, Europe, the Philippines, Asia, and South America—in the latter area, pioneered and maintained largely by C. W. Webster. Curtiss Flying Services, in addition to performing contract work and giving rides, conducted air and ground training, while establishing fields and offering demonstrations for prospective buyers.

Building on the technical successes of the *Oriole*, and especially of the wartime *Wasp/Hornet,* Curtiss produced a series of racers for the U.S. Army and U.S. Navy. These broke numerous world records, often in the hands of pilots such as Jimmy Doolittle, Bert Acosta (Fig. 11.4), and Billy Mitchell, setting a world standard for clean design. Elaboration of the C-6 and C-12 engines also continued, finally leading to the water-cooled D-12. [1, 5–7, 9–11]

Much capital and labor had been invested in the *Oriole, Eagle,* and *Seagull,* but the investment of hope was even more significant. The civilian market was simply not materializing. When the postwar depression settled in by 1920, Willys and his colleagues made a bitter decision. They needed to concentrate their attention on their automotive business, which was having troubles of its own. Rather than risk Willys-Overland any further, they would default on Curtiss loans.

Fig. 11.4 Bert Acosta with a Curtiss racer.

Clement M. Keys, Curtiss vice president for finance, saw the future differently. He offered to buy up common stock for the $650,000 that was immediately falling due. His offer was accepted, and Keys was now chairman of the board. He further reduced the size of the company, concentrating even more heavily on military orders, at home and abroad. Curtiss became chairman of the engineering committee in the reorganization, retaining his own holdings but not investing further with Keys. [7, 10]

Plans for conversions and new machines came from the subsidiary Engineering Corporation, where Curtiss was president and chairman of the board.

At Garden City, Curtiss had gathered his key design staff—Charles Kirkham, Henry Kleckler, William L. Gilmore, and others. There were three wind tunnels, one of which was 70 ft long and could generate flow approaching 100 mph. With a diameter running from 7 to 17 ft, it was believed to be the largest wind tunnel in the world. These tunnels tested products from the Curtiss Model Shop. The company's article in 1920s *Aircraft Year Book* boasted that mahogany-and-aluminum models up to 3 ft in span were made accurate "to thousandths of an inch," while wind tunnel balances "can record wind

pressures in all desired directions to 0.0001 of a pound." The *Year Book* article continued, "new Curtiss machines perform like seasoned types . . . the aeroplane has been
reduced to a problem like the railroad bridge, and solved in the laboratory and factory preliminary to its first actual use."

Garden City was also a prototype shop, where 800 people had worked on the NC boats
alone. There was also a chemical and metallurgical research laboratory, scientifically testing wood, metal, dope, and fabrics. In the motor laboratory, new engine designs were
developed. This department had a 400-hp dynamometer with dedicated powerplant.
Underground conduits carried away exhaust gasses. In addition to equipment for physical
tests of the engines, "All gasoline, oil, etc., employed in laboratory work is scientifically
weighed, and results to date show that absolutely accurate tests for power, consumption,
etc., can be run." [5, 6]

How deeply was Curtiss involved at this time, as Florida exerted its siren call on him? A
company paper stated, "In 1919 Mr. Curtiss turned with full confidence to a task in which
he had always been interested and which now seemed capable of satisfactory completion:
the designing of special types of aircraft for practical peace uses." It further stated, "The
Engineering Corporation took form under the personal direction of Mr. Curtiss." Throughout his career, Curtiss seems to have recruited and inspired men who were more profi-
cient than he, while being able continuously to sketch advanced ideas and directions for
them to turn into reality.

Curtiss's businesses had always been highly personal, but he had stopped flying sometime
during the war, and aviation no longer gripped him as once it had. Airplanes were very
different now from those he had flown so brilliantly, and he would probably require complete retraining if he wanted to get back into one. Likewise, he still had only an eighth-
grade education. Aeronautic engineering was surely getting past him by now. The wonder
is that he was able to stay with it for so long.

Curtiss remained on the corporate board until his death, and from 1922 to 1929 was chairman of its Executive Committee. When a merger created Curtiss-Wright in 1929, he
served on the new board, and in particular on its Technical Committee. He was also on
the corporate board of the subsidiary Curtiss Flying Service, Inc., as late as 1929. He
maintained an office at the Engineering Corporation as long as he lived. However, the
challenges that Curtiss had once found in the open spaces of the road and the open
spaces of the sky he now found on the open spaces of southeastern Florida. [1, 5–7, 10]

With time and money on his hands, Curtiss indulged himself with plenty of camping and
hunting, not only in Florida but in the Adirondacks, around Hammondsport, and, once, on a
grouse moor in Scotland. As the war ended, he built on enthusiasm to bring out a new

product, the Adams Motor Bungalo, in partnership with his much younger half-brother, G. Carl Adams.

Trailers, many of them homemade, were starting to hit the road as Americans, fired by Henry Ford, became increasingly mobile. Adams and Curtiss made the Motor Bungalo in several different models, but it was usually a sort of pop-out. Awnings and extensions added to the space when it was stationary (Fig. 11.5). Bungalos had both sleeping and cooking facilities (Fig. 11.6). They had "fifth-wheel" tow hookups, with a prow sweeping back in a "V" shape from the tow spike. Roofs were hardtops. While energetically marketed, the product petered out in postwar hard times. The half-brothers made more than 100 of them, apparently at the old Hammondsport plant. [14]

Curtiss and Bright owned nearly 50,000 acres near Lake Okechobee, where they developed a new community called Brighton. Curtiss opened a hotel there and often used it as a base for hunting expeditions, frequently in the company of his old pal Tank Waters. At this hotel, Curtiss treated many guests to what must have been an utterly unforgettable experience.

Spectators had always marveled at Curtiss's incredible ability to judge distances at speed, shaving obstacles and racing pylons shockingly close. By now, Curtiss had realized that this ability extended to other areas of life as well. Packing guests into his car, he would

Fig. 11.5 The Adams Motor Bungalo. Notice the phonograph at the right.

Fig. 11.6 Home away from home.

without warning back up, at speed, not down the driveway but through the palm forest. "I looked around to see what the back seat dudes looked like," Waters wrote of one occasion. "All had very white faces and never said a word for a long time." One day, Curtiss and Waters were driving through the Everglades when they found their path newly cut by a 10-ft canal. The dirt trail on which they were driving, barely wide enough for the car, had water-filled ditches along either side. Curtiss backed the car two miles without stopping.

On at least one occasion, his practical jokes backfired. Another favorite stunt was to drive full tilt toward the edge of a swamp and brake with the front wheels in the swamp and the rear wheels on dry land. One night he forgot that he was driving a new Cord with front-wheel-drive. "[W]as his face red," Waters wrote, "because it was after working hours and help was two miles away and his passengers were prominent officials of Miami."

Despite the ranching, airplane business, and outdoor life, Curtiss remained restless. Waters remembered, "Even while he was engaged in some sport, his brain was continually working on some project in his business. After sitting in a boat for a half hour, I would usually have to tell him when he had a bite on his line, for he was either dreaming a new method of doing something or scribbling marks on an old envelope."

Curtiss and Bright experimented with papayas (Fig. 11.7) and other exotic fruits, with indifferent success. Tank Waters attributed these ventures to Curtiss's feeling that "things

*Fig. 11.7   The agricultural researcher,
inspecting his papayas.*

were not busy enough for him." Waters shrewdly concluded that such agricultural attempts call for true experts, which Curtiss decidedly was not. "Banana stalks grew so luxurious that he thought ensilage should be made of it and be a great feed for cattle. He forgot to ask the cattle if they liked the banana, which they did not. He started a couple of vegetable farms, but he placed city men on them and they did not prove profitable. On another very large farm, it was in a location that is now known as a frost belt and only now used for dairying. Goats got a stomach worm. Chicks got pneumonia and virus. Sheep wouldn't grow a marketable coat. Rabbits could not stand the heat of summer in close confinement." [9, 10, 12, 13]

More success sprang from Bright's notion to develop a flat stretch of their holdings for a new community. "Jimmy, nobody but you would want to live there," Curtiss scoffed, but went along with his partner's proposal. They flabbergasted themselves by selling $100,000 worth of lots in ten days, giving birth to the city of Hialeah (Fig. 11.8). [10]

The Florida Land Boom, joyously satirized by the Marx brothers in *Coconuts*, was on. Again, Curtiss, whether by insight or by accident, was poised to make millions of dollars.

Fig. 11.8 Curtiss built this "handsome home" when he developed Hialeah, but he didn't stay there very long—he wanted to build a big place.

In addition to his personal financial investment, Curtiss was genuinely and generously concerned about boosting the development of the Miami region. He offered land valued at $100 an acre for a racetrack in Hialeah at $15 an acre, with no money down and three years to pay. He later gave the land for the municipal golf course in what is now Miami Springs, and the water source to supply Miami and surrounding communities. He also handed out land lots to old pals and employees, such as Henry Kleckler. Kleckler decided to remain in Bath, while others took advantage of the opportunity and became Floridians, or at least snowbirds.

Moving ahead from the success of their Hialeah venture, Curtiss and Bright issued a prospectus for a new planned community—Country Club Estates, later renamed Miami Springs. The central feature of this town was to be the large country club that had been gifted to Miami. This settlement was also conceived as a themed development, with houses and public buildings in the Pueblo style, inspired by Curtiss's trips through the Southwest (Fig. 11.9).

Despite financial incentives, many buyers elected to build traditional homes. Regardless, the country club, a luxurious hotel, the municipal buildings, and many businesses used the Pueblo style. So did many private dwellings, including the two homes Glenn built for his

Fig. 11.9 Building large in such an unusual style epitomizes those frenzied days of the Roaring Twenties and the Florida Land Boom.

mother. (She didn't like the first one.) Most spectacularly, Curtiss spent $150,000 building a new home for himself, Lena, and Glenn Junior. [10]

Money like that went a long way in 1925, and Lena spent another $70,000 to decorate and furnish their new home. Built in an asymmetrical Pueblo style on the edge of the golf course, the home boasted a five-car garage, a two-story living room with massive fireplace, a swimming pool, a terrace and barbecue, gatehouses, and a waterfowl pond. Tank Waters was hired as groundskeeper. He recalled that Curtiss, in giving water rights to the city of Miami, had failed to stipulate that he himself should be exempt from charges. Bills were so high that Curtiss installed his own private water system. [9, 10, 12, 13]

Furnishings were lavish if eclectic. Lena, of course, had bravely soldiered on through years of legal battles, near-bankruptcy, and death-defying feats on Glenn's part. Now that she had luxury and money, she seemed to develop an enthusiasm for spending. Lena indulged in multiple silver sets, jade, porcelain, cut glass, and collections of elephants, ceramic shoes, and figurines in eighteenth-century style. Contracting an art specialist to help make selections, she bought two turn-of-the-century French oils after being told, "Don't buy a painting because of the name on it; buy it because you like it and want to have it in your home." [Personal communication from Mrs. Glenn Curtiss, Jr.] Interestingly, the paintings involved two staples of Steuben County agriculture: potatoes and grapes. Many of Lena's treasures are now on exhibit at the Curtiss Museum.

Lena liked the family to dress for dinner, a practice Glenn Junior, now in his early teens, found irksome. She also indulged herself in lavish entertainments, edging away from the quiet persona by which she had been known back home in Hammondsport. Her husband, however, continued his uneasiness with formal engagements. At one of her parties, he would appear, visit for a little while, and then disappear up a spiral staircase to his private office. [Personal communication]

Whenever he was resident on Long Island, Curtiss frequently bicycled to work at the Engineering Corporation. Although his Florida home was on the edge of the golf course, Curtiss never took to the game. Instead, he revived yet another boyhood interest— archery—and promoted the game of archery golf. Four-inch rings were set up on each green at the country club. Two archers made up a foursome with two golfers, one pair shooting arrows from the tee, the other driving balls. The golfers, as usual, scored by holing out. The archers scored by putting their arrows through the ring. Shots counted equally with strokes, and Curtiss with his bow often beat the club golf pros with their clubs (Fig. 11.10). [12, 13]

Fig. 11.10 Archery golf foursome on the links. Curtiss (far right) is partnering a Seminole man.

Curtiss gave local Seminoles free run of his Brighton land for hunting and grazing, frequently visiting them in company with Waters, and in the process picking up the names of Hialeah and Opa-Locka. "One day in calling at the Seminole camp, " Waters wrote, "we saw some of the Indians practicing with their bows. They did not seem very good at the game so Glenn threw his nice Stetson hat as far as he could throw it and told one of the men to shoot at it. He tried several times and never hit it. Then he saw that one of the cowboys had a pretty good hat and asked him to throw it as far as he could so he could shoot at it. Glenn had five arrows and put four of them through the hat. He spoiled the hat so he gave the cowboy money to buy another one. Beating the Indians pleased Glenn." On occasion, Seminoles would come into town and see Curtiss for medical help. [12]

While making Florida his main home, Curtiss continued spending part of each year in Hammondsport and on Long Island (Fig. 11.11). At the Engineering Corporation in 1922, he developed the flying boat glider, testing it himself on the Long Island Sound. Towed up to air speed by a motorboat, the craft soared well enough, and Curtiss saw it as the birth of a new sport along the shallow waters of Florida (Fig. 11.12). This probably was the last aircraft he oversaw from start to finish and probably the only time he flew during the post-war decade.

In Hammondsport, Curtiss summered on the lake, went fishing and hunting, and dropped in on old friends and employees, often dropping off $400 gifts to those who had worked with him in the old days. He also promoted new businesses for the town, some of them using the old airplane or motorcycle facilities. Kleckler in 1920 had started the Aerial Service Corporation to buy and sell surplus *Jenny* parts. He did not remain with the business

Fig. 11.11 Similar to his father, Glenn Junior loved fast cars. Apparently, he got his start at their Long Island place with this Smith Flier, powered by the Motor Wheel at the rear centerline.

Fig. 11.12 The flying boat glider was another of Curtiss's great ideas that never caught on. Tom Swift would have liked it, though.

long, and the new owners renamed it Mercury Aircraft, Inc. As the twenty-first century opened, the company was a metal and plastics fabricator, rather than an aircraft manufacturer, but it retains the name and is the largest employer in the area—an indirect benefit of those early Curtiss days. Two lighter-than-air companies—Airships, Incorporated and Meadowcroft—soon passed from the scene, although Meadowcroft, now called Air Cruisers, survives as a New Jersey company specializing in escape equipment.

✮ ✮ ✮

The Motor Bungalo business was gone but not forgotten. Curtiss had an oversized model he used himself. (Now pushing 50, he may have wanted a little more comfort in his outdoor life.) He used several more as mobile billboards to promote his land developments, catching the eye of Carl G. Fisher. No stranger to automotives, Fisher had founded the Indianapolis Speedway and the Prest-O-Lite Company. He took several test rides, startled Curtiss by announcing that he wanted to buy four, and urged the former aviator to start manufacturing. "Glenn Curtiss has the greatest trailer that was ever made in America," Fisher wrote. [14]

Curtiss had not been thinking about resuming manufacture, but he revealed that he had been looking for ways to attract more industry to south Florida. Fired by Fisher's enthusiasm, Curtiss joined him and several others to form the Aerocar Corporation in 1928. Briggs Body Corporation and Hudson Motor Car both took licenses to manufacture, but Aerocar also manufactured and sold on its own behalf, first in Curtiss's new development of Opa-Locka and then in Coral Gables (Fig. 11.13).

Fig. 11.13   The younger (but bigger) brother of the Motor Bungalo, the Curtiss Aerocar. In the background are the municipal buildings at Opa-Locka, which Curtiss planned with an Arabian Nights theme. Most actual development in Opa-Locka took place well after Curtiss's death.

The Aerocar name and its propeller trademark were obviously designed to capitalize on Curtiss's aeronautic reputation, but they were more than merely a pretty conceit. The company advertised that an Aerocar was built like a *Jenny*. It was wood, wire, and fabric, depending on internal turnbuckled cross-braces for its internal support. Even though the trailer was more than 19 ft long, it was remarkably light.

Aerocars (and their licensed cousins) had a single axle set far aft, with a fifth-wheel hookup set slightly forward of the rear axle of the tow vehicle. This required retrofitting. (Hudsons were usually recommended, because of the business relationship, but owners used vehicles of many makes.) The tow spike dropped into the open axle of an airplane wheel cushioned by a Goodyear tire.

Curtiss believed that automotive engineering was sloppy because it could get away with being sloppy. Aeronautic engineering, as he saw it, did not have that luxury. After World War I, he had devoted a good deal of study to automotives, several times having autos custom-built to test his conclusions. He had long since decided that a three-axis chassis and a passenger compartment independent of the engine compartment would make for a smoother ride. Naturally, being Glenn Curtiss, he wanted to decrease weight and increase speed. He applied all these concepts to the Aerocar, which he saw not so much as a trailer but as one component of a complete articulated vehicle. Aerocars traveling from Florida to northern states were clocked as having average speeds approaching or exceeding 40 mph. Considering that there was no interstate highway system, and that at some points the vehicles were either traveling quite slowly or stopped altogether, cruising speed would have been much higher. Curtiss claimed that the rig could travel easily and comfortably at 55 mph. He also claimed that because of the aerodynamic design, an auto with the trailer could travel even faster than the same auto without one! [14]

Aerocars were available in varied configurations, including an ambulance, a school bus, an open tour bus, and a horse trailer. Cities Service used one as a traveling movie theater touting its wares. Enna Jettick Shoes outfitted a fleet for its sales force, whose members no longer needed to lug sample boxes in and out of stores. They could take buyers out to their rolling show rooms, where all the styles were tastefully displayed along the walls.

The Aerocar's main market, however, was people interested in luxury travel. While there were some gestures toward a mid-range market, Aerocars remained an upper-end product throughout their existence. The elegant design, with its sweeping V-shaped prow and its aerodynamic lines, was more than modern—it was futuristic. Many featured an Art Deco–style interior. Bunks were concealed when not in use. There was a single-seat "facility," a stove, a shower, a sink, an icebox, and, in many units, a built-in radio. There were crank windows at a time when many automakers still supplied windows with straps. One disconcerting feature was the decorative interior use of tiny fylfots—the reverse swastika that was regarded as a good luck symbol in the days before Hitler seized power.

As time passed and models proliferated, prices ranged between $2,600 and $6,000. Because the Great Depression was raging through much of the period, these were indeed luxury items. Production ran into hundreds of units at the Florida firm alone, although demand dwindled as more competitors entered the field. Manufacturing ended about the time of Pearl Harbor. [2–4, 10, 14]

The Aerocar, the movie studio, Curtiss-Bright Properties, and sundry other ventures were, of course, separate from the Curtiss Aeroplane and Motor Corporation. Curtiss remained involved with the old company, although more distantly as the years passed.

Clement Keys continued to head Curtiss Aeroplane, and relations between the two men were good enough so that each served on boards of several of the other's corporations. Keys had kept the company's head above water and, by the late 1920s, even had it moving ahead. Good times had returned in the U.S. economy. The World War I–era airplanes were becoming technically obsolete and individually senescent. The Lindbergh Boom of

1927 had sparked an explosion of enthusiasm for aviation. Military establishments across the globe were recognizing their need to keep current. As the U.S. armed forces updated their inventories, previous models became available for second-tier powers overseas.

Keys envisioned a vertical consolidation—not a monopoly, but a huge conglomerate that would offer nearly every service in aeronautics. Within the company, he already had experienced operations for research and development, for airframe manufacture, for power-plant manufacture (although Curtiss no longer led in that field), for air and ground schools, for field operations, and for small-scale flying services. Now Keys invested heavily in airlines, including passenger, mail, and cargo routes. He purchased strong stock positions in a number of smaller firms, including Sikorsky and Cessna. He arranged mergers that created Curtiss-Robertson in St. Louis, Curtiss-Reid in Canada, and Curtiss-Caproni, which would manufacture Italian-designed seaplanes. He acquired Pitcairn Aviation and Sperry Gyroscope and set up the Curtiss Airports Corporation to buy or create modern airports for key U.S. cities. The Keys Group (sometimes called the Curtiss Group, after its star holding) was a loose collection coordinated largely by interlocking directorships. [1, 7]

Meanwhile, at Wright Aeronautical, after Glenn Martin's disgusted withdrawal from the merger during World War I, the company had saved itself by manufacturing Hispano-Suiza engines under license. This continued to be a profitable business after the war, and Wright purchased the Lawrance Aero Engine Company to acquire its new air-cooled radial engine. Wright was not particularly enthusiastic about the product, but the U.S. Army and U.S. Navy were interested in the technology.

Charles Lawrance stayed with the merged firm, continuously elaborating and developing what would eventually become the premier product of the company, the Wright Whirlwind Engine. Lawrance himself eventually became company president. Richard Hoyt, chairman of Wright Aeronautical, began an expansion campaign similar to that of Keys, with whom he served on several corporate boards. Wright Aeronautical held strong positions in two airframe manufacturers (Keystone and Travel Air), not to mention several airlines and several financial firms that were concerned with aeronautics.

After considerable discussion between Keys and Hoyt, the Curtiss-Wright Corporation was announced in June 1929. With assets exceeding $75 million, it was second in size only to General Motors among U.S. companies. Besides Hoyt and Keys, the leadership included Charles Lawrance, Walter Beech, and Glenn Curtiss. Curtiss served on the corporate board, heading its technical committee. With the star-studded leadership, the gigantic assets, the experienced and widespread holdings across nearly the entire spectrum of aeronautics, a rising market, and the oldest names in the business, Curtiss-Wright seemed set for gratifying profitability. Unfortunately, four months later, the stock market crashed, leaving Curtiss-Wright scrambling again until World War II restored its fortunes, which sadly but almost inevitably declined again thereafter. [7]

The Florida Land Boom had started to bust in 1925–1926, leaving Curtiss with a good deal of land on his hands. He had started the development of Opa-Locka with an Arabian Nights theme. The municipal hall and the street names remain, but most residential development did not revive until after World War II, and future builders did not choose to continue the Baghdad look.

Curtiss served on various governmental boards, generously gave away land and water rights, and founded 18 corporations (including a movie studio) in Florida alone. When a hotel he had started in Miami Springs failed to develop its anticipated clientele, he turned it over to Dr. Henry Kellogg for $6. Kellogg used the place as a sanitarium, and it is now a nursing home. Finding one of his old contract pilots, Jimmie Ward, gravely ill with tuberculosis and alcoholism, Curtiss hurried him into a hospital. The two men had not parted on good terms, but Curtiss paid Ward's debts and cared for him until the "Minnesota Shooting Star's" death.

Curtiss's generosity had become such a byword that he was constantly beset by those in need, those who had little need but optimistically hoped for a handout, and those who had various business schemes to float. Tank Waters would bring Curtiss's car around to the back of his office building. Curtiss would go out his window, cross a roof, and drop down to the waiting car, after which the two friends were off to the great outdoors. In addition to hunting and fishing, they sometimes snared nuisance alligators and relocated them. Once while riding with Curtiss company official C. W. Webster, Curtiss leaned out the window of a moving car and brought down a flying hawk with a single rifle shot. [10, 12, 13]

In keeping with his policy of encouraging the development of southeastern Florida, Curtiss contributed heavily to the fledgling University of Miami. For its second commencement in 1930, the university honored Curtiss with a degree. [10]

Curtiss remained, as ever, allergic to formal occasions, and photographs of him in cap, hood, and gown are somewhat amusing. An appealing legend insists that he was inveigled into the ceremony and the platform party (not to mention the regalia), but correspondence in existence at the university demonstrates clearly that arrangements were made with Curtiss's full participation (Fig. 11.14). He must have been pleased to accept his honorary degree as Doctor of Science. It was, no doubt, more than he could have aspired to when

Fig. 11.14 Glenn Curtiss, Doctor of Science (honoris causa).

he dropped out of school and went to work after finishing eighth grade in Rochester, many years earlier. He was a forward-looking guy even in those early days, but it is unlikely that even his wildest dreams projected the life he had lived in the interim.

On Memorial Day of 1930, nine days after his fifty-second birthday, Curtiss was in Albany for the twentieth anniversary of his flight down the Hudson. In 1910, he had piloted what resembled a powered box kite, perched on a tiny seat in the midst of all that bamboo and rigging, directly in front of the droning 50-hp engine. Now he would ride in a Curtiss Condor carrying 18 passengers and two crew members. This was a closed-cabin biplane airliner, designed for luxury rather than speed. Twin 1250-hp Curtiss Conqueror engines were mounted between the wings, minimizing vibration and noise in the fuselage. Joined by Lena, Glenn Junior (who would turn 18 in little more than two weeks), Henry Kleckler, Augustus Post, the mayor of Albany, and other dignitaries, Curtiss, with gray suit and Panama hat, would ride in comfort. [10]

Except that Glenn Curtiss did not plan simply to ride. After a luncheon hosted by Lieutenant Governor Lehman, pilot Frank Courtney took off from the Municipal Airport, which had evolved from Curtiss's 1910 takeoff site. Once they were airborne, Glenn Curtiss took the controls.

Courtney gave him some coaching. Curtiss had never handled craft similar to this and almost certainly had not flown since his seaplane glider experiments in 1922, with a likely gap of several years preceding that time. "He reared up like an old war horse scenting battle," Courtney wrote. "In his time he had hardly ever known a plane that didn't have to be manhandled all the time, so he kept up a series of small control motions just on principle."

On reaching the Catskills, they ran afoul of a west wind and increasing turbulence. "Curtiss, as in days of yore, worked purposefully to correct every gust and bump. Above all, he kept in mind the pioneer pilot's ingrained principle of precaution against the risk of stalling: 'When in doubt, push the nose down.'" Curtiss gleefully dove and climbed, according to Courtney, who "glanced inquiringly at Glenn with a view to taking over from him. But he obviously had no remote desire to relinquish the controls; he was having the time of his life. So I felt that this was his day, and short of impending disaster, I was going to let him enjoy it." Both pilots had forgotten the passengers until one of them staggered forward to shout that they were all getting sick. "Reluctantly I took over," Courtney concluded, "and Glenn sat back with the air of a man who has proved his point." (Fig. 11.15)

Augustus Herring had died in 1926, but his family continued the lawsuit against Curtiss. Lena repeatedly urged her husband to settle and put the mess behind them, but Curtiss flatly refused. His erstwhile partner claimed that Herring-Curtiss had never been properly extinguished, and that the three Hammondsport directors (Curtiss, Tom Baldwin, and Judge Monroe Wheeler) had conspired against him, defrauding him by taking the company into bankruptcy and thereby violating their fiduciary responsibility toward him as a stockholder. It turned out to be true that Judge Wheeler had never formally dissolved the company. Whatever Curtiss's own defaults may have been in these matters, his lawyers certainly served him poorly in this case and in the early stages of the Wright suit.

A 1923 ruling by Judge Hazel (who by then must have been tired of seeing Curtiss in court) came down squarely against Herring. However, an appeals court in 1928, while

*Fig. 11.15
Final flight.*

dismissing charges against all lesser defendants, ruled against the three directors, of whom only Curtiss was still living.

Further proceedings absorbed much of Curtiss's time when he returned to Hammondsport after the Hudson River anniversary flight. Traveling back and forth to Rochester, he once testified for five days straight. Heading north for another such session, he was seized by severe abdominal pain, bouts of which had been troubling him for some time. His driver hurried him home.

Lawyers for the Herring heirs charged that this was a dodge, and the referee appointed three Rochester doctors to examine Curtiss in Hammondsport. Their report was swift and firm: Curtiss was severely ill from appendicitis and required immediate surgery. An ambulance took him to Bath, where he transferred to a private compartment on the DL&W. Arriving in Buffalo, he walked (with difficulty) to the ambulance that carried him to Buffalo General, where he was operated on the following morning, July 11.

The operation was a complete success, and surgeons took the opportunity to detach some adhesions from old motorcycle injuries. Lena stayed at the hospital as telegrams rushed in from well-wishers, including Richard Byrd, Jack Towers, Dr. Kellogg, the mayor of Miami Springs, the governor of Florida, and Glenn Junior's old nursemaid. Half-brother G. Carl Adams rushed with his wife by train from Florida to Buffalo, taking many responsibilities off Lena's shoulders. Glenn and Carl's mother, who was by now quite elderly, remained in Florida with Glenn's sister Rutha. Carl wired her, reporting his arrival and address and stating that Glenn was "resting comfortably after successful operation for appendix probably caused by old bruise years ago." (On the telegraph blank, Carl had substituted "bruise" after striking out "motorcycle accident." Apparently, he felt there was no need to burden mother with memories of motorcycle accidents a quarter-century past.) "No cause for concern will keep you fully advised love Lena and Carl."

Indeed, no cause appeared. Curtiss was recovering nicely and arranged to return to Hammondsport by rail. On July 22, a Christian Science practitioner visited; Curtiss had become interested in Christian Science, which had captivated his mother 20 years earlier. He gave some dictation to Florence Illig. The next morning, as he was preparing for discharge, he suddenly slumped toward the floor. His private nurse caught him, and Lena was instantly summoned from the Statler. However, a staff doctor declared Curtiss dead two minutes after he was stricken. He was felled by pulmonary embolism, a small blood clot near his heart. The very short, very active life of Glenn Curtiss was over.

The Episcopal rector in Hammondsport conducted funeral services in the Curtiss home two days later. Lena wore white mourning, supported by Glenn Junior, Carl, and Carl's wife Dot, not to mention lifelong village friends. Three of Glenn's first cousins attended, although Lua and Rutha remained in Florida. Jack Towers was an honorary pallbearer, as were Holden Richardson, Lanny Callan, and Miami mayor C. H. Reeder. The active bearers were all old friends—Tank Waters, Henry Kleckler, Harry Genung, Rumsey Wheeler, Jim Bauder, and K. B. MacDonald.

Glenn Curtiss was buried by the side of his baby son Carlton, only a few feet from the graves of his father and his Curtiss grandparents. Stony Brook Farm, site of the *White Wing* and *June Bug* flights only 22 years earlier, was clearly visible from the family plot. Ten airplanes flew overhead and dropped flowers on the crowd. [8, 10, 11]

REFERENCES

1.   Bowers, Peter M., *Curtiss Aircraft 1907–1947,* Putnam, London, 1979.

2.   "The Curtiss Aerocar," Curtiss Aerocar Company, Coral Gables, FL, circa 1936, GHCM 93-10-1.

3.   Curtiss Aerocar catalog, Curtiss Aerocar Company of Florida, Coral Gables, FL, (n.d.), GHCM 83-82-3.

4.   Curtiss Aerocar catalog, Curtiss Aerocar Company of Florida, Coral Gables, FL, (n.d.), GHCM Aerocar Files.

5.   "The Curtiss Aeroplane and Motor Corporation," *The Aircraft Year Book 1919,* Doubleday, Page and Company for the Manufacturers Aircraft Association, New York, 1919.

6.   "Curtiss Aeroplane and Motor Corp.; Curtiss Engineering Corp.; The Burgess Company," *Aircraft Year Book 1920,* Doubleday, Page and Company for the Manufacturers Aircraft Association, New York, 1920.

7.   Eltscher, Louis R., and Edward M. Young, *Curtiss-Wright: Greatness and Decline,* Twayne Publishers, New York, 1998.

8.   The *Hammondsport Herald,* published weekly throughout Curtiss's lifetime, includes multitudinous references to Curtiss, his works, and his times. (Curtiss Museum holds a microfilmed set.)

9.   Mitchell, Charles R., and Kirk W. House, *Glenn H. Curtiss, Aviation Pioneer,* Arcadia Publishing, Charleston, SC, 2001.

10. Roseberry, C. R., *Glenn Curtiss: Pioneer of Flight,* Doubleday & Company, Garden City, NY, 1972.

11. Studer, Clara, *Sky Storming Yankee: The Life of Glenn Curtiss,* Stackpole Sons, New York, 1937.

12. Waters, C. Leonard, to Nancy Hutches, undated typescript, GHCM Yorkers Collection.

13. ———, to Nancy Hutches, undated typescript, GHCM Yorkers Collection.

14. White, Roger, "Planes, Trailers and Automobiles: The Land Yachts of Glenn Curtiss," in *Automobile Quarterly,* vol. 32, no. 3, January 1994, pp. 30–47.

Chapter 12

Close-Up:
Land Yachting

★ ★ ★

Curtiss probably loved driving even more than he loved flying, cycling, or motorcycling. Speed and maneuverability were always his goals, and as time passed, he added a third goal—comfort. It is difficult to say whether this was simply a goal he now had the luxury to pursue, whether it was a sign of encroaching middle age, or whether comfort was a potential marketing ploy.

Curtiss had never pursued auto manufacturing, although he had held multiple dealerships in Hammondsport, going back as far as the one-cylinder Orient Buckboard days. Although automobiles had developed rapidly in the first two decades of the twentieth century, they did not keep pace with airplane evolution. Of course, Henry Ford—as principal manufacturer at that time—had opted for democratization rather than for advancement (not that the two are necessarily incompatible). Ford also exerted a considerable conservative influence, clinging to the Model T and the later Model A as long as possible (or even longer) and vigorously resisting any move past four cylinders.

However, Curtiss had done a certain amount of experimenting with auto technology. The 1917 Autoplane was an extreme example, and he had made his propeller-driven wind wagons as far back as 1905. He also fitted several cars with his 90-hp OX engines, apparently finding the resultant speed and power quite satisfying. Beyond that, over the years he ordered several automobiles to be custom-built to his specifications, experimenting with more streamlined designs than were typically found on the contemporary market (Fig. 12.1). [13]

As far as Glenn Curtiss was concerned, auto technology in general was unsatisfying. Perhaps this is not surprising because autos were—to some extent—still a hybrid technology. In ways, they were powered wagons or powered carriages. Why shouldn't they step forth as a new type of vehicle altogether?

Fig. 12.1 One of Glenn Curtiss's custom-built autos.

Curtiss saw several drawbacks in autos of the 1920s. [16]

1. Noise was transmitted to the passengers.

2. Vibration was transmitted to the passengers.

3. Passengers had to ride in cramped positions, causing toxins to accumulate.

4. Auto bodies were not well designed, presenting considerable problems with weight and drag.

5. Weight and drag meant that overpowered engines were required (producing even more vibration, noise, and weight).

6. Paradoxically, despite overpowered engines, excess weight and drag sacrificed speed.

7. High net weight and cramped conditions limited carrying capacity.

Noise, vibration, and cramping problems were not simply matters of creature comfort to Curtiss. He recognized that all three factors contributed to fatigue, limiting both safety and time on the road. Weight, drag, and power problems also contributed to excess fuel consumption, although I am not aware of any record indicating that Curtiss explicitly addressed this issue.

The Adams Trailer and Motor Bungalo (sometimes MotorBungalo) business in the early 1920s laid the groundwork for the more successful Aerocar. "Make that extra power serve," urged an Adams brochure. The focus of this particular advertising piece was the cargo trailer, "always ready to serve at a moment's notice and at no expense, utilizing only the power which is otherwise wasted in your motor. . . . It will work just as efficiently as a one-ton truck at merely one-tenth of the initial cost and no upkeep expense." Paralleling "Adams Trailer service for the motorist" with "Railroad Trailer service for the nation," Adams proclaimed, "The Pulling Power is Greater Than the Carrying Power." [2]

Adams (and Curtiss) offered at least 15 models: the top-of-the-line Motor Bungalo, at $1,200; four "Camp Trailers," ranging from $485 to $655; and ten "Commercial Trailers" starting at $215 ("with Dumping Attachment") and rising to $370 ("with Solid Delivery Body").

The Model R Camp Trailer Light weighed 855 lb. Commercial Trailers, while standardizing beds as much as possible, varied considerably in weight. Model B-2 (with top and 32-in. rack) was 655 lb. The B-1, with its 14-in. rack, weighed 30 lb less. The more basic Model A and Model B came in at 410 lb and 485 lb, respectively, while a Cattle Rack Trailer, retailing at $240, weighed merely 160 lb. [14] The crating for shipping added 50 lb. Two trailers (model not stated) could be packed for export in a crate 166 × 58 × 18 in.—shades of Curtiss's arrival in France with his *Reims Racer*! Crating two trailers with tops varied only the depth, from 18 to 30 in., thereby increasing cubic footage from 100 to 167. [15]

The makers, working with a basic design kept standard as much as possible, paid careful attention to interchangeability, quick conversions, and add-ons, themes that had been stressed in the "Curtiss Aeroplanes" catalog ten years earlier. The basic bed had a single axle with two wheels. [2] It was rectangular with a leading triangular prow, from the apex of which the tow spike descended. The bed on a basic model was open (Fig. 12.2).

Starting with a basic Model A at $195, customers could select—or purchase at a later date—from among various options, designed to fit into any of the beds. The $50 cattle rack had vertical pieces spaced every 12 in., but most attachments used only five uprights, one at each vertex of the five-sided bed. A Standard Top gave the buyer an enclosed cab with a rear door. The Express Top had a solid waterproof roof but relied on Tufhyde side curtains with Murphy buttons to make the unit "absolutely water- and dust-proof." For $40, the buyer could get a double deck, raised 27 in. above the bed, which could be used

Fig. 12.2 The Adams Trailer in its most basic form.

for light deliveries and for carrying items that should not be stacked. Adams suggested that this top be used in conjunction with the Express Top. [1]

A 35-in. woven rack of 1-1/2 in. wire mesh could be used with the express top for theft protection, or it could be used independently for additional loading height. The 14-in. rack could be mounted, if desired, with a 45° outward flare.

Forty dealers, distributors, and agencies offered Adams Trailers in Connecticut, Florida, Massachusetts, New Jersey, New York, Ohio, Pennsylvania, Ontario, and Quebec. [10] Inevitably, there were teething problems. Tailgate brackets caused trouble, and workers scrambled to find a standard part to replace their spring snap (stressing "cost and simplicity of operation"), before concluding that the problem was caused by inaccurate location of the hinges on the body and tailgate. A 1921 memo from Carl Adams ordered, "Solid pins should be substituted for the cotter pin in the front stand at the earliest possible moment. THIS IS IMPERATIVE!" [4]

Nelson Parker of Asbury Park, who seems to have been involved with promoting the trailers, wrote about problems he experienced "on the road home." While making a short turn, he found the electric light wire was too short; it burned out, causing "considerable damage." He then discovered that the lamp, which also burned out, would have done no good anyhow, requiring 6.8 V while his Dodge battery produced 12.16 V. [10] On top of that, the glass lens fell out and broke. "Merely as a suggestion, I believe it would be quite advisable not to connect up these cars until you know what kind of a car they are to be used on," Parker wrote, rather mildly under the circumstances.

Parker's night was not over yet. One of the rollers on the right wheel was missing a bearing, and the paint on the rear doors was peeling and blistering. He also requested a new washer and felt washer for the inside of the wheel, although not explaining whether these were needed because of a factory defect. "Outside of this, I believe everything is all o.k.," he added cheerfully. The next day, Parker wrote, "We had a large crowd at the show last night and they kept us very busy. The future looks very bright." [12]

Referring as he did to the rear doors, Parker may have had one of the camp trailers, or even a flagship Motor Bungalo. These were "a most luxurious outfit," featuring two full-length clothes closets ("dustproof"); a gun and fish-pole locker; food lockers opening from inside and outside the cab; water tank; ice chest; screens ("absolutely insect proof"); interior in either white enamel or dark oak; steel kitchenette ("to comply with the standards of the most exacting housekeeper"); table seating for six (although this appears as if it would have been a bit cramped); felt mattresses with springs that did not sag; and electric light. "It meets all the known requirements; it anticipates many others." You could break camp, advertisements earnestly assured shoppers, in three minutes.

Motor Bungalos packed a lot into a space that was 12 ft 6 in. long by 5 ft 8 in. wide, with a height of 6 ft 4 in. When parked, campers could "pop out" enclosed bunks on either side to expand the sleeping space. The trailers had 15 in. of road clearance. Weight was approximately 850 lb.

"Purchasers of Adams Trailers," the company suggested, "can change or complete any desired model in the Adams group by the simple addition of one or more of the accessories which are specially designed and interchangeable. They can be attached or detached in a jiffy." For $75, buyers could have a kitchenette and wardrobe installed in the bow. A toilet and tent (folding into a dustproof case $15 \times 24 \times 7$ in.) cost $30. Fire apparatus for commercial units was negotiable. A complete Camp Equipment set for four sold for $150. [9]

The inventory of these sets, with sources and costs, is detailed in an interesting memo to Carl Adams from purchasing agent Bert Channer. Folding chairs came from Abercrombie and Fitch. A Kamp Kook Stove from Baker, Murray, and Imbrie cost $6.50, while a four-person aluminum cooking outfit was the most expensive component at $23. Kitchen supplies also included galvanized dishpan and enamel washbasin, a bread knife, kitchen knife, and combination cork screw/can opener. Scott Tissue Paper supplied paper towel rolls at 49 cents apiece and paper towel racks for 25 cents. Napkins, from B. Gertz, were $2 per thousand. There was a 36×72 in. rug, four pillows, a folding toilet, and a $9 tent for the same.

Of course, a buyer had to expect to rough it. The axe cost Adams $1.25, the spade 58 cents. One duffel bag was supplied. The lowest cost on the list of accessories was

7 cents for a locker key. It would seem that truly this was, as a sales brochure put it, "Gypsie Life Modernized." [1, 9; for more detail, see 3, 5, 11]

The sales and export offices were located at Grand Central Palace in New York City, headquarters and factory at Garden City, Long Island (also home to the Curtiss Engineering Corporation). At least some production went on at Keuka Industries, which also was a distributorship, in Hammondsport; Curtiss had sponsored Keuka Industries in an effort to provide as much business as possible in his home village. The Adams camp trailers were widely acknowledged as top of the line immediately after the war, although they also were priced accordingly. Postwar economic troubles depressed sales, and the business gave out around 1922. Ironically, on November 28 of that year, Glenn Curtiss received his patent for the "Camp Car." [16]

Many of the trailers remained in service, but the business itself seemed safely, if sadly, interred. Curtiss continued his auto experiments, however. In 1925, he applied for a patent on a three-axle auto with independent suspension of the passenger and engine compartments. [17] By 1928, he had further refined the trailer, applying for another patent on the new design. [18] He seems to have made one for personal use and to have employed several more as rolling billboards and sales offices in the frantically booming region of southeastern Florida. These few units led Carl Fisher to rhapsodize, "Glenn Curtiss has the greatest trailer that was ever made in America. . . ." Inspired by Fisher, Curtiss joined him to create the Aerocar Corporation. [16]

The patent application described Curtiss's invention as "a simplified trailer unit in which there is no chassis, as distinguished from the body structure itself." [18] He accomplished this with "a body structure having its sides constructed in the form of light trusses, said trusses being connected at top and bottom by transverse members forming with the trusses a box girder of substantially the full length, depth, and width of the body." The patent drawings (Fig. 12.4) showed horizontal and vertical members with interior wire cross bracing along the sides, an arrangement with which Curtiss had been intimately familiar as far back as the AEA Chanute-type hang glider 20 years earlier. Curtiss had squared off the *Jenny* fuselage, blown it up, and converted it into a road vehicle.

This arrangement, Curtiss pointed out, could be manufactured at lower cost than "the traditional chassis-body structure now in use." It could carry the same (or a greater) useful load as a much heavier "vehicle built according to current practice." Curtiss added that the new trailer "permits of more economical transportation of merchandise, passengers, and the like, by virtue of its greater carrying power for a stipulated gross weight, and by reason of the decreased tractive effort required to draw it."

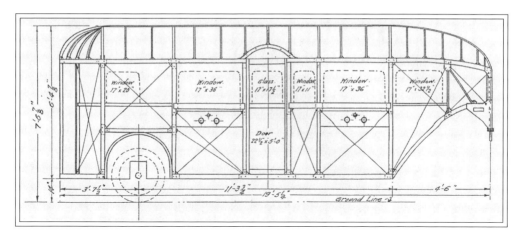

Fig. 12.3   Aerocar construction, as shown by sales brochure.

The trailer certainly was light. Besides dispensing with the load-carrying chassis, Curtiss kept the rest of the vehicle as light as possible. The frame was anchored in two chord members, generally U-shaped, which footed and headed the sides and rear of the trailer. Curtiss suggested that these be made of wood, as well as the uprights joining the longitudinal chords (they used laminated spruce in actual construction). The diagonal cross bracing, he further suggested, could be made from piano wire. Because the body covering did not support the load, it also could be made of any desirable light material. The patent application suggested using a sound insulator, "thus insuring practically noiseless transportation in the trailer."

Curtiss had a box girder on wheels, using "a single trussed structure to perform the functions of both" the chassis and the body. "I am able to attain the needed strength while reducing the weight of the structure because of the extreme beam depth available in the load carrying trusses, which enable them to be built in the lightest possible manner." These arrangements, he added, readily lent themselves to cheap mass production (Fig. 12.3).

Two wheels on a single axle were secured to the box girder near the rear end. At the front, converging members swept forward and upward to form the dramatic prow with its tow spike.

A concurrent patent application covered the hitch. This Aero Coupler generally was a 25-in. square compartment, set at least 10 in. forward of the rear axle of the tow car, in which an airplane wheel and tire lay horizontally (Fig. 12.5). The spike slipped into the hub of the wheel (where it would normally be mounted on the axle of the aircraft). The inflated tire provided cushioning in the horizontal plane, while seven rubber disks cushioned vertically. This improved tracking, but it required using something along the lines of a

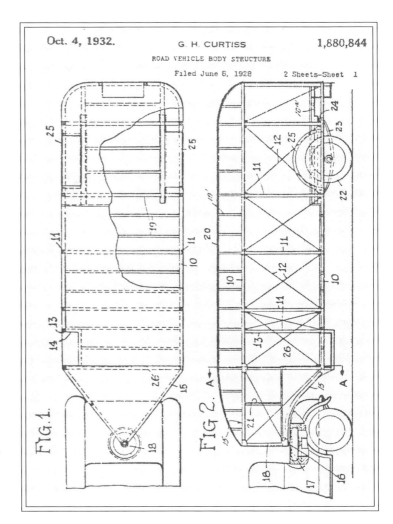

Fig. 12.4 Aerocar patent diagram.

roadster or a coupe for the tow vehicle. "In most cases, it is only necessary to install one or two extra leaves in the rear springs of the power unit." [8] The hitch was forward of the drive axle of the power unit, so that the trailer in a sense was being pushed rather than towed.

While making the cargo capabilities of the trailer perfectly clear, Curtiss obviously envisioned the Aerocar as a superior passenger vehicle. In addition to suggesting ways to abate noise in the trailer, he also opined in his application that a trailer would diminish skidding on the part of the tow vehicle, and that the passengers would be safer in the rear than they would be in a standard four-wheel vehicle. He further stated—probably optimistically—that passengers would be safer in this vehicle than in a traditional model because

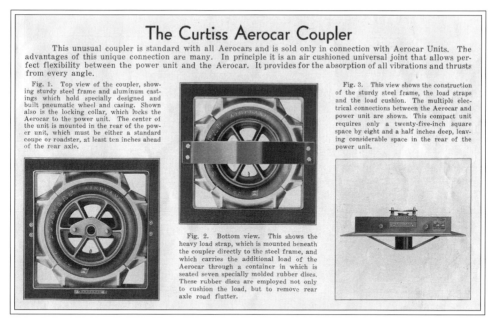

Fig. 12.5 Even the hitch of the Aerocar emphasized aeronautic connections.

the body was unlikely to break or twist if turned over. Riding qualities, he also suggested, would be "greatly improved" in this vehicle.

☆ ☆ ☆

References in company literature to the tow car as the "power unit" reflected thinking that seemed to view the Aerocar not as a trailer but as the carrying component of an articulated six-wheel vehicle. Commercial users signed on quickly; some listed in company literature had previous or prospective connections with Curtiss. Pan Am ferried passengers to, from, and around airports with a fleet of four 12-seat versions. Florida Year-Round Clubs used a dozen 18-passenger models. Enna Jettick Shoe Company (owned by a distant relative) equipped four for its sales staff, who could now bring buyers to view neatly stocked shelves, rather than lugging boxes in and out of stores. Carl Fisher reported traveling 12,000 miles through 18 states with no more problems than two punctured tires. The city of Miami used an open-bed Aerotruck to haul garbage, reporting that 200-stop trips, averaging 4.67 tons a load, were accomplished at 5.39 mpg. W. L. Philbrick, an undertaker at Miami and Coral Gables, was enthusiastic about his ambulance model. [6]

Other unconnected entities seized on the transportation and promotion opportunities offered by Aerocars. Georgia Warm Springs used one to transport guests, as did many resorts and hotels. Foster Brothers of Owings Mills, Maryland, used the four-stall horse trailer version, for which the low clearance of the Aerocar was extremely useful. In addition to moving their own animals, they used the vehicle to transport horses commercially. General Electric brought its appliances directly in Aerocars to prospective customers— some were even tricked out to resemble a row of refrigerators on the exterior. Cities Service used its Aerocar as a roving theater. Pure Oil made an Aerocar into a sound truck, selling 1800 gal of gasoline in one day at a station in a town where the previous maximum had been 800 gal. Grolier outfitted a tasteful, dignified reading room on wheels. [6]

An early catalog listed nine commercial models: Ambulance Type, Commercial Type (the open-bed truck), two Horse Car versions, two Observation Types, Passenger Transportation Type, and Streamline Club Car Type. Most of these (and most passenger versions) were built on the basic Model 61, which was 19 ft 4 in. from nose to tail. These were all described as being "Custom built at Opa-Locka," Florida, and so could be readily adapted to the specifications of the commercial customer. [7]

However, it was in personal use that the Aerocar shone with its true glory. Streamlined, designed with an Art Deco feel, dramatic, huge, lightweight, efficient, and lavish, Aerocars seemed to be the wave of the future. Emphasis on the aeronautic connections—advertising "sturdy airplane construction" and Curtiss's successful career in aeronautic engineering and manufacturing, using the Curtiss name, the prefix "aero," and even a propeller on the trademark—only added to its forward-looking mystique.

Personal Aerocars were marketed as luxury items, and many owners had their cars customized, usually before delivery. A forward observation dome seems to have been a popular choice, and some units had a graceful rear taper rather than the uncompromising "back wall" typically seen. The $2,500 Model 61 was essentially a shell. Upper berths retailed at $110, lowers at $250. Linoleum was the original equipment for floors, but customers could upgrade to carpet for $40. Chemical toilets went for $25, marine types for almost three times as much. A monel lavatory with marine pump and 6-gal supply tank cost $105. [7]

Windows had crank handles at a time when many autos continued to depend on straps. Four types of cushioned seats were available, including two that could come in side-by-side arrangements. Some seats could recline or fold out to form beds. Pullman-style curtains could give each berth a measure of privacy. A divan with genuine leather upholstery would set a buyer back $142.50. Other amenities included flower vases, luggage carriers, fans, radios, a cigar lighter, and window drapes. For $45, a buyer could have a telephone installed and talk with the driver. Two refrigerators (actually iceboxes) were available.

This was a far cry from the Adams Motor Bungalo! However, those camping days were not forgotten, and the catalog illustrated the $2,600 Model 61-C with a set of suggested options: daybed; four seats (which could be combined to form two beds); two cabinets;

closet; refrigerator; toilet; wash basin; two-burner stove; two cigar lighters; and radio. All of this would cost in excess of $600. Original equipment included two doors, three dome lights, stabilators (shock absorbers), a push-button signal to the driver's seat, linoleum floors, ivory lacquer finish in the galley, and leatherette finish in various colors for both interior and exterior. Similar to most models, the Model 61-C was 19 ft 4 in. long and 6 ft 2 in. wide. There were no longer any "pop-out" features. [7]

Although Curtiss emphasized those features that were allied to aeronautics, he also referred to these vehicles as "land yachts." If we imagine ourselves on the road in the 1920s or 1930s, an Aerocar with tow vehicle must have resembled a majestic ship cleaving through the sea of lesser craft. I spoke once with one of the Tuskegee Airmen, and near the end of our conversation, he asked whether we had a Curtiss Aerocar in our museum. "When I was a young man," he said, "it was my ambition to own a Curtiss Aerocar." I told him that I could certainly see why—it probably would have been my ambition, too.

Marketing a large luxury product during the Depression certainly had its drawbacks. In the mid-1930s, Aerocar announced that the Series 61 models would henceforth be the deluxe line (Fig. 12.6). The new Series 161 would be "less expensive and within reach of all," or at any rate all who had $1,985 for a basic unit with no interior equipment (Fig. 12.7). Fitting this with kitchen and sleeping accommodation for four raised the price to $2,840 and the weight from 1900 lb to 2800 lb. The 161-C Standard Model was now 19 ft 9-5/8 in. long × 6 ft 2 in. wide. It had 14 ft of clearance and 6 ft of interior headroom. [8]

In addition to two other 161 subtypes, Aerocar also offered Model JC-100, "A Permanent Mobile Home with Two Bedrooms, Kitchen, and Bath." All new versions were being marketed not simply as land yachts but as true "mobile" homes, with hot water heaters,

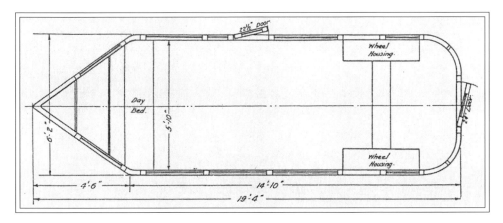

Fig. 12.6   Model 161 as a shell.

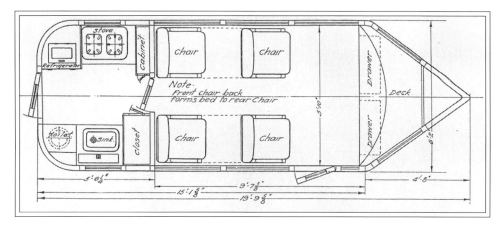

Fig. 12.7 Even the lower-priced model seems luxurious.

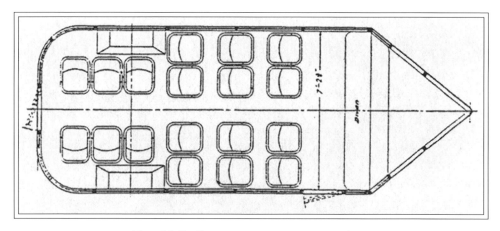

Fig. 12.8 Passenger transport version.

showers, wardrobes, flushing toilets, and other features aimed at comfort. There were also three passenger versions (Fig. 12.8), ranging from 17 to 22 seats. [8]

✯ ✯ ✯

The Aerocar (Fig. 12.9) in the Curtiss Museum is a 1937 Model 161-E, acquired through the generosity of Jeanne Curtiss and of former owner Ed Smith. It bears serial number 251, although it is unknown to which subtypes this refers.

The E series units, 8 ft in beam, are 22 ft long, shorter than the B series by 17 in. The galley, in the extreme rear, features a two-burner gasoline pressure stove and a stainless

Fig. 12.9   This may be the Aerocar in the Curtiss Museum collection.

steel sink with drain board. A hand lever pumps water from a 15-gal tank, the intake for which is on the back of the trailer. A valve handle opens and closes the flow of water to the pump, and an air valve is also provided. The icebox holds 50 lb. A clothes closet and a set of cabinets are fitted into the curving back corners. A drawer and two overhead cabinets are also included on each side, with racks to secure items while in motion. Facing each other from opposite walls, over sink and stove respectively, are two sliding windows (22 in. long × 15-1/2 in. high) with screens; a third window (22 × 11-1/2 in.) faces back, behind and above a small counter formed by the top of the icebox. A showerhead is set into the ceiling, with a drain in the linoleum directly beneath it. A Pyrene fire extinguisher and an Embury kerosene lamp (possibly not original equipment) are supplied. Fixed to the floor is a covered trash basket from Savery.

A doorway with privacy curtain leads forward, to where the toilet compartment on the left (port) side includes the fuel tank for the stove. Piping leads from the receiving tank of the toilet to a ventilation aperture on the curve joining the exterior wall to the roof. Set into this tank is a large bucket, showing that on this feature, the original owners decided to save a few pennies. The toilet compartment faces the single entry door, which has a crank-operated window ("regulator" window, according to the literature). Directly forward, space opens into the main compartment.

Here three crank windows on each side face each other. When combined with two small fixed windows, one angling in on each side of the prow, they create a truly impressive field of vision. In fact, each side is essentially a 10-ft window, broken only by three posts (Fig. 12.10). On the right side, this view is extended further by the 17-in. door window.

235

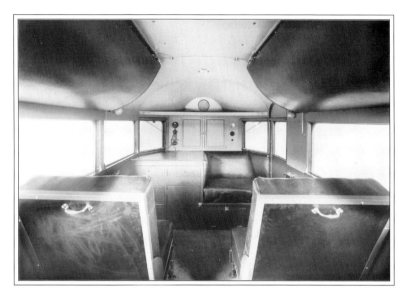

*Fig. 12.10 Imagine riding here—nothing could match the field
of vision in the Aerocar! Note closed Pullman-type
bunks overhead, telephone in front, dome light on the
centerline, cabinet space forward, and seats that fold
down for more sleeping space.*

Each of these windows in the main compartment is 22 in. high. The angled windows are 18-1/2 in. in length. The forward side windows are 28-1/2 in. long, while the two aft side windows (on either hand) each measure 35-1/2 in. All windows throughout the vehicle have roller shades.

Between the angled windows, the interior prow is squared off, creating some inconvenient cabinet space accessed by two hatches next to the windows. Electrical and heating services pass through this compartment, and fuses are mounted here. The uncovered vaulted ceiling of the compartment is particleboard, suggesting that the same may be true of the covered ceiling in the passenger spaces. Plywood is used for internal partitions in this space.

Directly in the center of this space is a built-in Philco radio with toggle switch for power and a built-in antenna. A rear-facing divan spans the entire width of the trailer. In the center below the divan is a heater, with a cabinet on either side. A tube communicating with the tow vehicle through conduit in the prow draws hot water from the cooling system to supply the heat, while a second tube returns the fluid.

Two individual seats face forward on the left side. On the right, two seats face each other, with a Pullman-type table set between them. Other pieces stowed in the trailer make it possible to add a second table on the left, or to extend the two tables into one running the width of the compartment. The table can be removed, and the seats folded down, to form two bunks. Above these are two concealed bunks, which are let down for use, creating upper and lower berths on each side. Concealed behind each of these upper bunks is a dome light and toggle switch. Snaps are provided for privacy curtains, which are no longer present.

The Aerocar has two small wall-mounted ashtrays opposite each other. Each is decorated grotesquely (to our eyes) with a fylfot—the backward-facing swastika that was considered a good-luck symbol until about that time. Several wall brackets are set to hold mugs or bottles. Each side has a button with which to signal the chauffeur.

Mounted on the ceiling centerline and evenly spaced are three screened ventilation hatches and three dome lights—two each in the main cab, one each in the galley. This, let us remind ourselves, was not the deluxe line but the standard line, and the smallest unit in the standard line at that. It would have cost $3,890 complete f.o.b. factory in Coral Gables, including brakes and shatterproof glass. [8]

Construction closely follows the pattern laid down in the 1928/1932 patent [18]. Working backward from the angle at which the prow begins, there are six uprights on each side, with two more in the stern. Each pair of uprights forms a window or door post, with the exception of the pair framing the toilet compartment. Transverse supports, on the other hand, are more numerous and more closely spaced, both in the floor and in the vaulted roof. The transverse pieces overhead follow the vault of the roof. Concealed cross-braced wires strengthen each perimeter cell formed by uprights, header, and footer. The two angled windows in the prow awkwardly force one short length of braided wire into the open on each side. A short upright forms the apex of the prow, and these visible wires are part of the cross bracing between that upright and those immediately aft, where the prow angles in from the main body. Cross braces also appear at the two sliding side windows in the galley.

A narrow bumper or fender runs along the foot of the trailer. Masonite panels, which are sealed by molding at the uprights, rise from this to another bumper at the level of the windowsill. Above this level, the Aerocar is covered with leatherette. The roof appears to be a separate section, but on the sides, the leatherette is in one continuous piece running from the left of the door entirely around the Aerocar to the right of the door. There are identical manufacturer's plates on each side of the prow, directly aft of the tow spike. In addition to model and serial numbers, trademark, and company information (it was at this time located in Coral Gables), the plates list applicable patents in Britain, Canada, and the United States.

Above each window is a shallow metal awning, and the wheel bays have metal fenders. As supplied, the wheels were "military type wood" with spokes, taking $31 \times 6 \times 19$ tires, but wheels on the Curtiss Museum unit were replaced at some time with more modern models. A bumper curves around the foot of the stern, which also features taillights and turning lights. A running light is set at each corner of the rectangular body.

Under the prow, the surface moves upward and forward in four flat wooden sections, each angled slightly more than its predecessor. All the jointures are at a transverse brace, and one makes a slight step. A bit of overhang provides some semi-sheltered space here, and in that space near the spike are utility hookups. Two foldaway tripod legs can be used at the front angles of the main compartment when the trailer is freestanding.

In addition to the electrical hookup (including buzzer) and the in-and-out water tubing for the heater, a vacuum line also passes through conduits in the prow. This runs to a vacuum booster about halfway down the underside. From there, separate vacuum lines operate a brake at each wheel in the extreme rear. Interestingly, the axle is set well below the hub of the wheels, presumably to keep the floor low and to avoid a "tunnel" hump in the galley. In the wheel wells are found the "stabilators," shock absorbers joining wheel hubs to the body to dampen bumps and sways.

Curtiss was dead by this time, but his work was not yet finished. In 1931, Lena, as executor, filed for a patent that was granted three years later. [20; see also 21] This invention pressed ahead with the articulation of the two vehicles. Recognizing the inconvenience of separating operator from passengers, and aiming at the same time to push the hitch even farther forward of the drive axle, Curtiss proposed a four-wheel open tow vehicle with an open space between the driver's seat and the hitch socket, which was placed directly below it. A tongue from the trailer slid into the open space, dropping a tow peg into the fifth-wheel hitch.

When hitched, the prow of the trailer slid over the driver's seat, forming a sort of hood and placing the driver within the passenger compartment. A bathtub-type structure around the driver's position (I'm tempted to call this a "bucket seat," but I'll resist) fitted into the hood to seal driver and passengers from the elements, although we are certainly free to speculate as to how effective the seal was (Fig. 12.11). The driver was thus seated in the tow vehicle, but his seat was also enclosed within the trailer. The tow vehicle had no cab—it consisted simply of the engine, two axles, a hitch, and the driver's seat. Some tour lines found this quite a handy arrangement.

Three weeks before his death, Curtiss filed for patent 1,948,745, with yet another arrangement. [20] This assumed a front-wheel drive power unit and an engine with horizontally

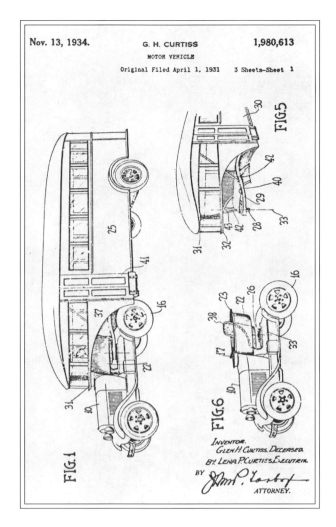

Nov. 13, 1934.

G. H. CURTISS

1,980,613

MOTOR VEHICLE

Original Filed April 1, 1931   3 Sheets-Sheet 1

Fig. 12.11   The articulated tour bus.

opposed cylinders. It placed the engine in the driver's cab and moved the improved resilient hitch backward, rather than employing a gap beneath the chauffeur's seat.

☆ ☆ ☆

Also granted posthumously were two more automotive patents applied for during Curtiss's lifetime, each aimed at improving the ride through independent suspension. Patent number 1,880,842 had been for a three-axle auto. [17] Engine and unroofed driver's cab composed a more or less typical two-axle vehicle with open cab (Fig. 12.12). The single-axle passenger compartment slid into place (providing the driver's roof) and was joined to the power unit through yieldable couplings (Fig. 12.13). This, the application stated, would improve the ride "very materially." Otherwise, it further pointed out, on "rough and

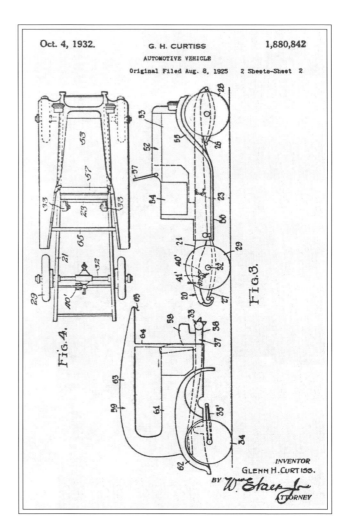

Fig. 12.12 Independent components of the proposed six-wheeler.

undulating" roads, the passengers, especially rear-seat passengers, "are jolted and jostled about in a most objectionable manner; in fact, so much so that riding becomes irksome, tiresome and uncomfortable in the extreme." This vivid language in a patent application (typically a repository of rather dry prose) suggests personal experience with the phenomenon. It is fun to speculate on whether it was Curtiss's experience or that of his attorney. Possibly both, of course.

Patent number 1,948,744 likewise took up the problem of independent suspension. [19] This time, Curtiss proposed an articulated two-axle front-wheel-drive vehicle (Fig. 12.14). The power and passenger compartments would each be "unstably mounted" on two wheels. They actually would be joined at only three points arranged triangularly. "Yielding coupling devices" made up of "annular cushioning members" at these three points, and

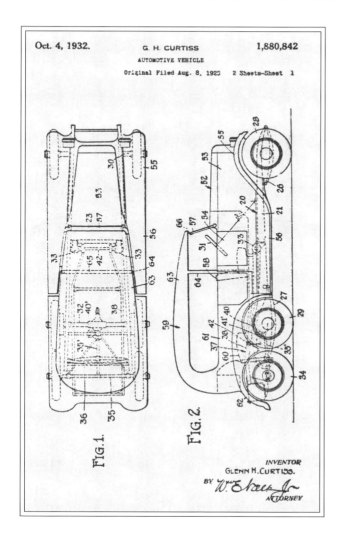

Fig. 12.13   The same vehicle, as shown in Fig. 12.12, completely articulated.

acting as tertiary protection (after pneumatic tires and springs), would shield the passenger cab (which could "teeter" transversely to the power unit) from all but the worst of shocks. Curtiss's commitment to independent suspension and vehicle articulation wove themselves throughout his automotive projects that occupied so much of his last decade of life.

REFERENCES

1.   "Accessories and Equipment," Adams Trailer Corporation, March 29, 1921, GHCM Channer Collection.

2.   "Adams Trailer Motor Bungalo," circa 1922, GHCM Channer Collection.

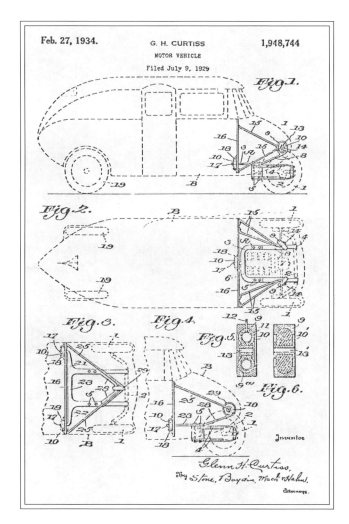

Fig. 12.14 Was Glenn Curtiss the father of the streamlined minivan?

3. Channer, Bert, to G. Carl Adams, June 2, 1921, GHCM Channer Collection

4. Church (initials illegible), memo to Bert Channer, May 12, 1921, GHCM Channer Collection.

5. "Cubic Measurements of Trailers Packed for Export," manuscript, circa 1921, GHCM Channer Collection.

6. "The Curtiss Aerocar," Curtiss Aerocar Company, Coral Gables, FL, circa 1936, GHCM 93-10-1.

7. Curtiss Aerocar catalog, Curtiss Aerocar Company of Florida, (n.d.) GHCM 83-82-3.

8. Curtiss Aerocar catalog, Curtiss Aerocar Company of Florida, Coral Gables, (n.d.) GHCM Aerocar Files.

9. Adams, G. Carl, "Gypsie Life Modernized," Farmingdale, Long Island, circa 1922, GHCM Channer Collection.

10. "List of Dealers, Distributors and Agents," typescript, June 14, 1921, GHCM Channer Collection.

11. Mitchell, Charles R., and Kirk W. House, *Glenn H. Curtiss, Aviation Pioneer,* Arcadia Publishing, Charleston, SC, 2001.

12. Parker, Nelson S., to Adams Trailer Corp., April 4, 1921. Includes typescript of an April 5 letter from Parker, a memo to Adams from "M. K. C.," and two handwritten notations by Jack Doris, GHCM Channer Collection.

13. Roseberry, C. R., *Glenn Curtiss: Pioneer of Flight,* Doubleday & Company, Garden City, 1972.

14. "Standard List of Models/Adams Trailer Corporation," typescript, circa 1921, GHCM Channer Collection.

15. "Weights on Trailers," manuscript, circa 1921, GHCM Channer Collection.

16. White, Roger, "Planes, Trailers and Automobiles: The Land Yachts of Glenn Curtiss," in *Automobile Quarterly,* vol. 32, no. 3, January 1994, pp. 30–47.

U.S. PATENT REFERENCES

17. 1,880,842 G. H. Curtiss, Automotive Vehicle, August 8, 1925–October 4, 1932.

18. 1,880,844 G. H. Curtiss, Road Vehicle Body Structure, June 8, 1928–November 4, 1932.

19. 1,948,744 G. H. Curtiss, Motor Vehicle, July 9, 1924–February 27, 1934.

20. 1,948,745 G. H. Curtiss, Motor Vehicle, July 3, 1930–February 27, 1934.

21. 1,980,613 G. H. Curtiss, Motor Vehicle, April 1, 1931–November 13, 1934.

22. Des. 85,815 Glenn H. Curtiss, Deceased, Design for a Tow Car and Trailer Combination, January 8, 1931–December 22, 1931.

Chapter 13

Final Frame:
Afterword and Evaluation

★ ★ ★

Afterword

Telegrams expressing shock and condolence poured in to Lena from Richard Byrd, Charles and Anne Lindbergh, Juan Trippe, and other noted names in aviation. Leading citizens of southeastern Florida and public officials from Albany added to the stream, plus old village friends such as Butz Hoyt, who had worked as a mail carrier in the Hammondsport plant. (Butz died in 1997, the last-known veteran of the original facility.) Jack Vilas's wire arrived a week late. He had only received word after returning from a hunting trip. [17]

Lena, who was only 49 when her husband died, later married H. Sayre Wheeler. Wheeler, an old Steuben friend and the son of Judge Monroe Wheeler, had been an honorary pallbearer at the funeral. He was associated with the Curtisses in the Aerocar business; he and Lena continued manufacturing until the beginning of World War II. The couple became well known for their entertainments at the Miami Springs mansion of Dar-Err-Aha, including evenings for enlisted men during the war years. Glenn Junior remembered that they would arrive at the doorstep wide-eyed and certain that they could not be in the right place. Lena would drag them inside to enjoy performers (including a very young Desi Arnez) whom she had imported from the hotels in Miami Beach. [Personal communication] Lena, who died in 1951, was buried next to Glenn under a stone marked "Lena Curtiss Wheeler."

Soon after her husband's death, Lena put an end to the 20-year-old Herring struggle. Harry Genung, representing the widow, sat down with representatives of the Herring heirs, telling them that Mrs. Curtiss was prepared either to fight it out or to come to immediate terms. The case was settled out of court. As Tom Crouch sardonically pointed out, "Augustus Herring had at last made a fortune in the airplane business." He never lived to see it, and his lawyers probably did at least as well as his heirs on the deal. [5, 14]

Glenn Junior did well in the Volkswagen business after the war. Similar to his father, he liked fast cars, although he hated flying. He had been quite heavy for many years, but late in life his slim build, baldness, and mustache gave him an almost eerie resemblance to his father. He followed the family pattern by dying young, of cancer, in 1972. He was buried next to his mother in Pleasant Valley. Glenn Junior, Rutha, and half-brother Carl Adams did not have children. The nearest Curtiss relatives today are either relatives by marriage or descendants of Glenn's first cousins.

Jack McCurdy, who led Canadian aircraft production during World War II, survived the other members of the Aerial Experiment Association. While being flown into Cape Breton Island for the golden anniversary of his making Canada's first flight, he looked out of the airplane and saw the reproduction *Silver Dart* in flight below him. Naturally, he was thrilled. [12]

Jack Towers found his career stymied by a combination of his prickly personality, his political maneuverings, and his commitment to naval aviation at the expense of battleships. However, Towers had given Franklin D. Roosevelt his first airplane ride, and President Roosevelt remembered Towers well from the days when he had sponsored the NC mission as assistant navy secretary. FDR elevated Towers to head the U.S. Navy Bureau of Aeronautics, with automatic promotion to flag rank. He was in that position at the time of the attack on Pearl Harbor, later becoming aviation chief and then chief of staff for Admiral Nimitz. A major architect of Pacific victory, Towers stood at attention on the deck of *Missouri* as the surrender was signed in 1945. [12] Missing from the ceremony was the empire's minister of munitions, Nakajima Chikuhei. Lt. Nakajima had arrived in Hammondsport about the same time as Towers, equally enthralled with learning to fly. He later started the first private airplane factory in Japan, pitting Curtiss warplanes and Nakajima warplanes against each other across Asia and the Pacific.

Hitting high and low at Pearl Harbor was U.S.S. *Glenn H. Curtiss*, the first U.S. purpose-built seaplane tender. Commissioned in 1940 (with Lena as sponsor), *Curtiss* helped to sink a midget submarine and shot down two Japanese airplanes (out of a total of 29 lost that day). One of these slammed into the ship, as did a bomb, causing 21 U.S. deaths. Quickly repaired, *Curtiss* won seven battle stars, suffering one death at Saipan and 35 at Kerama Retto (Okinawa), where she was struck by a kamikaze. Henry Fonda served on board, and Admiral John McCain, father of the Arizona senator, used *Curtiss* as a flagship. Another vessel, U.S.S. *Hammondsport*, served in the Pacific during the war as an aircraft transporter.

Curtiss deployed both U.S. and British seaplanes during the Korean War, participating in several nuclear tests and in the International Geophysical Year before being decommissioned in 1957 and scrapped in 1972, because the navy had deleted seaplanes from its arsenal. U.S.N.S. *Curtiss*, an aviation logistical support vessel, served in the Gulf War and keeps the name alive on the navy list.

Curtiss-Wright endured, weathering the Depression, the death of its namesake, and the removal of Clement Keys for misuse of corporate funds. New leadership slashed operations back to their original core of engines and airframes, depending largely on worldwide military orders. As World War II came to a boil, Curtiss-Wright was already manufacturing its Model 81, known in the U.S. army service as the P-40 *Warhawk*, often called *Kittyhawk* or *Tomahawk* overseas. Curtiss ground out nearly 14,000 of these in various subtypes. In the early years of the war, P-40 production dwarfed all other U.S. military aircraft production combined. Two other wartime products proved especially significant, the C-46 (Navy R5C) *Commando* cargo plane and the SB2C *Helldiver* navy dive bomber—the latter one after dreadful teething problems.

During the war years, Curtiss-Wright invested heavily in capital expansion, most of which became instantly extraneous with peace. Its gigantic expansion had left it continually short of experienced management. The military insistence on dedicating corporate resources to available, but increasingly outdated, products such as the P-40 left the company behind on the design curve as the jet era opened. Finally, stockholders were eager for distribution of wartime profits. Although still in business as a publicly traded corporation, Curtiss-Wright is much smaller now. Its business is diversified among aerospace components, aircraft service, valves, and rescue tools. Who could have imagined that such a business would grow from two nineteenth-century bike shops? [7]

Curtiss remains a living, breathing presence in the village of Hammondsport, which continues to be home to a precious few who knew him. Any family that was in town during those days preserves its fond items of Curtiss lore. The same holds true in Miami Springs, which celebrates an annual Curtiss Week. Both communities have streets named after their joint favorite son, while Hialeah boasts the Lua Curtiss Branch Library. The Miami Springs mansion, which later became a hotel, was derelict as the twenty-first century opened, with a local group hard at work on restoration.

The largest employer in Hammondsport is Mercury Aircraft, founded in 1920 as Henry Kleckler's Aerial Service Corporation. In 1976, Mercury workers built and flew a copy of *June Bug.* Plans for a Glenn Curtiss Airport in Pleasant Valley were vetoed (probably wisely) by Governor Franklin Roosevelt. In 1935, most of the ramshackle factory buildings in the village were removed, and the old house was moved a few yards to make room for the Glenn Curtiss Memorial School. This facility now hosts grades four through six. The house itself later burned down.

Otto Kohl, a Curtiss machinist in the Hammondsport plant, opened the Glenn H. Curtiss Museum in 1961, using the 1859 school building where Glenn and Rutha had attended classes. The museum moved to modern facilities in 1992. Its collection includes all that survives of the house, the cupola Glenn Curtiss added in 1911.

A monument stands near the seaplane launching site and another on the grounds of Pleasant Valley Wine Company. U.S. bonded winery #1 remains in business, and on the grounds (now owned by Mercury Aircraft) stands the Stony Brook Farm barn, immortalized in photos of that dazzling flight on the Fourth of July. Near this barn, within sight of the graves of his father, his grandparents, and his little boy, Glenn Curtiss celebrated his thirtieth birthday by piloting his first thousand feet in an airplane.

Evaluation

"God made many men," Chief Scout Dan Beard wired Lena at the time of the funeral, "but only one Glenn Curtiss." [17] While other opinions may vary, it's certainly hard to argue this one.

A famous man even before taking up flying, Curtiss can certainly be described in many ways. He was at once brilliant and flighty, and certainly accomplished far more than his education or his childhood opportunities would have led one to predict. He had no training in mechanics or engineering, but he was able to lead development in several fields.

Part of this success grew from getting skilled men to work for him. Especially as time passed, Curtiss worked increasingly by sketching initial ideas, turning them over to men such as Kleckler, Kirkham, and Pfitzner to be realized. It is fascinating that most of these men continued to hold him in awe, even though their skills may have been far beyond his. Curtiss could perhaps be described as a "maestro of technology," to use the words of Arthur M. Squires. He was the kind of leader who could appear on the shop floor at 2:00 A.M., run a machine, and get straight talk from the workers, and still keep the entire enterprise moving enthusiastically forward. [3]

Evaluations of the pioneer figures in aviation often wheedle down to arguments about who was the better pilot, whose were the safer airplanes, who had the most firsts, and similar controversies. Pro-Curtiss observers and anti-Curtiss observers alike often overlook the fundamental truth that Curtiss was a businessman. Long before becoming involved with airplanes, young Mr. Curtiss had been manufacturing a significant transportation product, marketing and distributing it nationwide. Although he was always fascinated by exploring the potentials of nearly anything mechanical, he never lost sight of the fact that his job was not only to invent things, or even to make things, but to sell things. Among significant U.S. pioneer aeronautics manufacturers, perhaps only Starling Burgess had a similar background in previous successful manufacturing. [12]

It is possible that neither the Wright brothers nor Alexander Graham Bell ever quite realized this about Curtiss. Bell and the Wrights saw themselves as scientists. Curtiss certainly saw himself as an experimenter, but he also saw himself as a businessman.

What about the great controversies of Curtiss's career? What did Curtiss steal from the Wright brothers? The answer is simple: nothing. He would not even see a Wright airplane until the time of the army trials in August 1908, by which time had already won the *Scientific American* trophy and was assisting with the creation of *Silver Dart*. The legend of Curtiss visiting the Wrights and being shown all their secrets is, in fact, only legend. On his one visit, in company with Tom Baldwin, the older man chided Curtiss for asking too many questions. Getting together with the Wright brothers was only incidental. The two Hammondsport friends were on a dirigible exhibition tour. Neither Curtiss nor Baldwin was shown an airplane or the plans for an airplane. Apparently, they did not ask. Although Curtiss could have piloted one of Baldwin's dirigibles at any time, he would not take that opportunity for another year and would not become involved with airplanes until later yet. Baldwin started heavier-than-air work even after Curtiss did, so it is evident that neither of them had particular interest in making airplanes at the time of their visit to the Wrights. [6, 10, 11, 14, 16]

Likewise, Wright biographer Fred Howard has pointed out that, although the AEA wrote many workers for information, the Wrights' response was limited to materials that had already been made public, with the exception of some data on calculating the center of pressure, which there is no evidence that the Bell group ever used. [10] The AEA made such rapid progress because the five members and their colleagues were highly competent, highly enthusiastic, collaboratively oriented, and eager to pool information.

Did Curtiss's products infringe the Wright patent? Therein lies an entirely different question. Certainly, a creation may infringe without stealing from, or even without knowledge of, prior art. The ailerons were almost universally judged superior to the Wright wing-warping technique. They were certainly worthy of their own patent because they were, at minimum, a significant advance. [15] But did they fall under the previous patent and thus owe royalties to the Wrights or their successors? One can certainly make the case. In part, one's conclusion lies in the weight one assigns to the fact that the Wright patent described manipulations of the surface of the wing, which would seem quite a broad application to control surfaces mounted midway between the two wing planes.

What about the legal pettifoggery? Whatever position one takes, Curtiss certainly had the right to defend himself, and he did so by legal, if annoying, means. Posting bonds and taking advantage of loopholes, he put his own assets on the line in the event of final adverse judgments. He assumed the risk of his actions. This was, of course, the end of the age of robber barons, in which society even encouraged businessmen to press beyond the limits in quest of growth. One conclusion seems trustworthy: even if he misled the Wright brothers about his plans during the AEA period, Curtiss seems honestly (if, it may be argued, erroneously) to have *believed* that his products did not infringe. With his go-ahead, move-faster, big-picture approach to life, he may not have had the patience to follow the opposing view. As far as he was concerned, ailerons were distinctly different and thus were not covered.

When he began airplane manufacturing, did Curtiss make use of the pending AEA patents, in which he owned only a one-fifth share, without due consideration of his colleagues? This may be the case, although apparently none of the other members raised objections. Indeed, Baldwin, McCurdy, and Bell seem to have followed a parallel course in Canada, "the only civilized country," according to the Wright brothers, that did not recognize the Wright patents. By keeping their work in Canada, Bell shrewdly avoided the patent problem. Curtiss in practice took the entire risk upon himself. In addition, Curtiss seems to have believed that Herring's (supposed) patents, to which his organization theoretically had rights, were early enough and broad enough to swallow most of the Wright and AEA work. Continued friendly relations among the AEA veterans suggest that there may have been a tacit "division" of U.S. and Canadian territories. They also appear to have seen each member as fully possessed of their joint patent. [8, 14]

When his firm was finally reorganized in the wake of Herring and in the van of war, Curtiss joyously passed out blocks of shares to old employees and supporters, including the Bells. Mrs. Bell, who had bankrolled the four AEA airplanes, sniffed that this gift of stock in an untested company appeared to be in the nature of a tip. Curtiss, it should be remembered, had gone bankrupt and then rebuilt in the interim, at no risk to the Bells. Shares in that untested company soon made him a multimillionaire. [8]

Did Herring create the Curtiss airplane? He certainly implied as much, and the door is wide open for speculation. Curtiss #1 (*Gold Bug/Golden Flier*) was distinctly different from the AEA machines and from Bell's contemporary Baddeck machines. *Gold Bug* was far smaller than its predecessors. It did away entirely with the dihedral wings, adopting a Chanute-type biplane. Moreover, four triangular wingtip ailerons were discarded in favor of two rectangular interplane ailerons. Because Herring was entering the Curtiss operation at about this time and had been closely associated with Chanute in the past, could he have been the source of the new design?

The Chanute arrangement was certainly already well known at the time. Indeed, Curtiss had built the AEA hang glider in that arrangement as far back as January 1908. Kleckler later reported that neither he nor Curtiss had ever been happy with the opposing dihedrals on the AEA machines. Finally, all reports are that Curtiss and Herring, already beginning to be at odds, each tried to keep his partner away from the two private projects already in progress—Curtiss #1, and Herring's mysterious army airplane. Given Herring's failure to make a workable powered aircraft (at least one that anybody else ever saw), it seems likely that Curtiss, rather than Herring, was in fact responsible for the post-AEA design. Of course, anything that Herring might have let drop about his work with Chanute probably would have been swept up by Curtiss's voracious mind. [2, 4, 14]

Alternatively, could Curtiss have picked up ideas from the Wright machine he had seen at Fort Myer the previous summer? Curtiss seemed unimpressed, writing to Bell that the airplane contained no secrets and no special features. The Wright machine was quite different from the Curtiss machine. Because Curtiss had already worked with Chanute-type wings, there is no reason to think that the Wright machine inspired his future use.

Did Curtiss fail in his fiduciary responsibility, in effect defrauding Herring? Two courts issued exactly opposite rulings on the question. A contemporary suggested that Curtiss had all the moral right in the matter and none of the legal right, while Herring had all of the legal right and none of the moral right. Curtiss, who had no grounding in law, was abominably served by his legal advisors, both with respect to the original merger and with respect to forcing the cuckoo out of the nest. After putting all his assets (including his house, business, and factory) into the new concern, Curtiss slowly realized that Herring was not bringing in promised patents, tools, or cash. Despite this, Herring controlled large blocks of watered stock. To prevent his voting these at the first annual meeting, the three Hammondsport directors sought and received legal injunction, and eventually Curtiss bought his business and his home back at a bankruptcy sale that was postponed twice to give Herring a chance to organize a bid (which never materialized). Curtiss certainly acted on legal counsel and no doubt considered himself in the right. [7, 9, 14]

What about those two attempts to demonstrate "prior art" in the Wright case—*Langley* and *Duck*? Curtiss was certainly entitled to try to defend himself in this manner, although it is difficult to see how they would have had much influence on a court. In fact, they were never presented as part of the case.

As far as *Duck* was concerned, Goupil's published drawings were not actually plans. The resultant aircraft, although quite faithful to what little Goupil had provided, in all likelihood benefited from aeronautic knowledge available at the time it was made. It certainly seemed to demonstrate that Goupil had worked out a practical three-axis control system. However, to have any effect in court, it would need to survive "cross-examination" by opposing counsel. Any such project presented by a party to the suit would certainly require extremely strict scrutiny. [2, 5]

The case of *Langley* is a bit thornier because it involved restoration of a damaged and dismantled machine. Curtiss and his associates insisted that they had made no material changes involving airworthiness, simply substituting water gear for the original catapult. While this made launch even more difficult than it had been in 1903, Grover Loening objected that the installation of floats had incidentally made the wings rigid, correcting a flaw in the original design. Moreover, *any* provision for landing corrected a glaring omission in Langley's work. [2, 4, 5, 14]

Curtiss, who had suggested that he build a reproduction of *Langley*, could hardly be criticized for the Smithsonian's decision to have him restore the original. Nor can he be faulted for having accepted its offer, although any insertion of the restoration into the court case (which, be it recalled, never occurred) would have had to bear very strict opposing scrutiny.

Of course, Curtiss could hardly be held responsible for the egregious informational label initially placed by the Smithsonian.

What were Curtiss's actual contributions to the new twentieth century? Rather than list his particular firsts and records, we may summarize them by saying that he demonstrated great skill, great daring, great confidence in his own machines, great engineering, great public-relations sense, and great sales sense in his exhibition flying and in his motorcycle racing. He did a great deal to publicize and popularize the very concept of airplane flying and the practice of motorcycling.

On October 13, 1924, readers of *Time* magazine found Glenn's diamond-drill eyes boring into them from the cover. Reporting inside on the recent air meet at Dayton, *Time* wrote: [1]

> Though his works were everywhere present, his name on every man's lip, the face and figure of Glenn Hammond Curtiss were not in evidence at Dayton. At least every other plane of those assembled bore a Curtiss motor. Not one plane but bore some evidence to the contributions he has made to mankind's knowledge of the air and his agility in it. . . .
>
> In Hammondsport, N.Y., where Curtiss was born, they used to call him "handy at fixing things." Also they would say: "I knew he could do it." Ingenuity, mechanical skill, persistence, enterprise, daring—these were Glenn Curtiss' qualities as early as the days when his bicycle was the speediest, his sled coasted farthest, his motor-cycle was the wonder of the day, his skate-sail unique, his birds'-egg collection largest and rarest of all his

comrades. His appetite for speed has always been insatiable. Now 46, he still ponders engine construction, streamline, weight reduction in hopes of letting man move faster.

On his own, in collaboration with others, and by stimulating competition, Curtiss pushed development of internal combustion engines, both small air-cooled models for motorcycle use and large water-cooled models for aeronautic use. His innovations apparently include the first V-twin motorcycle, the first V-8 motorcycle, one of the first V-8 engines in the United States, and one of the first water-cooled aero engines.

On his own, in collaboration with others, and by stimulating competition, Curtiss pushed development of the airplane. These developments include the foundational features of the aileron and the tricycle landing gear. Even the single centerline propeller was a departure from the work of the Wright brothers.

By attention to merchandising and to infrastructure, Curtiss contributed mightily to the creation of an aviation industry. He made the first airplane sale in the Americas, the first sale to an individual, and the first sale for pleasure purposes. He set up flying fields, flying schools, and exhibition teams. He continuously introduced new civil and military applications. He struggled to make the airplane more "user-friendly," even to the level of planning better ways to ship dismantled parts. He recognized that it was not enough simply to *make* an airplane. He needed to create a setting in which the buyer could actually *use* an airplane. Perhaps this aspect of his work, more than any other, justifies the title "Father of American Aviation."

Curtiss developed the first practical float plane, leading many to call him "The Father of Water Flying." The purchase by the U.S. Navy in 1911, and Curtiss's continued close work with that service, led to him often being described as "The Father of Naval Aviation."

Curtiss developed the first flying boat.

He was the first American to turn aviation into a truly big business, seizing opportunities offered by World War I.

In the Curtiss Engineering Corporation, he created an outstanding enterprise for rigorous research and engineering in the field of aeronautics.

Curtiss founded a corporation that grew to huge dimensions, contributed strongly to the Allied victories in both World War I and World War II, and still endures a century later.

He was a strong force behind the development of southeastern Florida.

He created, produced, and marketed an advanced, industry-leading, streamlined, articulated travel trailer.

Curtiss was a significant contributor to pioneer American dirigibles, although that endeavor always remained essentially a curio. He was a significant figure to the more enduring development of southeastern Florida. However, he was an even more foundational figure in four new fields, in each case both on the level of technology and on the level of business: the internal combustion engine, the motorcycle, the airplane, and the travel trailer.

Not bad for a guy with an eighth-grade education.

What was Curtiss like as a man?

Some obvious features of his personality have already been mentioned. He was athletic and daring, and he had an excellent mind with a special facility at mechanics. He had a fixation with speed. He was extremely determined and intense, with drive to achieve and succeed, but his mind often raced from one topic to another, even, at times, to the point of ineffectiveness.

Curtiss manifested some aspects of personality—such as intensity, drive to achieve, and addictive risk-taking behavior (his "speed craving," in his own words)—often seen in children of alcoholic backgrounds. It is possible that there was also some form of a learning disability.

Curtiss was quiet, even withdrawn, but he had close friends and seems to have been able to work well with people. Townsmen, workers, and colleagues remembered him as "G. H.," and reported that he was always open to their ideas and suggestions. It is likely that all the engine work over decades led to increasing hearing loss, which doubtless contributed to his withdrawn nature. Despite this quiet, withdrawn nature, Curtiss had a startling flair for drama when the occasion suited. He also enjoyed practical jokes, although his verbal wit ran to laconic, dry, New England-style zingers.

Similar to the Wright brothers, Curtiss was a "straight arrow," pursuing neither liquor, tobacco, nor women, and even eschewing bad language. He loved the outdoors, finding many of his favorite hours in hunting, fishing, or camping.

While Curtiss could be death on someone such as Herring, whom he felt had deceived and betrayed him, he remained dedicated to his family and his old friends throughout life. His generosity with cash and other assets was abounding.

Obituaries written at the time, reports by contemporaries looking back over the decades, and oral history preserved in families, often contain the same telling phrase: "Mr. Curtiss was a very kind man." Who wouldn't wish to be so remembered?

> [A]s the planes of tomorrow roar down eternal airpaths, the gleam of their wings in sunlight, the sound of their motors at night will forever remain symbols of that man's greatness.

John H. Towers [13]

REFERENCES

1.   "Aeronautics: At Dayton," *Time*, October 31, 1924, p. 15.

2.   Bowers, Peter M., *Curtiss Aircraft 1907–1947*, Putnam, London, 1979.

3.   Bowser, Hal, "Maestros of Technology: An Interview with Arthur M. Squires," *American Heritage of Invention and Technology*, vol. 3, no.1, Summer 1987, pp. 24–30.

4.   Casey, Louis S., *Curtiss: The Hammondsport Era, 1907–1915*, Crown Publishers, New York, 1981.

5.   Crouch, Tom, *The Bishop's Boys: A Life of Wilbur and Orville Wright*, W. W. Norton & Co., New York, 1989.

6.   Eklund, Don Dean, "Captain Thomas S. Baldwin: Pioneer American Aeronaut," Ph.D. dissertation, University of Colorado, 1970.

7.   Eltscher, Louis R., and Edward M. Young, *Curtiss-Wright: Greatness and Decline*, Twayne Publishers, New York, 1998.

8.   Grosvenor, Edwin S., and Morgan Wesson, *Alexander Graham Bell: The Life and Times of the Man Who Invented the Telephone*, Harry N. Abrams, New York, 1997.

9. The *Hammondsport Herald,* published weekly throughout Curtiss's lifetime, includes multitudinous references to Curtiss, his works, and his times. (Curtiss Museum holds a microfilmed set.)

10. Howard, Fred, *Orville and Wilbur: A Biography of the Wright Brothers,* Alfred A. Knopf, New York, 1988.

11. Mitchell, Charles R., and Kirk W. House, *Glenn H. Curtiss, Aviation Pioneer,* Arcadia Publishing, Charleston, SC, 2001.

12. Morehouse, Harold E., and Marvel Dyer, *The Flying Pioneers Biographies of Harold Morehouse,* GHCM.

13. Reynolds, Clark G., *Admiral John H. Towers: The Struggle for Naval Air Supremacy,* Naval Institute Press, Annapolis, MD, 1991.

14. Roseberry, C. R., *Glenn Curtiss: Pioneer of Flight,* Doubleday & Company, Garden City, NY, 1972.

15. Scott, Phil, "Wright v. Curtiss," (two parts) in *Air and Space/Smithsonian,* 12:1 (April/May 1997) and 12:2 (June/July 1997).

16. Studer, Clara, *Sky Storming Yankee: The Life of Glenn Curtiss,* Stackpole Sons, New York, 1937.

17. Telegrams on the death of Glenn Curtiss, GHCM Curtiss Biographical Files.

Index

★ ★ ★

An abbreviation is used after the page number to indicate a figure (*f*).

About the Author

✯ ✯ ✯

For six and a half years, Kirk W. House was either curator or director-curator of the Glenn Curtiss Museum in Hammondsport, New York. Before that, he spent 21 years as a schoolteacher and administrator.

Widely known as a historian of early aviation, he has written extensively on the subject (including two earlier books and nine encyclopedia entries), in addition to making several appearances on national television.

Kirk W. House
(Courtesy of Joshua B. House)

"That open-cockpit era has always fascinated me," House says, "the days when men and women set off across a countryside that was encountering wings for the first time. I'm also absorbed by the human and social side of innovation—how those factors drive the process, and find themselves then changed in turn by the changes they have wrought. Curtiss is a natural for that field of study, and his life makes a whale of a story."

House holds degrees from Rhode Island College and Lehigh University. Today, he is an independent writer, editor, and researcher, working largely in the fields of history and tourism. He lives with his wife and their two sons in Bath, New York.

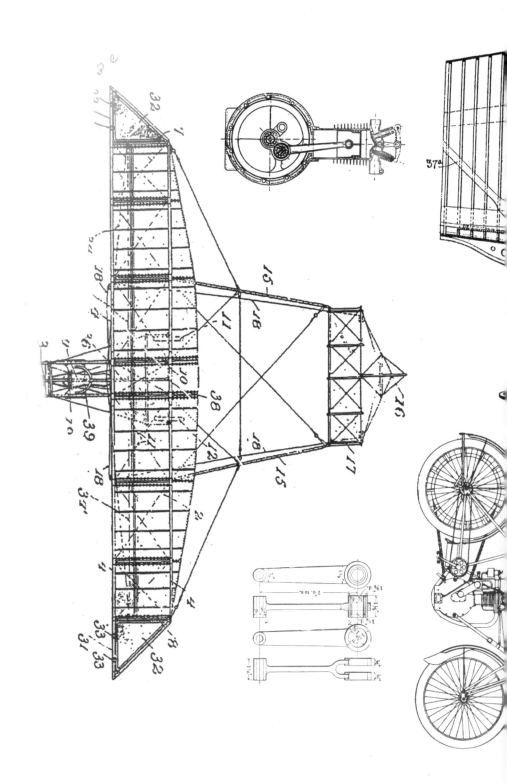